Optimum Utilization

OF

Scientific and Engineering Manpower

by

WILLIAM G. TORPEY, Ph.D.

Manpower Specialist, 1959-1969
Executive Office of the President of the United States
and
Faculty member, The George Washington University

1970

PREFACE

As program director of a unique national effort designed by a White House committee to maximize the utilization of scientific and engineering manpower, I was in a most fortunate position to participate, from the administrative level of the Executive Office of the President of the United States, in the ebb and flow of efforts channeled toward this objective.

My career experience in laboratories, at plants, in conference rooms, on campuses, in offices, and on speakers' platforms throughout the nation have forcefully impressed upon me the need for OPTIMUM UTILIZATION OF SCIENTIFIC AND ENGINEERING MANPOWER as an essential national goal. As I have been stimulated by groups and individuals across the country who have been actively pursuing this objective, it is my sincere hope that this book will stimulate the extra efforts which are required if the goal is to be attained.

In unfolding this challenge, I wish to express appreciation to my Mother, who was a source of inspiration throughout my efforts, and to my sister, Dr. Dorothy M. Torpey, who read the complete manuscript and offered constructive suggestions.

W.G.T.

CONTENTS

Role of Employers
Role of Educators
Role of Professional and Technical Societies
Role of Federal Government: Policies and Programs
Role of Federal Government: As Civilian Employer
Role of Federal Government: Military
Present Status of Continuing Education

Chapter V

Increasing Flow of Documents
In-House Scientific and Technical Information Facility
Scientific and Technical Information Centers
NSF Science Information Program
Federal Coordination
General Programs Related to Scientific and Technical
    Information Retrieval
Proposals for National Scientific and Technical
    Information System(s)
Roles in Facilitating Storage and Retrieval Service

Chapter VI

Nature of Graduate Education in Science and Engineering
Importance of Continuous, Adequate Flow of Graduate Students
Establishment of Concept of Graduate Deferment
Legislation in 1967
Action by the National Security Council
Impact of "No Graduate Deferment" Policy on
    Graduate Enrollment
Impact of "No Graduate Deferment" Policy on
    Occupational Deferment
Military Use of College Graduates as Enlisted Men
Changes in 1969
Overview

Chapter VII

Reductions in Large Scale Funding
Employment of Scientists and Engineers in the
    Defense Effort
Employment of Scientists and Engineers in the
    Aerospace Industry

OPTIMUM UTILIZATION OF
SCIENTIFIC AND ENGINEERING MANPOWER

I

VIEWING UTILIZATION FROM A NATIONAL PERSPECTIVE

•

CONCEPT OF UTILIZATION

Scientific and engineering manpower utilization refers to the use which scientists and engineers make of their abilities and their unique background of education and experience in their work situations. Optimum utilization of scientific and engineering manpower means that scientists and engineers are making greatest possible use of their abilities and unique backgrounds. Much more effective utilization of the scientific and engineering talent of the nation, than is characteristic of combined current efforts, is required if the goal of optimum utilization is to be achieved.

The word "scientist," as used in this book, refers only to physical scientists (including mathematicians). Furthermore, although the word "scientists" precedes the word "engineers" in references to these two professional groups, it is believed that scientists and engineers play coequal roles in today's world.

It is impossible to analyze scientific and engineering manpower utilization in quantitative terms. Obstacles, such as identification of behaviors to be measured, methods to take measurements, and means to validate evaluations, loom as difficulties to a quantitative approach. A worker in a factory may produce a certain number of units of a predetermined quality during a specified time; his output can be calculated, and a degree of utilization of his talent can be roughly estimated. Due to the nature of their duties, scientists and engineers usually do not produce countable work units. Actions, such as evolving new ideas, devising new methods, combining known concepts, and applying new informa-

[3]

tion, cannot be satisfactorily measured against existing or projected standards.

Steps to improve the current utilization of scientific and engineering manpower embrace numerous group and individual efforts. All sectors of society directly concerned with scientists and engineers—employers, educators, government, scientists and engineers, professional and technical societies, and related groups—are involved in taking such steps. Hence, a review of activities pursued to increase utilization requires consideration of a wide range of policies, programs, and actions of each sector.

The concept of utilization is distinct from the subject of manpower shortage. Statements are sometimes made that, in view of a temporary surplus of scientists and engineers in a particular geographical area at a particular time, there is no need to give serious consideration to manpower utilization. However, the aim of optimum utilization is to induce at all times the highest level of professional effort on the part of scientists and engineers in a work situation. Striving for maximum utilization of scientific and engineering manpower is a worthwhile endeavor whether or not there is a manpower shortage.

INVOLVEMENT OF PERMANENT AGENCIES AND ORGANIZATIONS

During the past decade several permanent agencies in the Executive Branch of the Federal Government have given attention to specific aspects of scientific and engineering manpower utilization, beyond the normal role of these agencies as employers of scientific and engineering personnel. Among federal agencies showing an identifiable concern are the National Science Foundation; the Department of Labor; the Department of Health, Education and Welfare; and the Civil Service Commission. The National Science Foundation, for example, has sponsored studies of scientific and engineering manpower utilization. The Department of Labor, for example, has conducted analyses of the role of technicians in industry. The Department of Health, Education and Welfare, through the U. S. Office of

Education, for example, has provided continuing education programs which involve scientists and engineers. The Civil Service Commission, for example, has conducted training programs for federal scientists and engineers.

A few permanent, non-government, national organizations have shown realistic concern from time to time for particular issues directly related to scientific and engineering manpower utilization. Among such organizations are the National Society of Professional Engineers, the Engineers Joint Council (and the Engineering Manpower Commission), the Scientific Manpower Commission, and the American Society for Engineering Education. Collectively, these groups have sponsored special meetings to exchange views on the subject of utilization, conducted studies on individual elements of utilization, included topics directly related to utilization on the programs of their annual meetings, provided advice on phases of utilization related to their organizational interests, and administered individual programs to improve the utilization of their membership.

The efforts of permanent federal departments, agencies, and offices and the efforts of permanent, non-government national organizations, useful as they have been, have been directed to identifiable but partial aspects of the utilization problem. None of the efforts by the permanent groups has attacked the issue of scientific and engineering manpower utilization from an overall, multi-sector viewpoint. By contrast, concerted national attention to the comprehensive problem of scientific and engineering manpower utilization, through an approach which integrated the views of employers, educators, government, scientists and engineers, professional and technical societies, and related groups, was initiated in 1956 by the President of the United States.

UTILIZATION PROGRAM OF THE PRESIDENT'S COMMITTEE ON SCIENTISTS AND ENGINEERS

The President's Committee on Scientists and Engineers was established by President Dwight D. Eisenhower in 1956 as the result of a recommendation by an interdepartmental committee under the chairmanship of the Director of the Office of Defense Mobilization in the Executive Office of the President. The interdepartmental committee, in its report to the President, pointed out that science and engineering had made such remarkable progress in recent decades that the nation which holds the lead in these fields holds the initiative in world affairs. Information available clearly showed, the committee advised the President, that the Russians were approaching comparability with the United States in both quantity and quality of scientists and engineers and might overtake the United States in some of the physical science fields. The committee stressed that the struggle for military supremacy was being waged in the fields of science and technology. Therefore, it was appropriate, the Committee informed the President, that the nation concern itself particularly with the development of men and women in science and engineering.

The interdepartmental committee believed that, in addition to the role of government, primary responsibility for the solution of many problems in the field of scientific and engineering manpower rested with leaders in education, professional and technical societies, industry, and related groups. The committee recommended to the President the creation of a White House group to deal with a portion of these problems and to be composed of representatives of major national, non-government organizations in these fields.

The recommendation was accepted by the President who established the President's Committee on Scientists and Engineers as a temporary group to respond to the concern posed by the interdepartmental committee. The President charged the committee to assist the Federal Government in identifying problems associated with the development of more highly qualified scientists and engineers, to enlist the cooperation of all interested individuals and groups in analyzing the problems and developing programs to deal with them and to take the lead in coordination of interested organizations outside of the Federal Government, to make available to all interested organizations information on effective ways of overcoming the obstacles to the training of more qualified scientists and engineers, and to publicize the problem and possible solutions in order to stimulate widespread public understanding and support.

The nineteen members of the Committee were presidents or chairmen of leading, national, non-government organizations concerned with the education, training, and use of scientific and engineering personnel. Included on the Committee were the national heads of such groups as the American Council on Education, the American Association for the Advancement of Science, the National Academy of Sciences, the American Association of Land Grant Colleges and State Universities, the U.S. Chamber of Commerce, the AFL-CIO, the American Society for Engineering Education, the Engineers Joint Council, and the Scientific Manpower Commission.

One key phase of the Committee's activity was its scientific and engineering manpower utilization program, initiated in 1957. The program consisted of two parts: (1) the stimulation of a series of scientific and technical manpower conferences having as their basic purpose the motivation of individuals and organizations with scientific and technical manpower responsibilities to enhance the utilization of this type of brainpower and (2) the initiation of contacts and maintenance of liaison with national organizations of educators, employer organizations, government agencies, professional and technical societies, and related groups in order to ascertain and to participate in activities of these organizations pertaining to scientific and engineering manpower utilization.

With respect to the stimulation of a series of scientific and technical utilization manpower conferences, the program director consulted with college and university presidents, deans of engineering, heads of departments of the physical sciences, officials of professional and technical societies, and other key individuals. The purposes of such consultations were to relate the urgency for maximum scientific and engineering manpower utilization as an action to keep the nation technically superior, to explain conference concepts as an effective device for promoting maximum use of scientific and engineering manpower resources, to urge as appropriate such individuals to undertake to sponsor and conduct a local conference, to provide informal advice (upon request) concerning planning and to participate (upon request) in the conference, and to insure that the methods for attaining objectives of one conference were considered for translation into programs of conferences and meetings in other geographical areas. Such actions were a means for achieving greater utilization of scientific and engineering manpower.

The pattern which evolved as a guide for the administration of the conferences had the following characteristics:

1. The conferences were local in character and were sponsored by local organizations vitally interested in science and engineering fields.

2. The local planning group was composed of representatives of major groups directly concerned with scientific and engineering personnel in the area.

3. The conferences were directed at policy formulators and policy makers as well as supervisors of scientists and engineers.

4. Topics covered were of such a nature that conferees could subsequently take specific actions to improve the utilization in their own organization.

5. Depth of program content leading to subsequent action by individual organizations, instead of breadth of coverage, was considered more desirable.

6. The groups sponsoring the conference determined responsibilities for conference management, according to local needs and resources.

7. The conferences were usually one and one-half days in length and featured an opening general meeting with keynoters, a series of concurrent panel sessions, two luncheon sessions, a banquet session, and a closing general meeting (which included an oral résumé of conference ideas).

8. Since a college or university was usually a basic sponsor

of the individual conference, the precise time for holding the conference was related to the total educational institution activity during an academic year and the availability of conference facilities.

9. The decision to hold a conference and the conducting of each conference (including selection of topics, speakers, and invitees) were matters wholly for the local sponsor.

10. The Federal Government did not administer the individual conference.

11. No federal funds were provided for any of these conferences; the total cost to the Federal Government for this program was the salary of the program director, the service of a secretary, and travel expenses of the program director to participate in conference planning, execution, and follow-up.

No two conference programs were identical. Each was geared to phases of the scientific and engineering manpower utilization problem of particular concern to sponsors in the geographical area covered by the conference. For example, individual conferences explored such areas as reduction of obsolescence of scientific and engineering knowledge and skills, the education and use of engineering technicians, the relationship of liberal arts programs to the effective utilization of scientific and engineering talent, improvement of management of R&D personnel, and a role for trained womanpower in science and engineering. In the aggregate, however, the conferences covered all major aspects of the problem of scientific and engineering manpower utilization.

The quality of the program and the genuine enthusiasm of the participants to consider and to apply conference ideas to their own organizations were regarded as fundamental to conference usefulness. Numbers in attendance at the conferences usually exceeded local planning committee expectations. Average attendance ranged from 100 to 150 participants. The largest attendance was 343, at Omaha, Nebraska. On the other hand, a very fruitful conference was held on the Purdue University campus, with approximately 50 persons in attendance. The ma-

[9]

jority of the conferees were from top or middle management of large-scale and small-scale employers, but all sectors directly concerned with the utilization problem were involved in each conference.

A follow-up plan was adopted by local planning committees in an effort to gauge the effectiveness of the individual conference, as well as to provide further help to the participants. Questions included on a follow-up questionnaire were matters for determination by the local planning committee. However, the usual follow-up questionnaire had two parts: Part I consisted essentially of a series of questions related to conferee opinions on the format, mechanics, and general values of the conference; Part II comprised a list of positive utilization policies and procedures which had actually been developed during the conference. The list was arranged to solicit participant response concerning follow-through on each item. The follow-up not only served as a reminder of helpful techniques reviewed at the conference, but the follow-up also elicited information from participants about particular policies and practices which participants were following which might be useful elsewhere.

Written evidence obtained by planning committees during the follow-up period indicated that, as a result of the conferences, officials of many organizations seriously considered recommendations made during the conferences from the viewpoint of local application and that specific changes were made in policies and practices of particular organizations with respect to the utilization of scientists and engineers. Officials reported that as a result of the conference, they had:

1. Delegated non-professional duties to engineering technicians and to clerical employees,
2. Recruited and trained engineering technicians,
3. Set up a program of equitable recognition of individual scientific and engineering achievement,
4. Given greater management concern to suggestions and desires of scientists and engineers,

[10]

5. Outlined specific duties of scientists and engineers on an individual basis,
6. Revised the employment interviewing system for scientists and engineers,
7. Provided in-service training,
8. Transferred qualified engineers from drafting board operations to professional tasks,
9. Initiated studies toward improved utilization of scientific and engineering personnel in their own organizations,
10. Made an evaluation of the utilization problem as related to a particular organization,
11. Included action plans for the utilization of scientific and engineering manpower in management training programs,
12. Made graduate education arrangements under which employers and educational institutions worked together to reduce the impact of obsolescence of scientific and technical knowledge,
13. Broadened course offerings to reflect rapidly changing science and technology,
14. Changed the organizational structure of individual companies to improve the utilization of R&D personnel,
15. Increased the use of support manpower to maximize the extent of bona fide scientific and engineering assignments to scientists and engineers,
16. Established committees to clarify reciprocal responsibilities of employers and of professional and technical societies with respect to granting recognition for individual and/or group scientific and engineering accomplishment.

Other conferees reported to planning committees that certain points stressed at a conference supported policies which they had already instituted in some cases.

The second part of the utilization program established by the President's Committee on Scientists and Engineers concerned the initiation of contacts and maintenance of liaison with national organizations of educators, employer organizations, government agencies, professional and technical societies, and related groups. The program director met periodically with officials of organizations which were members of the Committee and others to learn of current scientific and engineering manpower utilization programs and plans; to suggest programs for improving the education, training, and use of scientific and engineering manpower within the scope of activities of the individual organizations; and to participate in conferences and committee meetings of such organizations to assure appropriate attention to particular phases of scientific and engineering manpower utilization consistent with national policy. The objective of these actions was to strengthen the national manpower base.

Under the same program, periodic assessment was made of the changing nature of the scientific and engineering manpower utilization problem. For example, an interagency committee composed of representatives of five federal agencies and chaired by the program director assessed the problem of scientific and engineering manpower utilization in 1969. In the opinion of the group, the problem of utilization appeared to be more acute than it had been three years earlier. Among conditions cited as mitigating against effective utilization were rigid and unrealistic selection standards, lack of sufficient motivation on the part of some scientists and engineers, and a shortage of qualified engineering technicians. Among factors contributing to effective utilization were realistic opportunities for scientific and engineering personnel to advance professionally, meaningful continuing education opportunities, and the existence on a wider scale of a professional atmosphere under which scientific and engineering personnel thrive. In its evaluation of the status of scientific and engineering manpower utilization in 1969, the interagency committee concluded that much more positive action to increase effective use of scientific and engineering personnel is required in the national interest.

Under the same program, new contacts were initiated and liaison was maintained with numerous national, non-government organizations concerned with scientific and engineering

manpower. Illustrative of such contacts and liaison were informal suggestions and advice to the Association of Higher Education, to the Technical Association of the Pulp and Paper Industry, to the American Power Conference, and to the American
Petroleum Institute. In such cases, suggestions and advice were
directly responsible for the inclusion of a special panel on scientific and engineering manpower utilization on one or more annual national conference programs of each of these organizations. The program director was a formal speaker at annual
conferences of many member organizations, as well as of other
groups, such as the National Conference on Industrial Hydraulics
and the Silver Bay Conference on Human Relations in Industry.
He also participated in policy deliberations of national organizations dealing with scientific and engineering manpower, such as
the American Council on Education, the American Association
for the Advancement of Science, the National Society of Professional Engineers, the American Society for Engineering Education, and other national scientific and engineering societies.

A collateral benefit of the utilization program was that an excellent cross-section of non-government leaders in many fields
associated with the education, training, and use of scientific and
engineering manpower came in direct, personal contact not only
with leaders of permanent federal manpower programs but also
with persons outside of government who had similar interests.
These individuals formed a leadership pool from which responsible scientists, engineers, managers, and educators were subsequently chosen for special utilization assignments in private and
public endeavor.

By the time the Committee was terminated on December 31,
1958, nineteen local conferences had been held under the auspices of the Committee. In its final report to the President, the
Committee strongly recommended to the President that the Federal Government at the White House level assume the responsibility for coordinating and stimulating the nation's efforts in the
development and utilization of highly trained manpower; this responsibility should cover the continued close government liaison

[13]

and cooperation with the private agencies of the nation which educate and utilize this manpower; and pending the assumption of full responsibility for these functions by a White House agency, the key programs developed by the Committee be continued without interruption as being of vital importance to the further development of the scientific and engineering potential of the country.[1]

Based upon the recommendations of the Committee to the President and after subsequent discussions by the Director of the Office of Civil and Defense Mobilization (which had superceded the Office of Defense Mobilization), by the Secretary of Labor, by the Director of the National Science Foundation, and by others, the utilization program (both parts) was transferred, effective January 1, 1959, to OCDM. Among responsibilities of OCDM (pursuant to provision of the National Security Resources Act of 1947, subsequently applicable to OCDM), was the function of advising the President concerning the coordination of military, industrial, and civilian mobilization, including "policies concerning industrial and civilian mobilization in order to assure the most effective mobilization and maximum utilization of the nation's manpower in the event of war" and "the relationship between potential supplies of, and potential requirements for, manpower resources and productive facilities in time of war." In a sense, the utilization program was a communication device to reflect elements of scientific and engineering manpower policy useful for mobilization purposes.

When the Office of Emergency Planning was created in 1962 as successor agency to the Office of Civil and Defense Mobilization, the utilization program became a responsibility of OEP.

The first part of the utilization program, namely, the stimulation of scientific and technical manpower conferences held under the auspices of the Executive Office of the President, was ended in 1964 after a total of seventy-seven conferences had been held under PCSE-OCDM-OEP auspices over an eight year

1. The President's Committee on Scientists and Engineers, *Final Report to the President,* 1958.

period. The second part of the utilization program, namely the initiation of contacts and maintenance of liaison with national organizations of educators, employer organizations, government agencies, professional and technical societies and related groups, was ended in 1969.

CONCERN OF OTHER COMMITTEES

In addition to the scientific and technical manpower utilization program initiated by the President's Committee on Scientists and Engineers and continued by the Office of Civil and Defense Mobilization and by the Office of Emergency Planning, the Federal Government showed a broad integrated concern for scientific and engineering manpower utilization through the efforts of five other White House inspired, or Executive Office level, temporary committees established during the decade of the 1960s.

The membership of these five committees appointed during the 1960s was different in each case; hence, each committee provided a fresh look and brought additional ideas to bear on aspects of the utilization problem under its purview. These committees in the aggregate dealt with several utilization issues which had been examined by the PCSE-OCDM-OEP utilization program and, in addition, gave attention to new utilization issues. Continuity was provided, in part, by the program director of the PCSE-OCDM-OEP utilization program who was assigned, collaterally, to perform staff work for each of the five temporary committees.

At the initiation of President John F. Kennedy, two temporary groups were created to examine aspects of scientific and engineering manpower. Both groups became involved with the scientific and engineering manpower utilization problem.

President Kennedy requested his Science Advisory Committee to examine the nation's scientific and technical manpower resources to determine the quantity and quality required to meet future needs. A Manpower Panel was appointed by the Chairman of the Committee to analyze manpower problems and to submit recommendations for an action program to the Committee. Members of the Manpower Panel came from education, industry, government, and professional and technical societies. The Manpower Panel, and subsequently the Committee, examined the role of scientific and technical personnel in connection with national activities. The report issued in December 1962 set forth a series of national scientific and technical manpower goals which involved an increase in the number of doctor's degrees to be awarded each year in science and engineering and an increase in the number of students to complete a full year of graduate education in these fields. The report also favored an increase in the number of qualified engineering technicians and the improved use of such technicians. The Committee stressed that the use of technicians in all areas of science and engineering conserves professional skills and thus enhances total manpower resources.[2]

President Kennedy also approved the undertaking of a study of the utilization of scientists and engineers to be conducted by a committee appointed by the National Academy of Sciences. The Academy in 1962 set up an ad hoc group called the Committee on Utilization of Scientific and Engineering Manpower. The seventeen members of the NAS Utilization Committee were selected from government, industry, and education.

In its deliberations the Committee viewed utilization in a broad context—concerned with humanistic as well as economic goals. The Committee report, published in 1964, dealt with the distribution of personnel in relation to needs, productivity in various working environments, and effects of education upon productivity. These elements were considered in two dimensions: the value of the work done and the development of the people doing the work.

The recommendations of the Committee were divided into four parts. Concerning the Federal Government, the Committee urged, in part, assessment of the impact of large technological programs

2. President's Science Advisory Committee, *Meeting Manpower Needs in Science and Technology, Report No. 1; Graduate Training in Engineering, Mathematics and Physical Sciences,* 1962.

on deployment of scientists and engineers before future program approval, top official agency responsibility for supervising the utilization of scientists and engineers, use of fixed price and incentive contracts, and greater emphasis on high level professional competence in the federal science establishment. Concerning industry, the Committee urged, in part, action to enable promising scientists and engineers to develop and apply their competencies fully, provision for a climate for creativity and productivity, and programs for management improvement. Concerning colleges and universities, the Committee urged, in part, augmentation of efforts to improve professional engineering education and curriculum development. Concerning research, the Committee urged that government, industry, and universities should expand or initiate research to provide broader perspectives and increased knowledge for dealing more effectively with utilization issues.[3]

President Lyndon B. Johnson appointed a National Commission on Technology, Automation and Economic Progress in 1964. The law which established the Commission charged the Commission to identify and assess past effects and the current and prospective role and pace of technological change, to identify and describe the impact of technological and economic change on production and employment, to define areas of unmet community and human needs toward which application of new technologies might most effectively be directed, to assess the most effective means for channeling new technologies into promising directions, and to recommend specific administrative and legislative steps which it believed should be taken by federal, state, and local governments in meeting their responsibilities. Members of the Commission came from industry, education, and related groups and were aided by an advisory committee of government representatives. One aspect of the Commission's activity was its concern for facilitating adjustment of manpower—including

3. National Academy of Science Committee on Utilization of Scientific and Engineering Manpower, *Toward Better Utilization of Scientific and Engineering Talent, A Program for Action,* 1964.

scientific and engineering manpower—to technological change, a vital utilization issue.

The Commission created a Panel to explore the role of technological forecasting in manpower adjustment. The Panel subsequently set forth reasons for the inadequate use of existing forecasting data: employers, government officials, educators, and others at the local level found it difficult to translate national occupational information into local meanings; requirements for immediate placement were generally given priority over prospective placements; and occupational forecasting information was considered difficult to interpret. The Panel believed that although much information about occupational demands—both short and long range—was potentially available, many announced efforts by responsible officials in and out of government to anticipate and ease dislocations tended to "evaporate" upon close inspection. The Panel likewise felt that many actions were best undertaken by the organization responsible for the dislocation, partially because such an organization had, to some extent, the timing and character of the dislocation within its control. Forecasting may contribute to effectiveness of efforts to ease job dislocations by guiding counseling and retraining and by enabling an amelioration agency to anticipate and prepare helpful counteraction. The overwhelming need, according to the Panel, was for local and short range (0-5 years) forecasting information. The Panel recommended that for the support of local manpower adjustment activities, forecasting data should be assembled on a locality basis in a systematized manner and be made available to local manpower adjustment mediators in the public and private sector; local information centers should expand their influence by assisting in the establishment of regional information centers; certain kinds of information, national in scope and centrally generated, should be made available to local and regional forecasters; and a central agency should support continuing work on methodology for technological forecasts as well as assess the usefulness of available technological forecasts.

On a broader scale, the Commission concluded that sufficient knowledge about potential capacities of employees was lacking and consequently many individuals were not given training for jobs at the highest levels of their capabilities. To the extent that this condition prevailed, the Commission said, existing human assets were being wasted.

Among its recommendations, the Commission favored lifetime opportunities for education, training, and retraining; creation of a national computerized job-man matching system; regional technical institutes in each Federal Reserve district to serve as centers for disseminating scientific and technical knowledge relevant to the region's development; encouragement of federal, state, and local governments to conduct themselves as model employers in the development of adjustment techniques; and increased efforts to make available for non-government use results of government performed or funded research.[4]

Pursuant to legislation which President Johnson signed in 1966, the President established a temporary Commission on Marine Science, Engineering and Resources, composed of fifteen members appointed by him. The purpose of the Commission was to make a study of all aspects of marine science in order to recommend an overall plan for an adequate national oceanographic program. Members were selected from industry, education, and government. The Commission undertook, among its functions, to review aspects of scientific and engineering manpower utilization as applied to marine personnel. A peculiarity of marine personnel is that most scientists and engineers engaged in marine work obtain their degrees in basic disciplines (such as physics, chemistry or electronics engineering) and are not technically identified as marine scientists or marine engineers. Hence, consideration of marine professional manpower requires broader treatment than concern only for those who are formally classified as marine scientists or marine engineers.

---

4. National Commission on Technology, Automation and Economic Progress, *Technology and the American Economy,* 1966.

[19]

A Committee staff study on marine scientific and engineering manpower pointed out a lack of midcareer training programs for those in the marine field whose assignments are so limited as to provide them with a narrow perspective of marine developments. A major conclusion of the staff study was the need for a stronger mechanism for obtaining and analyzing data on education and training programs and on manpower needs and for coordinating federal activities to support the education and training of marine personnel. The staff study recommended an increase in funding for the sea grant college program, greater emphasis on midcareer training and on post-doctoral education, and the creation of a series of national centers for marine education and training.

The Panel on Education, Manpower and Training of the Commission pointed out the lack of reliable manpower data, including lack of a concensus on definitions of job categories for work in the marine field. The Panel recommended that within a proposed new oceanographic agency an office be established to assess marine education and training needs. The Panel also favored increased funding for the sea grant program and urged greater emphasis on midcareer training and post-doctoral education.

The Panel on Basic Science and Research of the Commission, observing that the supply of oceanographic technicians is likely over the short term to prove the most critical manpower area in basic marine research, recommended the creation of additional training programs for marine technicians. The Panel stated that these programs should involve junior colleges and technical institutes. The Panel also favored, as part of an expanded program of professional training, support of postdoctoral programs at marine science research centers.

In its report to the President and to the Congress in 1969, the Commission expressed concern for elements of scientific and engineering manpower utilization. The Commission recommended that a proposed new oceanographic agency be assigned responsibility to help assure that the nation's marine manpower needs are satisfied and to help devise uniform standards for the nomenclature of marine occupations. Among other functions, the new agency would give special attention to methods for updating skills and for aiding interdisciplinary transfers; in some specialties transfers require re-education or reorientation. The Commission favored expansion of federal support for marine technician training through the sea grant program. The Commission also recommended that the National Science Foundation should plan postdoctoral and midcareer marine orientation programs in consultation with educators and industry.[5]

In the same legislation establishing the Commission on Marine Science, Engineering and Resources, a temporary National Council on Marine Resources and Engineering Development was created, composed of the Vice-President as chairman, six cabinet officers, and the heads of two agencies. Input from industry and education was obtained through use of panels and consultants. The act stipulated that the marine science activities of the United States should be conducted so as to contribute to the effective utilization of the science and engineering resources of the nation in close cooperation among all interested agencies, public and private, in order to avoid unnecessary duplication of effort. The act also gave the President the duty, with the advice and assistance of the Council, to survey all significant marine science activities (including policies, plans, programs, and accomplishments) of the Federal Government and to develop a comprehensive program of marine science activities. In addition, under separate legislation the Council was required, as the President requested, to advise the National Science Foundation with respect to policies, procedures, and operations of the Foundation in its carrying out the sea grant program. In connection with its responsibilities, the Council not only provided positive guidance for the administration of the sea grant program but also prepared and disseminated data related to scientific and engineering manpower utilization, such as information on graduate education opportunities and on the training and use of techni-

5. Commission on Marine Science, Engineering and Resources, *Our Nation and the Sea*, 1969.

cians to relieve scientists and engineers of nonprofessional duties.[6]

The work of each of these temporary committees appointed during the 1960s ended with publication of a report which crystallized, from an integrated viewpoint, approaches to the utilization problem as related to the mission of the committee. Each report offered constructive suggestions for consideration and implementation by groups and individuals having responsibilities in the area of scientific and engineering manpower utilization. In a few cases, the work of these temporary committees contributed to legislative and administrative change. For examples, the concern of the Manpower Panel of the President's Science Advisory Committee for technicians aided the passage of the Vocational Education Act of 1963; views of the National Council on Marine Resources and Engineering Development assisted in the implementation of the sea grant program of the National Science Foundation. However, insofar as scientific and engineering manpower utilization was concerned, the immediate outcome of the work of the five committees appointed during the 1960s was orientation and education for those groups and individuals involved with the utilization problem. No specific administrative mechanism was created for subsequent follow-through with those groups to whom the utilization recommendations contained in the reports were addressed.

Through the activities of the utilization program initiated by the President's Committee on Scientists and Engineers and through the activities of the five subsequent temporary committees cited, the Federal Government, at the Presidential level, acted as a listening post to identify the problem of scientific and engineering manpower and to ascertain its changing nature; as a point of information exchange; and as a stimulator of action on the part of government itself and on the part of employers, educators, scientists and engineers, professional and technical societies, and related groups. The influence of these temp-

6. National Council on Marine Resources and Engineering Development, *Marine Science Affairs, Second Report of the President to the Congress,* 1968; *Third Report of the President to the Congress,* 1969.

orary committees, coupled with policies, programs, and actions both of permanent government departments, agencies, and offices and of permanent, non-government organizations, has been highly beneficial.

ASPECTS OF THE PROBLEM

When one views the whole period from 1956 to the present time, progress in achieving better utilization of scientists and engineers is distinctly recognizable. Some responsible officials and individuals in all sectors involved with the problem—employers, educators, government, scientists and engineers, professional and technical societies, and related groups—appreciate the problem and have introduced on a sustained basis successful solutions to individual phases. For other officials and individuals, constructive action has accelerated or waned as the immediate availability of scientists and engineers for employment in a particular geographical area has decreased or increased. Countless others have acquired a serious concern for the utilization problem but have not been able to take adequate steps toward its solution.

Another characteristic of the utilization problem has been that aspects of the problem itself have changed. For example, the need for off-campus formal academic courses to provide continuing education for scientists and engineers has lessened considerably in several geographical areas because of acceptance of the concept of off-campus courses by educational institutions which previously did not regard such service to be within the purview of their responsibility. On the other hand, the proliferation of the printed word has compounded the need for effective ways to store and retrieve scientific and technical information. The ever-changing nature of the utilization problem means that no official or individual can afford to be complacent after positive steps to improve utilization have been successfully taken. The currently accelerated pace of science and technology brings forth new challenges to the goal of maximum utilization.

As the nation embarks upon the decade of the 1970s, six major current aspects of the goal of optimizing the utilization of scien-

[23]

tific and engineering manpower are identifiable. These aspects are strengthening selected personnel functions, increasing the availability and use of engineering technicians, broadening the role of continuing education, facilitating the retrieval of information, deferring graduate students, and minimizing the impact of defense cutbacks. The thrust of the following chapters is to describe each of these aspects, to analyze factors involved, and to present suggestions for consideration and for follow-through action.

II

STRENGTHENING SELECTED PERSONNEL FUNCTIONS

•

NATURE OF SELECTED PERSONNEL FUNCTIONS

The operation of a science-oriented or technology-oriented organization involves the execution of personnel functions which especially influence the performance of scientists and engineers. The administration of particular functions may be deliberately and uniquely focused in order to promote maximum utilization of scientific and engineering personnel employed in an organization.

To achieve this objective, employers engage in a series of special activities designed to strengthen selected personnel functions. The number of employers presently engaged in any one of these activities varies considerably. Any one employer does not normally pursue all of these activities. A range of activities has been chosen to illustrate tested actions, worthy of consideration and adoption by employers on a wider scale.

The range of selected activities are grouped into four categories: (1) activities related to the accession of scientists and engineers and their entrance on duty for their initial assignment in an organization, (2) activities related to work operations of scientists and engineers, (3) activities related to rewards for scientific and engineering achievement, and (4) activities related to the training of scientists and engineers as managers.

ACCESSION AND ENTRANCE ON DUTY

Activities related to the accession of scientists and engineers and their entrance on duty for their initial assignment in an organization involve using selection standards attuned simultaneously to both current and prospective assignments, avoiding under-rating of actual or potential scientific and engineering talent, and providing in-house training to facilitate performance of initial duties.

USING SELECTION STANDARDS

Criteria in selection standards which are too high or too re-stricted to the immediate job vacancy bring into an organization scientists and engineers whose progressive professional growth may be impeded. For example, a selection standard under which only those persons in the top 10% of a baccalaureate graduation class are eligible for consideration for employment in entry science and engineering positions may be unrealistic because the capabilities of graduates falling between the top 10% and 25% may more nearly approximate actual and potential requirements of positions for which selections are being made.

In an effort to bring talent in harmony with assignment needs, employers devise and use standards simultaneously attuned to the short and long range manpower requirements of the organiza-tion. Under such standards, employers select scientists and en-gineers having capabilities reasonably related to both current and prospective assignments. When employers choose for po-tential growth assignments, they weigh basic attributes, such as formal education, experience acquired, extent of currency in one's specialized field, capacity to grow, and evaluations of applicants made outside the organization.

Realities of supply-demand relationships at a particular time and place may cause compromises with respect to the nature of the attributes possessed by those finally selected. A shortage of qualified applicants may force a lowering of minimum criteria in established standards and thus, in the long run, tend to dilute the quality of the scientific and engineering manpower in an organi-zation. A surplus of qualified applicants may cause a raising of minimum criteria in selection standards so high that subsequent satisfactory utilization of talent may be nearly impossible.

The fact is that criteria in selection standards which reflect elements of individual potential growth, as well as elements of

[26]

current performance, are vital to a concern for scientific and engineering manpower utilization. Scientists and engineers who enter employment in an organization become, over a period of time, the manpower base with respect to which actions are taken to improve personnel utilization. A factor in optimizing the use of scientists and engineers is the quality of this talent, determined to a large degree by properly designed selection standards.

AVOIDING UNDERRATING

Avoiding underrating of actual or potential talent in the accession process pertains to three identifiable types of applicants for scientific and engineering positions: (1) women, (2) senior scientists and engineers, and (3) minority group members. Rating equitably and choosing qualified applicants from among these groups, according to ability, promotes better utilization of scientific and engineering talent. It is anticipated that the numbers of qualified and available scientists and engineers in each of these groups will increase in the years ahead.

Women as scientists and engineers

Women have made progress in science and engineering during the past decade. A total of 10,215 women reported themselves in four fields of the physical sciences identified in the 1960 census. It is estimated that there are approximately 13,400 women so employed at present.

In the 1960 census, 7,211 women reported themselves as engineers. It is estimated that approximately 11,500 women are currently employed as engineers.

Valid questions can be raised concerning the meaningfulness of the above figures because of such problems as occupational definition and the self-reporting procedure associated with census taking. Nevertheless, even if these increases are only approximations, they represent important employment advances.

The number of degrees in science and engineering awarded to women is also increasing. For academic year 1967-68, a total of 13,751 women received degrees in science, as shown in Table II-1.

[27]

Table II–1

DEGREES IN SCIENCE AWARDED TO WOMEN, 1967-68

Areas	Bachelor's Degrees	Master's Degrees	Doctor's Degrees
Computer sciences and systems analysis	55	30	0
Mathematical subjects	8,786	1,331	52
Physical sciences	2,674	635	188
TOTAL	11,515	1,996	240

Source: OE data

It is estimated that, during academic year 1968-69, approximately 16,400 degrees were awarded to women in the three areas cited above. Because of the time lag associated with undergraduate science degree selection and the nature of undergraduate statistics, no estimates are available on the total number of women who are now studying for degrees in science.

Women were awarded 312 degrees in engineering during academic year 1967-68. It is estimated that approximately 400 engineering degrees were awarded to women during 1968-69.

The number of women who are now studying undergraduate engineering is estimated to be more than 1,800. A survey of women undergraduates enrolled in engineering schools having one or more engineering curricula accredited by the Engineers Council for Professional Development revealed that 1,289 women were so enrolled during academic year 1967-68.[1] According to the survey, conducted by the Society of Women Engineers, the 1,289 women pursued the engineering curricula shown in Table II-2.

Table II–2

WOMEN ENROLLED IN UNDERGRADUATE ENGINEERING CURRICULA, 1967-68

Field	Number of Women
Aeronautical/aerospace	75
Agricultural	3

1. Society of Women Engineers, *Report on Women Undergraduate Students in Engineering*, 1968.

Table II–2 (Continued)

Field	Number of Women
Architectural	5
Ceramic	33
Chemical	209
Civil	150
Electrical/electronic	194
Engineering mathematics	33
Engineering physics	4
Engineering science	42
Engineering mechanics	11
General engineering	156
Geological	19
Industrial	43
Materials	13
Mechanical	107
Metallurgical/mining	25
Nuclear	6
Petroleum	4
Other/unspecified	157

Source: SWE study

Thus, women undergraduates centered their engineering education, in order of frequency, in chemical, electrical/electronic, general, and civil branches.

Comparison of women undergraduate engineering enrollment over a ten year period reveals the general growth pattern shown in Table II-3.

Table II–3

COMPARISON OF ENROLLMENT OF WOMEN IN
UNDERGRADUATE ENGINEERING CURRICULA

Survey year	Schools Reporting	Total Enrollment
1959-60	128	1,035
1961-62	116	902
1963-64	148	1,038
1965-66	149	1,426
1967-68	118	1,289
1969-70	—	(est.) 1,810

Source: SWE study

[29]

The irregular number of schools reporting makes a comparison, in terms of absolute numbers, impossible; however, one may conclude that total enrollments during the decade, as reported at two year intervals, has shown a steady increase.

Federal employment represents about 12% of total science employment in the United States and about 14% of total engineering employment. According to the U. S. Civil Service Commission, there were 1,626 women in federal civilian positions classified as scientists and 379 women in engineering positions in 1968. Women thus represented 10.3% of the total federal civilian scientists and .5% of the total federal civilian engineers. This statistical picture is not impressive, yet data for 1969 showed an increase both in total numbers of women employed as scientists and engineers and in relative percentages of same.

However, the range of tasks represented by these women is impressive. Of the total number of women holding federal science positions in 1968, the largest single group was classified as mathematicians and statisticians (44%), followed by chemists (35%), cartographers (8%), physicists (4%), and general physical scientists (3%). Of the total number of women holding federal engineering positions, the largest single group was classified as aerospace engineers (23%), followed by electronics engineers (18%), civil engineers (16%), and mechanical engineers (11%). Other women engineers in the federal service are classified as general, safety, materials, sanitary, nuclear, electrical, marine, petroleum, agricultural, ceramic, chemical, and industrial engineers. The total list of branches in which women engineers are working in the federal service indicates growing interest among women in a wide variety of engineering fields, including newer technologies. Partially because women perform successfully in such a variety of science and engineering positions in the federal service, individual industrial employers are seeking to make better use of the talent of women in science and engineering assignments.

In spite of an increase in the employment of women in science and engineering, the talent of women who have scientific and engineering capabilities is often underrated by employers. Analysis of the accession of womenpower in science and engineering requires attention to attitudes and beliefs held by some employers concerning the role of women as scientists and engineers. These employers assert that:

1. Women are less objective than men in their approach to science and technology. However, the fact is that this claim is difficult to substantiate and apparently no statistical proof exists.

2. Women have substantially higher rates of absenteeism than men. However, the fact is that while experience in some cases has shown this statement to be true—especially in the first years of their employment, absenteeism rates for women who remain in employment compare favorably with absenteeism rates for men.

3. It is traditional for science and engineering positions to be regarded as men's work. However, the fact is that experience is showing that women perform very creditably in science and engineering positions and are becoming more accepted in their role in science and technology.

4. Women do not have the intellectual ability or the scientific and technical aptitude for work in science and engineering. However, the fact is that intellectual ability and scientific and technical aptitude are often found among women to the same degree as among men.

5. The probability of marriage makes it impractical for an employer to regard women as long term employees of an organization. However, the fact is that marriage does not necessarily reduce the total working life of women in science and engineering. Contrary to opinion that the education and training of women are wasted because of early separation from employment on account of marriage, evidence shows that married women scientists and engineers often return subsequently to such employment for relatively long periods of time.

More women are becoming available for employment in science and engineering positions. Educational institutions are making more flexible admission requirements for women who wish to enter or resume their educational programs in science and engineering, designing retraining programs in science and engineering to fit women's educational needs, and offering updating programs in science and engineering for women at convenient daytime hours.

Increasing numbers of employers are refraining from underrating women as scientists and engineers in the accession process. To increase the utilization of women in science and engineering, employers are undertaking a series of positive actions. Specifically, employers establish part-time positions for women qualified and available for employment in science and engineering, facilitate the establishment of day care centers for children of mothers who have been educated in science and engineering and who wish to accept employment in these fields, place women educated in science and engineering in challenging positions in these fields, provide continuing education opportunities for women in science and engineering, and choose women for a variety of types of assignments in science and engineering. Individual employers report that women have personal qualities of special value for science and engineering work such as an inquiring mind, imagination, a logical manner of thinking, and interest in precise measurement. The question of the capability of women as scientists and engineers is being resolved affirmatively as attested by accomplishments and honors bestowed on women for such employment. Growing acceptance of the principle of equal opportunity in the accession process means a more active role for women in science and engineering.

Senior scientists and engineers

The talent of senior scientists and engineers is sometimes underrated by employers in the accession process. As scientists and engineers approach fifty-five years of age, it becomes frequently difficult, or even impossible, for them to obtain an opportunity to utilize their knowledge and skills fully even though they are physically and mentally capable of so doing. Unfortunately, from the viewpoint of utilization, general concern of some employers and counselors has been based on an attitude which places a high priority on helping the senior person accept full time retirement gracefully. Professional and technical societies have usually been unwilling or unable to cope with the problem. As a matter of fact, the utilization of senior scientists and engineers has not been a primary concern of any national organization.

Obstacles to the effective utilization of qualified senior scientists and engineers include the following:

1. Compulsory retirement policy—The adoption of compulsory retirement programs in industry automatically bars continued utilization of senior scientists and engineers. A compulsory retirement policy prevents an employer from making decisions on the retention (or acquisition) of senior scientists and engineers on the basis of their individual current capabilities.

2. Age hierarchy—An age hierarchy in industry mitigates against the entrance of senior scientists and engineers into an organization. Also, industrial pension plans often restrict entry into employment in an organization at an advanced age.

3. Legal restrictions—Legal restrictions not aimed primarily at scientists and engineers may, nevertheless, make the employment of senior scientists and engineers especially difficult. For example, the willingness of senior scientists to accept teaching positions in secondary schools may be negated by state licensing laws. Local government residence requirements may impede senior scientists and engineers from entering municipal employment.

4. Individual inability to adjust quickly—Senior scientists and engineers are sometimes unable to adjust quickly to available opportunities. It may be difficult for individual scientists and engineers, once in highly essential assignments, to move to less significant positions in science and engineering. A consulting relationship is not always attractive to senior scientists and engineers because such an assignment means loss of administrative

[33]

prerogatives. Another aspect is that opportunities may require senior scientists and engineers to move out of a community in which they have held a responsible position for many years and take up residence in a new environment with lower prestige.

Adequate data on the incidence of the problem of utilization of senior scientists and engineers are not available. Census occupational categories are imprecise: where a census count singles out an occupational category in science and engineering, such as chemist, information on the number in such a category who are 65 years of age or older is ascertainable; however, such data are not known for several types of scientists and for many types of engineers. Furthermore, semi-retired and retired scientists and engineers are not tabulated by the census in a way that permits evaluation of the status of the over sixty-five years of age group.

Nevertheless, senior scientists and engineers who are capable and willing to continue in employment in science and engineering constitute a substantial underutilized reservoir of knowledge and skills.

An example of an effort to promote the utilization of senior scientists and engineers is the Mohawk Development Service of Schenectady, New York. This group was organized to find continuing employment for engineers retired from the General Electric Company and the American Locomotive Company. The Service is designed to provide engineering work for capable retirees who prefer to continue in employment and offers engineering services to several clients. Within the framework of community resources and requirements, this project suggests a workable approach for adaptation elsewhere.

Actions taken by employers to make better use of the talent of senior scientists and engineers include identification of precise types of scientific and engineering assignments best suited to the abilities of senior scientists and engineers, obtaining of more qualitative information on specific abilities of available senior scientists and engineers, and modification of terms and conditions of employment. As involuntary retirement programs in industry and government result in more senior scientists and engineers becoming available for employment, employers are finding greater opportunity to make full use of the expertise of this type of scientific and engineering talent through the accession process.

Minority Group Members as Scientists and Engineers

The talent of minority group members who are qualified as scientists and engineers is sometimes underrated by employers in the accession process. The number of minority group members who are qualified as scientists and engineers is presently small. It is estimated that six predominantly Negro institutions enroll approximately 70% of black students in engineering in the United States and that the engineering enrollment for academic year 1969-70 in the six institutions was approximately 2,100; slightly more than half of this number was in three of these institutions having programs accredited by the Engineers Council for Professional Development.

Factors, such as relative length of education programs in science and engineering, financial pressures, and inadequate secondary education preparation, which have often deterred members of minority groups from choosing science and engineering as a career, are being overcome through a series of measures aimed at providing better educational opportunities for minority group members at all levels of education.

One approach to broaden minority group member participation in science and engineering education is typified by the Newark College of Engineering. Twenty high school graduates who could not meet normal entrance standards but who showed promise of success and interest in engineering accepted, under the Engineering Opportunity Program of the College, an invitation to complete a program of academic assistance and review of basic course work during the summer of 1968. At the end of the summer session each student was given the option of entering as a freshman or receiving assistance to enter a nonengineering program at another institution. All twenty expressed a desire to

[35]

enter the college as freshmen and were admitted in the fall of 1968. Eighteen students completed the academic year 1968-69; of this group, five did not appear to be making sufficient progress toward the ultimate goal of an engineering degree, but they were given another chance to show achievement in academic year 1969-70. A second group of twenty students participated in the 1969 summer program and on the basis of their performance were continued for academic year 1969-70. Through its experience with the initial groups, the college is strengthening its program. The probable effect of this approach, tested and adopted by other institutions, will be to increase the availability of minority group members who have demonstrated talent for science and engineering.

Other programs, such as the "Three-Two" program of Atlanta-based liberal arts schools and the Georgia Institute of Technology and the Upward Bound program of the U. S. Office of Education, have been initiated to facilitate the development of both institutions and of members of minority groups and result in better educated minority group members in science and engineering. As minority group members who are prospective scientists and engineers are educated under accredited curricula, they become available to enter employment with knowledge and skills similar to other graduates. The use of scientific and engineering talent possessed by minority group members is likewise being utilized by some employers on the same basis as other graduates.

PROVIDING IN-HOUSE TRAINING

In-house training is provided by employers to facilitate the use of scientific and engineering talent in connection with initial regular assignments. This type of training, not to be confused with upgrading, takes a variety of forms.

Orientation training gives scientists and engineers entering upon duty an understanding of the mission of the organization and policies and procedures to be followed. Some form of orientation training takes place in most organizations. A formal orientation program may consist of one or more group sessions, a selective tour of the facility, and an introduction to administrative services provided by the employer to aid scientists and engineers.

Special short courses are established by employers to aid scientists and engineers in the performance of the duties of their initial assignments. Formal collegiate courses do not meet all of the training needs of scientists and engineers; the need for professional knowledge to carry out an initial assignment may not coincide with information acquired in a traditional college course. As a result, short courses are offered to provide additional information.

A rotation method of on-the-job training offers a broad experience to new scientists and engineers preparatory to their assuming their initial regular positions. The degree of success of such a plan depends upon several factors such as effective administration, enthusiasm of personnel trained, and acceptance of the plan by staff who supervise the personnel trained. Under the rotation program, a participant is given two or more assignments; usually some portion of training time is devoted to the phase of the scientific or engineering field in which the individual is to be assigned indefinitely. Training is normally provided by several supervisors. At the end of the rotation period and after consideration of such factors as positions available, types of work performed by the individual in the rotation process, his special aptitudes, supervisory preferences, and individual preferences, the scientist or engineer is given his first regular assignment.

Demands upon the total staff of scientists and engineers in an organization to meet deadlines may force emphasis on current output and tend to slow up the orderly transition of new appointees to their positions through in-house training. Where supervisors are too busy with current work schedules to give the necessary time to assist new personnel or where the regular work week extends to forty-five hours or more, supervisors may feel that they do not have the time or energy to conduct in-house training for new scientists and engineers. A feeling of indifference toward in-house training for scientists and engineers may

[37]

be characteristic of the attitude of a few senior supervisors who themselves "came up the hard way." However, many employers realize that in-house training provided in connection with initial regular assignment does help scientists and engineers to improve the use of their talent.

WORK OPERATIONS

Activities related to work operations of scientists and engineers involve maintaining a physical environment conducive to performance, applying the human relations approach, reassessing the match between capabilities and actual duties, keeping open the avenues of internal communication, fostering creativity, monitoring voluntary separations, and planning for future manpower needs.

MAINTAINING A PHYSICAL ENVIRONMENT CONDUCIVE TO PERFORMANCE

Concern for the nature of the physical environment in which scientists and engineers perform their duties and for the impact of the environment upon their efforts is accepted as a continuing responsibility by employers who seek to maximize scientific and engineering manpower utilization. At first, consideration of the physical environment may seem elementary, but an attractive physical environment exerts a very positive effect upon scientific and engineering manpower utilization. The physical environment consists of two aspects: the laboratory, office or plant and equipment.

Employers find that permanent buildings offer more suitable working conditions for scientists and engineers than temporary buildings. Moderate temperatures in the laboratory, office or plant are often maintained by air conditioning. A work locale free from noise irritants generally provides a desirable setting for scientific and engineering productivity. Where several scientists and engineers are assigned to the same large work area, effort is made to eliminate any feeling of crowdedness through use of properly designed space arrangements, such as the use of tem-

[38]

porary partitions, to provide a degree of privacy. If conditions become unpleasant, employers with a view toward better utilization either relocate personnel or eliminate or reduce negative environmental features.

Employers provide an array of modern equipment which saves time of scientists and engineers. For example, the use of electronic dictation equipment permits scientists and engineers to dictate directly to a machine without preparing handwritten drafts for typing. Pocket-sized dictating machines enable scientists and engineers to record while they are away from the office. Availability of a copy machine permits fast reproduction of charts, drawings, and other illustrative material needed at the moment and eliminates the possibility of error in the process.

The use of computers by scientists and engineers is increasing. Scientists and engineers have become so familiar with the capacity of computers that in some organizations the use of computers is almost as extensive as the traditional slide rule. Employers keep alert to computer developments in order that models which they rent or buy incorporate the latest degree of capability most useful for the type of scientific and engineering work performed in the organization. Calculations which in precomputer days involved days or weeks of the time of scientists and engineers are now performed in a few minutes by a computer.

In addition to the element of time saving, computers upgrade the character of the work which scientists and engineers are called upon to perform. Computers provide more challenging tasks for scientists and engineers who use them. Computers also play a major part in the solution of scientific and engineering problems. For example, the high speed feature of the computer permits making a large number of calculations applied to a vast mass of data—such as basic information used for weather forecasting—and hence brings solutions to problems which otherwise could not be solved within a reasonable time frame. The ultimate use of computers seems limited only by the imagination and intellect of scientists and engineers.

Employers find that the cost of providing expensive equipment may be surprisingly low when the depreciation factor is considered. If, for example, a piece of equipment worth $1,000 is purchased and is used by a $10,000 per year scientist or engineer, five minutes saved each day through use of the equipment may justify the purchase cost within a reasonable time. The use of a piece of equipment may so speed the completion of a particular assignment that the total time saved may be used to perform other assignments.

The acquisition of an arsenal of modern equipment in excellent working condition and easily available represents a vital part of an attractive environment for scientific and engineering effort.

Applying the Human Relations Approach

The human relations approach is a practice of employers in applying psychological principles of individual and group behavior to scientists and engineers in a work situation. This approach recognizes that behind the formal organization created to accomplish a science or technology objective is a group of individual scientists and engineers with varying human needs and goals. In the work situation, each scientist or engineer makes personal adjustments in the performance of the formal tasks which he is assigned. A series of adjustments become crystallized into behavior patterns which make up the social system of the organization. Although the social system in a science-oriented or technology-oriented organization is unique to that organization, there are comparable elements of the system in similar type organizations. Employers recognize the existence of a social system in their organization and develop policies which help to fulfill needs and aspirations of the scientists and engineers belonging to the system. Need and aspiration fulfillment generally results in improved utilization.

To illustrate specific employer action in this respect, employers recognize the presence of particular goals of scientists and engineers. These goals include a sense of belonging to an organization, relative independence in work practices, acceptance of work achievement by their peers, personal accomplishment, and professional respect. Employers then initiate steps to make these aspirations attainable by making known to scientists and engineers the importance of their contributions to the organization, maintaining opportunities for scientists and engineers to contribute to management decisions, assisting scientists and engineers to publish scientific and technical papers in their own name, providing for scientists and engineers a measure of self-determination in the selection of assignments, and encouraging extracurricular professional-satisfying activities.

The human relations approach stresses the importance of motivation in scientific and engineering manpower utilization. With an understanding of principles of motivation, employers engage in a series of actions designed to provide motivation for scientists and engineers in their organization. For example, employers encourage scientists and engineers to have contacts with outstanding leaders in particular areas of science and engineering who are respected for their superior accomplishment, to meet with colleagues who hold contrasting views, to maintain an independent frame of mind, and to take advantage of the open administrative door which is established to strengthen scientist-engineer-management rapport.

The crash program illustrates how motivation of scientists and engineers leads to increased utilization. In this instance, employers set forth a greater work challenge, pay special attention to the work effort, seek advice of scientists and engineers concerning the program, recognize the essentiality of teamwork, and indicate appreciation for the contributions which make up the total crash effort. Through such steps, motivation is increased, and scientists and engineers use their talents more fully to attain significant accomplishment during a limited time period.

The net effect of the human relations approach is to recognize the individual identity of scientists and engineers in the work situation and by satisfying their individual needs and aspirations help them to enhance the utilization of their capabilities.

[41]

Reassessing the Match Between Capabilities and Actual Duties

To help obtain maximum use of the talent of scientists and engineers, employers periodically make an assessment to ascertain the nature of the match between the qualifications and potential of individual scientists and engineers and the actual duties they perform. A proper match means that the duties performed by scientists and engineers are directly related to their professional capabilities and that they are developing in a professional manner. This aim is facilitated if the capabilities and duties are matched, not only at the beginning of employment in organization, but also during subsequent tenure of employment.

Greater endurance of a once-made match tends to occur in obvious situations. For example, a scientist with an insatiable quest for new knowledge may best be assigned as a sole researcher in a laboratory over a long period of time; another scientist with a flair for imparting knowledge may continue most properly as a leader of scientists engaged in developmental work. However, the proportion of scientists and engineers who typify the obvious match is small. Hence, periodic assessments are logical considerations for the majority of the scientific and engineering staff.

An essential part of the rematching process is identification of specific tasks being performed, methods used to perform the tasks, and an order of priority of individual professional efforts. In making these determinations, employers screen each professional task against a series of criteria such as the need for the performance of the task, the reason for performing the task in a particular manner, and the timeliness of the task being performed. The application of such criteria helps to eliminate unnecessary tasks and to revise the priority of specific tasks. To determine the most suitable assignments requires extreme care on the part of employers working in close association with scientists and engineers. The complex nature of making such judgments prompts employers sometimes to designate trial and error assignments to test their judgment with respect to the right match.

[42]

In the reassessment process, it is essential that administrative and clerical duties of scientists and engineers be reduced to the fullest extent possible. The effectiveness of scientists and engineers in their professional fields is often impaired by the failure of employers to provide staff assistance to relieve scientists and engineers of administrative and clerical detail. Administrative assistants, other staff specialists, secretaries, typists, and clerks provide this type of assistance. A certain amount of administrative detail is necessary for scientists and engineers involved in the administrative process. However, alert employers seek constantly to reduce administrative detail for scientists and engineers to a minimum consistent with efficient administrative practice and seek to provide adequate support personnel.

Periodic rematching of capabilities and the duties performed by individual scientists and engineers results in their spending much less time on peripheral and non-professional duties and their spending more time on utilizing their professional abilities.

KEEPING OPEN THE AVENUES OF INTERNAL COMMUNICATION

Action by employers to keep open the avenues of internal communication helps the exchange of needed information within the organization and enables scientists and engineers to utilize their knowledge and skills more extensively. The information transferred from a source to a destination within an organization is of two types, oral and written. For example, a scientist may make a verbal suggestion for further scientific exploration to a colleague in another division of an organization or an employer may issue a written directive on a revision of the patent policy. Both types of information are essential to the effectiveness of scientific and engineering personnel.

In the setting of science and technology, employers recognize that effective communication requires that a free flow of information take place in three directions: downward, upward, and outward in the organizational hierarchy. Employers promote downward communication through the use of face-to-face and intercommunication contacts, conferences, written messages, and instructions. Employers stimulate upward communication through provision for oral and written reports, suggestions, and interviews. Employers assist outward communication through emphasis on face-to-face contacts, informal meetings, and the routing of scientific and engineering papers within the group.

Unfortunately in many organizations the vertical communication is restricted to a downward flow. Upward flow is often limited for several reasons. Sometimes there is jealousy on the part of subordinates. Sometimes there is natural reticence at lower levels of a large organization. Sometimes there is general conservatism among young scientists and engineers who feel that expressing their opinions to their superiors may be misunderstood by experienced scientists and engineers. Sometimes there is a lack of a convenient mechanism to carry the information upward. For whatever the cause, serious impediments to the upward flow of communication often exist and mitigate against optimum utilization of scientific and engineering personnel.

A relatively simple device called a message form is used by employers to promote the flow of information in any direction. In an organization using this device, scientists and engineers are encouraged to use it on their own initiative. The subject matter is limitless and in practice ranges from complaints of administrative inadequacies to reports of conversations held with professionals outside of the organization. The subject matter includes innovative ideas as well as technical analyses of work. A requirement may be imposed that the individual use telegram style in order to reduce the length of the communication. A message form may be sent to any particular addressee within the organization whom the originator wishes to contact. Replies are provided within a reasonable time period. The message form has an advantage of reaching into organizational areas which otherwise seem to be isolated from normal communication.

Because of the nature of science-oriented and technology-oriented activity, the essentiality of the continuous flow of ideas in all directions emphasizes a requirement that the internal communications process be characterized by consistency, timeliness, adaptability, and acceptance. Employers seek to maintain their internal communication channels in such a way that the channels will operate accordingly.

In contrast to some non-professional types of positions where expected performance is highly routine, scientific and engineering personnel usually thrive through interaction with associates in various divisions and levels of an organization. To scientists and engineers, the inadequate receipt of information generated within an organization limits individual performance and induces under-utilization. A strong element of job satisfaction by scientists and engineers is the existence of open internal communication channels through which they easily exchange information and hence play a more active role in the organization.

FOSTERING CREATIVITY

Creativity has been called the "magic fluid" which fires the imagination and produces change from present workways. Acting creatively, scientists and engineers bring forth new ideas and concepts to meet needs of their organization. Putting forth creative effort increases the effective utilization of scientific and engineering personnel.

Employers who recognize the value of creativity take deliberate steps to foster creative productivity. Fundamental to employer action in this area is realization that an attitude of encouragement for ideas for change must be supported throughout the organization. Employers also recognize that motivation is an essential ingredient of creative effort, and they seek to provide positive motivation. For example, employers may reward creative effort in order to assure that scientists and engineers will continue to put forth additional creativeness.

For longer range results, employers establish formal training programs designed specifically to develop creativity in selected —often young—scientists and engineers on their staff. The more serious training efforts are reflected in programs held for two or four class hours per week on official time; such programs involve additional hours of study outside of the regular work week. Individual programs of this type may extend over a period of time, ranging from twelve weeks to one year.

The content of a formal training program usually stresses principles and practices of creativity. The first part of a course often involves reading assignments and individual problem solving. The reading assignments lead to class discussion of theory and practice. Identification of mass knowledge available for use in the invention process is also explored. Individual problem solving generally relates to inventive challenges actually facing the employer; each student analyzes the challenge and prepares a written report which is subject to subsequent class review and criticism. The second part of such a course may concentrate on analyses of critical scientific and engineering problems of a complex nature facing the employer; for each problem, an analysis may be made by a three or four man team of scientists and engineers assigned to the problem.

Extreme care is taken by employers in the selection of instructors for such a program. Minimum requirements of such instructors are the ability to be an effective discussion leader, the ability to keep discussion in a positive vein, and a personal interest in developing creativity. Instructors themselves are often creative scientists and engineers; nevertheless, they are frequently given a special training course before they begin their instructional duties. Instructors occasionally prepare manuals on creativity for class use or they may adopt text materials available on the open market for class use.

As a result of a formal training program, a pattern of behavior is developed on the part of individual scientist and engineer participants which henceforth they may apply to their work. The pattern includes a sincere willingness to take the initiative in exploring pertinent resources thoroughly, careful judgment to determine reliability of scientific and technical information secured, and use of a procedure for approaching creative work on a sequential basis. This procedure involves identifying a few major scientific and engineering needs, studying and proposing worthwhile solutions to meet these needs, completing development activity for appraisal purposes, and persuading the employer on the basis of evidence that a worthy scientific or engineering need will be satisfied.

A tangible measure of effectiveness of creative development programs administered by employers is the number of patents subsequently awarded to those who completed a program. Statistical studies comparing graduates of such a program with those of comparable qualifications who do not pursue the program show the number of patents per man as a function of the years since his graduation. Individual employers have found that graduates of their creative development program have averaged as many as three or four times the number of patents as a comparable group which did not pursue a formal program. However, all creative work does not result in invention; as a matter of fact, some of the most creative ideas are not patentable. The use of the number of patents as a measure of creativity takes into consideration only one aspect of creativity. Other measures of creativity include the number and quality of innovative ideas offered and accepted during a particular time frame and the extent of the significance of innovative ideas proposed to the program of the organization. Employers who have set up training programs are impressed with the creative progress which often takes place, following completion of such a program.

With respect to attaining more immediate results from creative thinking, employers regularly use communication channels to keep before the creative scientists and engineers in their organization a clear understanding of the basic objectives of the work being performed. Unless there is a continuing stress on these objectives, individual scientists and engineers with imagination and drive may seek to act on objectives in which they as individuals are interested but which may not represent employer objectives. If this condition develops, employer needs may unwittingly become secondary. When employers maintain clarity of objectives before the group, scientists and engineers usually aim to direct their creative efforts toward employer objectives and the challenges inherent therein.

Employers also establish a system of formal periodic reviews of the progress of projects calling for the exercise of creativity on the part of their scientists and engineers. The purpose of periodic reviews is to keep the pace of creative work at a generally constant level and thereby seek to minimize peaks and valleys of such effort. Periodic reviews compel individual self-analysis of progress made, provide an opportunity for employers to react to the progress reported, give employers a chance to offer further broad direction to projects, and enable employers to give recognition, if appropriate, during the progress of the work.

Employers sometimes use brainstorming sessions to detect and stimulate creativity among scientists and engineers. Brainstorming refers to a method of thinking in which an individual seeks to solve problems by stating to a group of colleagues possible solutions occuring to him, without immediate evaluation. Creative scientists and engineers often make false starts before they arrive at a practical innovative concept. At brainstorming sessions, the opportunity for criticism is denied to avoid fear of embarrassment which scientists and engineers may have because their early responses may appear to be unrealistic to their colleagues. During a brainstorming session, ideas are recorded but reviewed at a later time for possible use.

Employers also try to lessen negative attitudes that may prevail in their organization and that react against creativity. Thus, employers may refuse to accept, without factual support, statements to the effect that a proposed change is automatically useless because the proposal is against current policy, that a reorganization made necessary by the adoption of a proposed change would cost too much, or that the act of waiting and doing nothing more at the moment will provide the answer to a challenging need. Creativity is thwarted by a prevailing feeling on the part of those individuals in an organization who oppose change primarily because they are against change. Employers seek to eliminate nega-

[48]

tive attitudes of this type and seek to establish a work climate in which creative capabilities are permitted to develop.

MONITORING VOLUNTARY SEPARATIONS

In an effort to reduce turnover of scientific and engineering personnel, employers select a staff specialist or staff committee to monitor and assess on a continuing basis the voluntary turnover of scientists and engineers. Under this approach, the specialist or committee conducts interviews with scientists and engineers who signify their intention to leave the organization. A guarantee of complete confidentiality is usually extended during the interview. Where appropriate, the specialist or a representative of the committee is available to participate in a third party capacity to keep open channels of communication and to help with a solution to a personal problem which may be the basis of a pending separation.

It is recognized that a reasonable rate of turnover is desirable in any organization. Through normal turnover, for example, research and development in industry, in universities, and in government grows through the introduction of new ideas and workways by newly appointed scientists and engineers. However, there is a practical turnover rate above which the value of new ideas does not compensate for the loss of scientific and engineering talent through attrition. It is difficult to establish numerically an ideal rate. For example, a resignation of a junior scientist may not have the significance equivalent to the resignation of a senior scientist. Instead of emphasizing arithmetical percentages, employers scrutinize voluntary separations among scientists and engineers for the purpose of ascertaining bona fide causes, particularly those reflecting upon work operations. Analysis of controllable causes of separation is followed by an application of appropriate administrative remedies.

Satisfactory resolution of a turnover problem tends to have a favorable effect on morale of scientists and engineers. The success of the approach to monitor separations is attributable to the fact that scientists and engineers are satisfied that difficulties

[49]

which may potentially lead to separation are given careful consideration beyond the immediate supervisor, that adjustment of minor frictions is made adroitly, and that a change of supervisors which may result from a problem often acts as a spur to greater professional effort. Benefits also accrue to scientists and engineers not involved in a specific turnover situation because the approach provides an opportunity for the employer to accumulate information about the effectiveness of assignment procedures and about any developmental needs of supervisors. Employers having such a plan report that as many as two out of three cases of potential separations are resolved to the satisfaction of the scientists and engineers involved and to the enhancement of scientific and engineering manpower utilization.

Planning for Future Manpower Needs

Scientific and engineering manpower planning refers to a practice, on the part of employers, of estimating future needs for such manpower and of identifying specific means which will likely result in meeting the needs. Arriving at an estimate of decreased future needs requires the determination of steps to reduce excess manpower. Arriving at an estimate of increased future needs requires the determination of steps to attract additional manpower to an organization. Such planning promotes better manpower utilization.

Scientific and engineering manpower planning is not a luxury reserved for large employers. Such planning is a profitable undertaking whether the organization is large or small. Where planning is undertaken, the planning is carried out by line management alone, or by a staff specialist or staff group alone, or by a combination of line and staff effort. Except in small organizations, manpower planning is most effectively performed by a small staff group acting in a service capacity to, and working closely with, line management.

In some instances, very detailed scientific and engineering manpower planning is pursued by employers. In a typical case, an official of each operating unit of an organization develops estimates of manpower requirements based upon anticipated work load during a predetermined period of time. A staff specialist or group in the central unit of the organization receives the estimates from each operating units and merges them into a single plan. Top management considers the plan and, after possible modification, approves the plan which then becomes the pattern for an ensuing time period. In ultimate planning, future scientific and engineering manhours are budgeted in the same manner as are future dollar expenditures.

In a less sophisticated manner, employers establish an approach to planning under which supervisory justification and middle or top management approval are required before the acquisition of new scientific and engineering personnel is authorized. Occasionally, supervisors must certify to a check list of questions related to the need for replacement or for additional personnel. The effect of the certification process is to force supervisors to think through their future personnel needs and to help them arrive at a judgment of need. Top management reserves the right to modify any recommendation. Once a schedule of needs is approved, supervisors may not digress without subsequent approval. The objective of this approach is not to prevent the acquisition of necessary scientific and engineering personnel but to assure that new scientific and engineering personnel will have bona fide professional duties to be performed and will be utilized properly.

Employers adhere to a series of principles which serve as guides in scientific and engineering manpower planning. Employers seek to coordinate the scientific and engineering manpower needs of all parts of the organization developing the plan, to interrelate elements of implementing action, to be flexible and adaptable to extreme ranges of future requirements, and to promote acceptance of the concept of manpower planning throughout their organization.

The development and use of formal projections to ascertain future scientific and engineering needs of employers is gaining wide acceptance. With respect to making formal projections, employers follow a series of steps which may be summarized as follows:

1. An inventory of currently employed scientific and engineering personnel in the organization, together with an analysis of skills involved, is compiled.

2. Attrition rates for the future are determined. Classified by types of scientific and engineering position and by knowledge and skills, the rates are based on experience and supplemented by the judgment of planners. This step provides data on the number of additional scientific and engineering personnel required to maintain current manpower strength.

3. Requirements for additional or fewer scientific and engineering skills, due to changes in the need for products or services of the employer over a time span, are estimated. The time span for this purpose is usually from one to five years. Variables examined include market forecasts, availability of funds, existence of plant and equipment, extent of proper utilization of current and future work force, and scientific and technological change.

4. A total estimate of new scientific and engineering personnel required over the time span covered by the projection is made by combining the number of personnel required to maintain current strength with the number of additional or fewer personnel needed for the future. From a practical viewpoint, the projection is periodically reviewed and revised, not only to correct errors of judgment, but also to reflect subsequent developments affecting scientific and engineering manpower needs of the organization.

In manpower planning, employers give particular attention to scientific and technological advancement because it is a major influence upon changing employment requirements for scientific and engineering personnel. Such advancement impacts favorably and unfavorably upon scientists and engineers working in specialized fields. New areas of scientific and engineering opportunity are created. For example, progress in oceanography may challenge scientists and engineers to create and perfect more elaborate deep-diving maneuverable vehicles. Employment requirements also become more stringent as a result of such advancement. For example, the use of computers to regulate highway and subway traffic through automatically controlled lights lessens the need for traffic engineers incapable of thinking in terms of computers. The net effect of scientific and technological advancement is to change materially the nature of knowledge and skills required in an organization.

Employers of scientific and engineering personnel are a potential source of technological forecasting data used for manpower purposes. Other sources of such data for employers are government, industry, and the academic world in the form of reports, technical journals, seminars, conferences, and meetings. Available data usually lack specificity; they are also incomplete in connection with information on the rate of innovation and the rate of introduction of change. To link technological forecasting data to future scientific and engineering manpower needs, employers strive to make more detailed forecasts from the general data available to them. One emerging characteristic of such data is inclusion of two or three levels of assumptions instead of one level; multiple levels give a flexibility to the projection process. Greater use of currently available, although incomplete, data is made by employers as an understanding of the usefulness of technological forecasting data for manpower planning increases.

Planning for scientific and technological advance is a difficult task for employers because no one can predict with certainty the path of science and technology. Nevertheless, employers make profitable use of technological forecasting data for manpower projection purposes. Although forecasts may be imperfect and the interpretation of such data may not be done with complete confidence, employers find it practical to give due weight to this variable.

When the projection phase is completed, employers determine a series of steps to implement the manpower plan. These steps

[53]

usually involve one or more particular personnel activities designed to increase or decrease numbers and types of personnel consistent with the time frame of the plan. On the basis of the characteristics of the individual employment situation, employers take specific action, such as reassigning personnel, to meet scientific and engineering manpower requirements as set forth in the projections.

Employers use special manpower plans to protect and promote effective utilization of scientists and engineers in their organization as individual scientists and engineers are called upon to fulfill their military obligations. Employers recognize that they must plan for a continuous appraisal of the likelihood of loss of such personnel in the light of prevailing selective service and military reserve regulations. Use of a manpower plan minimizes scientific and engineering personnel dislocation. Under unusual conditions, a sudden expansion of the Armed Forces or a large military personnel replacement program may restrict occupational deferments or may result in a sudden call-up of reservists to active duty. Without a manpower plan, employers may find it very difficult to retain scientists and engineers having critical skills or to obtain, on a timely basis, replacements for those who are called for military duty.

To obtain and assemble personnel data in a meaningful manner, employers often use a manpower inventory plan developed by the Engineering Manpower Commission and the Scientific Manpower Commission. This approach, called "Employer's Inventory of Critical Manpower," gives specific advice to employers for identifying employees in vital activities, for assessing their relative vulnerability to call up for military service, and for planning to minimize interference with essential employer operations. To execute this plan, an employer obtains data on the liability of his male employees as selective service registrants and military reservists, analyzes the information, and assigns each employee a symbol to identify probable vulnerability. The employer then ascertains from the inventory chart answers to such questions as numbers of employees in designated occupations of draft age who are actually vulnerable, anticipated balances of vulnerable employees for one or more years hence, and the desirability of transferring particular employees to other duties to make better use of their knowledge and skills. Through use of the inventory plan or other similar device, employers establish and carry out training, reassignment, or other functions in order to initiate actions made pertinent by analysis of the assembled data.

There is no guaranteed formula for planning accurately future scientific and engineering manpower needs. The objective of such planning is reached if a series of useful approximations derived through careful judgment results. The cost of effective manpower planning is more than saved through improved utilization which follows.

REWARDS FOR SCIENTIFIC AND ENGINEERING ACHIEVEMENT

Activities related to rewards for scientific and engineering achievement involve providing a meaningful performance appraisal system, maintaining a realistic compensation plan, setting up parallel ladders for advancement, and insuring equitable recognition.

PROVIDING A MEANINGFUL PERFORMANCE APPRAISAL SYSTEM

Employers provide a meaningful system for the appraisal of the quality of individual performance of scientists and engineers. Such a system produces a professional judgment on the effectiveness of individual effort, suggests future application of knowledge and skills, offers guidance for personal improvement, and furnishes a mechanism for determining individual reward. To be helpful as a stimulant for improved utilization of scientific and engineering manpower, the appraisal plan has certain minimum features. The criteria for evaluating the individual must be realistic. The evaluation by supervisors must be free from bias. Scientists and engineers must be made fully and frankly familiar with all details of their own evaluation. Supervisory help—if needed—must be available to assist the individual in improving his proficiency in the directions set forth in the evaluation.

Special criteria are used by employers as they administer such a system. These criteria include the number of creative ideas the individual has proposed during the period of work activity covered by the appraisal, the number and quality of his publications, the number of his patents, scientific and/or engineering ability as reflected in his work efforts, his reputation among his peers, his activity to keep up-to-date, his efficiency in communicating, his degree of perceptiveness, his ability to get along with his colleagues, and his professional leadership. Not all criteria apply to the performance of any one scientist or engineer; the chief determinant for deciding which criteria do apply in any appraisal is the nature of the duties and responsibilities of the individual scientist or engineer.

A performance appraisal system may carry its own series of rewards such as an automatic pay increase for those employees achieving a premium rating. The prestige of an outstanding rating accompanied subsequently by peer recognition is regarded as another type of reward for unusual performance. In other instances, personal achievement formalized through a performance appraisal system is linked to further reward which is provided under another personnel program such as a program of awards for sustained superior service or a promotion program.

A meaningful performance appraisal motivates scientists and engineers to increase their efforts and to make wider use of their capabilities and unique background.

MAINTAINING A REALISTIC COMPENSATION PLAN

Salaries at competitive levels are necessary to attract and retain qualified scientists and engineers and to stimulate their productivity. Hence, employers who seek to improve utilization pay salaries which at least equal the salaries paid for similar work by other employers in the industry or geographical area. Such salaries are determined by a realistic compensation plan.

This type of plan is characterized by internal consistency among the administrative units making up the total work group in the organization, by correctness of differential based on the particular nature of tasks involved, and by due regard for years of individual service. Employers find it is not enough merely to pay competitive salaries; employers also take steps to disseminate among scientists and engineers information on methods used in salary determination and on details of the salary schedule in order to insure complete understanding and acceptance of the plan.

In establishing a realistic compensation plan, employers create a series of position levels, having salaries which range, for example, from $7,000 to $25,000. The levels are designated by a series of related position titles such as junior engineer, engineer, senior engineer, and engineering specialist. For each level employers set a minimum, mid, and maximum salary point. The differential between the midpoint of the lowest salary level and the midpoint of the next highest level may vary, often by 15% to 20%. In reality, employers may find it difficult to place individual scientific and engineering positions in predetermined levels of the plan. Since the salary plan is a guide, variation is permissible.

Employers periodically review their compensation plan to assure that salary levels reflect current competitive conditions. In the review process, data are obtained from salary surveys which employers conduct or sponsor in the industry or geographical area. One difficulty facing employers in analyzing data obtained through such surveys is the determination of precisely comparable data; comparability of salary quotations by different employers is not achieved solely because position titles in two organizations are identical. Another difficulty is the fact that the median of salaries reflects the approximate value of the work contribution of scientists and engineers of average proficiency; a median is only a guide for the midpoint of a particular range. A realistic value of the service of a particular scientist or engineer may be substantially higher or lower than the midpoint.

[57]

With these difficulties in view, employers consider very carefully the specific qualifications required to perform the duties of positions and the exact nature of the duties and responsibilities involved.

Employers in their desire to improve utilization now seek to provide for salary increases which give more weight to experienced groups of scientists and engineers in the organization than heretofore had been the usual case. Unfortunately, during the past decade, changes in salary rates for experienced scientists and engineers have generally shown a much slower rate of increase than the rate of increase for scientists and engineers who have been relatively new to the field. Specifically, salaries of scientists and engineers with twenty or more years of experience have generally not kept pace proportionately with salary increases for the total group, while scientists and engineers with ten to twenty years of service have generally gained only moderately. The effect of the differing rates of increase among groups is to narrow the salary range in an organization. The resultant compression has the greatest adverse effect upon the most experienced personnel, the group potentially most able to make very effective use of their capabilities and unique experience.

Employers find it useful to have at their disposal the results of national salary surveys from which employers ascertain information on medians and trends. National salary surveys pertaining to engineers are periodically conducted by the Engineers Joint Council and the National Society of Professional Engineers. Science-oriented organizations like the American Chemical Society make surveys of salaries of specific types of scientists. The National Science Foundation makes periodic comparisons of salaries of scientists and engineers, based on data contained in the National Register of Scientific and Technical Personnel. Median salaries in selected scientific and engineering fields, compiled in 1968, are shown in Table II-4.[2]

2. National Science Foundation, *Reviews of Data on Science Resources,* No. 16, December 1968.

Table II-4

COMPARISON OF MEDIAN SALARIES,
SCIENTISTS AND ENGINEERS

Field	Median Annual Salaries
Engineering	$14,800
Computer Sciences	14,100
Physics	14,000
Chemistry	13,500
Atmospheric & Space Sciences	13,400
Mathematics	13,000
Earth & Marine Sciences	12,900

Source: NSF study

The overall median income of $14,800 per year for engineers compares very favorable with that of scientists in the fields listed in Table II-4, particularly when it is realized that a larger proportion of advance degree holders are in scientific disciplines. The National Register contains data only from society members; hence, omission of data from individuals who do not belong to societies (such as some young engineers) acts to reduce the annual figures cited when one is considering the universe of employed scientists and engineers in the United States.

Examination of the results of national surveys conducted during the past few years reveals that, in general:

1. Highest median incomes have been found in private practice and among those scientists and engineers having administrative responsibilities.

2. Lowest median incomes have been found among those working for state and local governments.

3. Income differences among younger scientists and engineers have not been very great but these differences have increased with the number of years of experience.

4. Dollar-wise, the self employed have experienced the greatest absolute income gain; the largest proportionate increase in income has been reported by scientists and engineers employed by educational institutions.

[59]

5. Income in most age brackets has increased between 4% and 7.5% per year since 1966.

A word of caution about the influence of salary upon utilization may be noted. Certainly a non-competitive salary contributes to dissatisfaction, underutilization, and turnover while a competitive salary adds incentive and stimulates motivation. However, a competitive salary is only one factor in the array of factors which lead to increased scientific and engineering manpower utilization.

SETTING UP PARALLEL LADDERS FOR ADVANCEMENT

The concept of parallel ladders for advancement means that scientists and engineers find equal opportunity for advancement in an organization either by becoming a manager or by becoming a highly specialized scientist or engineer. When employers establish parallel ladders, they encourage scientists and engineers to continue in their professional fields.

Advancement of scientific and engineering personnel has normally been through a sequence of supervisory positions. Under this traditional method, each step up the administrative hierarchy has required of scientists and engineers either supervision of more persons or the exercise of more administrative responsibility or both. Supervisory personnel having a science or engineering background usually do not continue to specialize in depth scientifically or technically; increasing amounts of their time are spent on managerial duties.

If the administrative avenue is the way for ultimate advancement, some scientific and engineering specialists give up their expertise which has been acquired over a period of time and become managers. Many scientists and engineers become effective managers. However, employers believe that those scientists and engineers who have neither the desire nor the ability should not be forced to become managers in order to advance in an organization. A system of parallel ladders for administrative and for scientific and engineering advancement acknowledges that scientists and engineers can make as significant a contribu-

[60]

tion in their roles as specialists as they can in the role of an administrator.

To set up a program for scientific and engineering personnel growth to parallel administrative opportunity, employers establish standards for competence, applicable to the range of scientific and engineering positions. Within broad standards, various levels of performance, knowledge, experience, and potential are established. These levels of competence are related to salary; once broad salary ranges have been set, gradations of types of positions are fixed to reflect levels of competence. Scientists and engineers may move up from one level of performance to another without change in their basic field. Growth possibilities depend upon the ability of scientists and engineers as individual performers, not upon the limits of a particular position.

As an example of the parallel ladder approach, a graduate with a bachelor of science degree in chemistry enters an organization at level A as a chemist. After a minimum of one year of experience, he moves to level B; graduates having the M.S. degree in chemistry enter at this level. After experience for a specified minimum period of time, the chemist reaches level C and may be called a research chemist; graduates having the Ph.D. degree in chemistry enter at this level. Parallelism begins at level D. The chemist at level C who demonstrates outstanding scientific qualities moves either to a more specialized position in the chemistry field at level D or to an administrative position at level D. Choice of a specialized scientific position at level D eventually may lead to greater scientific specialization at level E. Choice of an administrative position at level D may enable the individual to progress to level E as an administrator. Thus, scientists and engineers may remain in their specialty field and progress or move from their specialty to the management field at a point in their career development (level D, in the example) and progress. Salaries are comparable for individuals at levels D and E whether the individuals are scientific specialists or administrators.

[61]

Under parallel ladders for advancement, scientists and engineers who continue in their specialized fields may receive over a period of time income and other benefits equal to, or even higher than, those of managers. Such opportunity reduces loss of scientific and engineering talent and induces greater manpower utilization.

INSURING EQUITABLE RECOGNITION

Recognition is attention and status given to an individual scientist or engineer, or group, for job accomplishment. The accomplishment is generally significant to the program of the organization or to the knowledge and skills of a field of science or engineering or both. The accomplishment may represent individual effort or group effort. A recognition program refers to an employer's total operation plan for granting recognition. Equitable recognition means that the program of an organization is administered on a basis fair and just to all members in the group covered by the program.

There are several types of recognition used by employers of scientists and engineers. Such types may be classified as monetary and non-monetary. With respect to monetary types of recognition, common forms are an increase in basic salary, supplemental salary, and lump sum salary amounts. Thus, as a result of achievement, the regular salary base of a scientist or engineer may be raised. The pay rate may be augmented for a particular period of time by a certain amount of money independent of any automatic pay increase. The scientist or engineer may be given a fixed sum for a particular accomplishment. Scientific and engineering personnel often do not consider monetary types of recognition as important as non-monetary types. With respect to non-monetary types, common forms are a change of the nature of assignment involving more scientifically or technically attractive duties, opportunity to attend meetings of professional and technical societies, opportunity to publish professional papers at employer expense, additional vacation, letters of commendation and of appreciation, outstanding performance ratings, and solicitation of ideas by employers on relevant matters of importance to an organization.

Appropriate credit for a significant contribution is essential to professional stature. Although engaged by different types of employers, scientists and engineers depend basically upon the same sources of knowledge and meet similar scientific and engineering obstacles in attaining professional achievement. Outstanding performance merits employer and peer approbation, regardless of work setting. Hence, effective recognition programs receive acceptance by the professional world.

Employers set up flexible rules for governing the administration of recognition programs. Individual recognition plans usually provide broad discretion for supervisors in fulfilling their responsibilities under such a program. By nature, scientific and engineering accomplishments are normally not subject to specific measurement. This aspect means that, although objectivity in the determination of the form and substance of recognition is the practice, the precise effects of the achievement are generally difficult for an employer to assess.

Standards in an effective recognition program are such as to assure recognition to individuals who actually deserve recognition, provided the standards are properly applied. Any recognition program which rewards average or mediocre performance soon becomes meaningless. Lack of equitable recognition results in job dissatisfaction, loss of productivity, and job turnover. The administration of an effective recognition program is a worthwhile approach by employers to foster the maximum utilization of scientists and engineers.

TRAINING OF SCIENTISTS AND ENGINEERS AS MANAGERS

Activities related to the training of scientists and engineers as managers refers to management development for those individuals having actual or potential managerial responsibilities. The purpose of such development is to help individuals plan, organize, staff, and direct a unit or division in a science-oriented or technology-oriented organization in an effective manner. Management policy, principles, and procedures are used as tools to provide an invigorating work environment. First line supervisors, project leaders, and other types of managers, by applying appropriate management tools, improve the utilization of scientists and engineers under their supervision. Employers establish management development programs in their own organizations or send their scientists and engineers to a program administered by an outside group, such as an educational institution.

Occasionally employers pursue concurrently both approaches. From one point of view, developing managerial skills of scientists and engineers may be considered a diversion of scientific and engineering ability, but those individuals selected to participate in the management process are given useful managerial training and subsequently provide leadership needed to stimulate optimum utilization of subordinate scientists and engineers in an organization.

It may appear to some persons that scientists and engineers do not have basic characteristics to become managers. One view of scientists and engineers is that their education and training point in a different direction than management and that they are opposed to detailed procedures, apathetic toward financial costs, anxious for a work environment of physical isolation, and accustomed to dealing with objects instead of people. However, such characterizations cannot be generally applied. Scientists and engineers also possess analytical ability, conduct their work in a systematic manner, show sound judgment, and develop communication techniques in reporting on their professional work. These latter characteristics are essential to managerial performance. The transition in behavior patterns which scientists and engineers with managerial ambitions and related abilities undergo to assume managerial duties is facilitated by management development programs provided by employers. Even scientists and engineers who have had trial and error work experience in supervision respond favorably to an orderly presentation of management philosophy and practice.

By its nature, a management development program does not provide scientific and engineering knowledge which is a highly desirable qualification for a manager. As first line supervisors, scientists and engineers require some degree of scientific and engineering proficiency because inspirational leadership which the supervisor provides depends to a large extent upon scientific and engineering acumen. Furthermore, in exercising their responsibilities for formulation, direction, and completion of projects, supervisors need scientific and engineering insight in order to understand the work efforts of their subordinates. Hence, at the outset, scientists and engineers obtain only part of their total professional growth through a management development program. However, as a manager advances from first line supervision, he usually proceeds with a lessening degree of scientific and engineering competency because he devotes more of his time to broader administrative problems. Eventually, the nature and demands of higher level management assignments do not permit him to maintain scientific and engineering competency. The usefulness of what he learns in management development, particularly with respect to factors associated with scientific and engineering manpower utilization, looms greater as he grows as a manager.

In the selection of scientists and engineers for participation in a management development program, employers seek to ascertain the personal career ambitions of their professionals as soon as practicable. Employers may observe the managerial ambitions of some scientists and engineers within the organization at an early stage. Thus, a young scientist or engineer may exhibit management potential early in his career by showing strong indications of possessing planning and organizing ability. Usually, employers look for manifestations of managerial interest on the part of scientists and engineers over a period of time and carefully make choices for participation in management development programs. One determinant is sensitivity to effective scientific and engineering manpower utilization. Although a management development program does not "make" a manager, it affords the individual an opportunity to acquire administrative understanding and to learn the administrative tools which helps him to be an effective leader and to promote optimum utilization of the group for which he is responsible.

Management development programs in which scientists and engineers participate by employer designation take a variety of forms such as courses, seminars, and workshops. The basic concepts of these programs also differ. Some programs stress basic principles of supervision and management techniques; others emphasize ramifications of mathematics and statistical techniques in management decision-making, operations research, or other recent managerial innovations. The time period for the individual program may be a few days or the period may extend as long as an academic year.

Some management development programs are not designed specifically for administering programs of science and technology; they are designed for general administration. Other programs are designed specifically for managing science and technology. The latter type is usually more successful in developing scientists and engineers to exercise management responsibilities and is increasing in usage. Individuals anticipating or experiencing managerial assignments in science and technology need to learn, within the framework of the environment of science and technology, how to delegate authority properly, how to provide subordinates with freedom of action, how to be a leader without being dictatorial, how to coordinate without being an operator, how to persuade instead of command, and how to act "person-oriented" instead of "object-oriented."

Employers sometimes utilize management development programs designed for managing science and technology with the objective of meeting needs of first line supervision. On other occasions, employers choose programs directly attuned to intermediate management. A third type of program which employers may select is addressed to needs of research directors, vice-presidents in charge of research, and other top management officials.

[66]

Approximately a dozen educational institutions conduct programs geared specifically to management development of scientists and engineers. Usually these programs are developed in close association with management needs of scientists and engineers, as suggested in part by employers. Such programs provide management knowledge and skills necessary for administration, often with special emphasis on research and development operations. Introductory courses or programs may include elements of personnel management, accounting, financial analysis, economics, statistics, quality control, and electronic data processing. In advanced management courses or programs for scientists and engineers, topics often include an understanding of creativity, leadership skills, communications, interpersonal relationships, motivation, and decision theory. The usual length of a university course or program is one week. Attendance in one course may be limited to a maximum of twenty-five or thirty scientists and engineers. Representative titles of these programs are Basic R&D Management Development, Advanced R&D Management Development, Management Development, Advanced Management Development, Research Management, Scientists in Modern Administrative Structures, and Concepts in Engineering Management.

Federal scientists and engineers attend universities for management training under the provisions of the Government Employees Training Act and as fellows sponsored by the National Institute of Public Affairs. Several federal agencies have developed their own management training programs for scientists and engineers. Some agencies permit scientists and engineers from other agencies to attend their sessions. The U. S. Civil Service Commission has developed and conducts several courses on an interagency basis to meet some of the needs for management competency on the part of federal scientists and engineers.

An array of interagency management programs is set forth in Table II-5.

Table II–5

INTERAGENCY MANAGEMENT DEVELOPMENT PROGRAMS PRIMARILY FOR FEDERAL SCIENTISTS AND ENGINEERS

Title	Focus of Program	General Participation
Institute for Executives in Science and Government Policy	science and government policy	scientists and engineers in executive and laboratory positions
Management Institute for Supervisory Scientists and Engineers	management of science programs and problems of laboratory management	scientists and engineers in supervisory or managerial positions in research organizations
Ideas and Authors Series in Science and Government	government and science issues, problems and policies	senior scientists and engineers
Introduction to Government for Scientists and Engineers	introduction to government R&D policies and programs	scientists and engineers new to federal agencies
Management of Scientific and Engineering Organizations	management functions, with an emphasis on human relations	scientists and engineers who are executives
Contracting Procedures for Scientists and Engineers	proper liaison between contracting officers and scientists and engineers	scientists and engineers responsible for technical aspects of a contract
Information Tools, Methods and Resources in Science and Technology	information retrieval	scientists and engineers whose work requires knowledge of advanced retrieval techniques

Source: CSC data

As a result of the findings of a Presidential Task Force on Career Advancement (1967),[3] the Civil Service Commission is expending more effort in defining and meeting scientist and engineer needs for management training. Additional seminars under consideration for scientists and engineers feature supervision with an emphasis on basic management tools and techniques for scientists and engineers preparing to begin their first supervisory experience, legislative theory, and international science policy.

The quality of most management development programs designed for scientists and engineers appears high, but the total number of participants from both industry and government is

3. Presidential Task Force on Career Development, *Investment for Tomorrow,* 1967.

unusually small, as compared with the total number of scientists and engineers having current management responsibilities.

The increasing importance of developing expertise in scientific and engineering manpower utilization through management development programs for scientists and engineers may be illustrated by the rise in the number of top managers who have scientific and engineering backgrounds. A Scientific American study revealed that the percentage of top industrial officials having a degree in science or engineering (or equivalent experience) increased from 6.8% in 1900 to 20% in 1950 and to 36% in 1964. The study asserted that, if the scientists and engineers in the 35-45 age group at mid-1960 subsequently supply their proportionate share to top management, the proportion of top managers with scientific and engineering background will have increased to more than 50% by 1980. A follow-up study referred to a recent survey showing that 45% of one group of 6,000 executives in industry had degrees in science or engineering; this survey indicated the younger the age group of managers, the higher the percentage with such degrees.[4]

The trend toward increasing numbers of scientists and engineers in top management posts underlines the essentiality of effective management development programs for scientists and engineers.

SUGGESTED ACTION

It is suggested that all employers of scientists and engineers carefully consider each of the preceding activities. To the extent that an employer already carries on these activities, he may find it profitable to evaluate their current effectiveness. To the extent that an employer does not carry on these activities, he may find it useful to adopt one or more activities in his own organization, consistent with its characteristics and needs. As the administration of personnel functions is strengthened, the goal of optimum utilization of scientific and engineering manpower is more likely to be attained.

4. Scientific American, *U. S. Industry: Under New Management,* 1966; *The New Industrial Management,* 1969.

III

INCREASING THE AVAILABILITY AND USE OF ENGINEERING TECHNICIANS

•

CONCEPT OF ENGINEERING TECHNICIAN

In numerous instances scientists and engineers regularly perform duties of a technical but non-professional nature. An aim of maximum utilization is that such personnel engage in strictly scientific and engineering tasks to the fullest possible extent. A practical approach toward this aim is the employment of technicians, generally known as engineering technicians, to work under the direct or indirect supervision of scientists and engineers and to relieve them of technical non-professional work. Wider availability and greater use of engineering technicians are essential to optimizing the utilization of scientific and engineering personnel.

An engineering technician is an individual whose education and experience qualify him to work in the field of engineering technology. Engineering technology is that part of the technological field which requires the application of science and engineering knowledge and methods combined with technical skills in support of scientific and engineering activities. Engineering technology positions lie in the occupational area between the craftsman and the engineer. The engineering technician performs activities requiring knowledge of appropriate technical theory as well as of craft practice.

DUTIES OF ENGINEERING TECHNICIANS

The work activities of engineering technicians may require highly developed, manipulative skills, such as those associated with the use of instruments, tools or special devices. The range of work activities varies in complexity but usually embraces a specialized field of research, design, development or construction; or exploration, measurement, analysis or application of basic scientific concepts; or control of production facilities and manpower. The performance of work activities is based on knowledge of underlying scientific, engineering or mathematical principles related to the specialized field of work and on the application of established scientific techniques and methods toward the solution of practical problems encountered in the field of specialization.

Examples of duties of engineering technicians in selected fields of engineering technology are contained in Table III-1.

Table III–1

EXAMPLES OF DUTIES OF ENGINEERING TECHNICIANS

Selected Fields	Examples of Duties
Aeronautical technology	assist in design and production of aircraft and helicopters
Air conditioning, heating and refrigeration technology	devise methods to test equipment
Chemical technology	conduct experiments, tabulate and analyze results
Civil engineering technology	prepare specifications for materials
Electronics technology	perform complex technical work in a specialized area of electronics
Mechanical technology	solve design problems such as those involving tolerances and vibration
Metallurgical technology	test metals and alloys to determine physical properties
Instrumentation technology	aid in developing and designing highly complex devices

Source: Dept. of Labor data

Types of duties performed by technicians who work with scientists and engineers are described in the "Occupational Outlook Handbook" prepared by the U. S. Department of Labor. According to the handbook, technicians work with scientists and engineers in virtually every aspect of science and engineering. In research, development, and design work, such technicians generally serve as direct supporting personnel. These technicians may conduct experiments or tests; set up, calibrate, and operate

[71]

instruments; and make calculations. They may assist scientists and engineers in developing experimental equipment and models, do drafting, and assume responsibility for certain aspects of design work. In jobs related to production, such technicians usually follow a course laid out by a scientist or engineer, but they often work without close supervision. They may aid in various phases of production operations such as devising tests to insure quality control of products, making time and motion studies designed to improve the efficiency of operations, and performing liaison work between engineers and the production department.[1]

Because of the wide variety of tasks performed by engineering technicians, a detailed description of the work actually performed by a single type of technician is only illustrative. Thus, an electronics technician may be assigned the construction of a single transistor amplifier. An assignment to construct an amplifier does not necessarily involve all of the fourteen steps described herein, but the steps cited typify a reasonable range of effort by this type of technician.

Step 1: Receive an assignment

A technician is asked by an engineer to construct a transistor amplifier which is to be incorporated into a test set used in development activity. The engineer usually describes orally what he wants done; he may provide a sketch or circuit drawing and a list of requirements. At the same time, the engineer explains the objectives sought. Such explanation enables the technician to draw upon his own experience when there is opportunity to decide which materials to use when he is constructing a piece of apparatus or which test equipment is appropriate for making measurements.

Step 2: Construct the initial model of a circuit

The technician begins by constructing the initial model of a circuit. The technician possesses certain craft skills; in this in-

1. U. S. Department of Labor, *Occupational Outlook Handbook*, 1968-69 edition, 1968.

stance he builds the chassis. He may use hand tools and simpler power operated machines such as a drill press. The technician may be responsible for the choice of materials and the mechanical layout. He draws upon experience to produce a design which is appropriate to the circuit requirements.

Step 3: Assemble and wire the circuit

After the chassis is built, the next step in the construction of the amplifier is assembling and wiring the circuit. This step involves the mounting and connection of such items as coils and resistors. At this stage, the technician is concerned with the placement of components which is important in an electronic circuit because placement often determines whether the circuit will work as it was designed.

Step 4: Obtain supplies

When the technician is building a circuit or piece of test equipment, he is a frequent visitor to a parts storeroom. The stock usually includes electrical components, hardware, chemical supplies, metals, and plastics. Regardless of size of the individual storeroom, it may not have in stock all items an experimenter may need. Often, it is necessary for the technician to use outside suppliers. In such a case, the technician examines trade catalogues and places his orders with the purchasing department. If the need is urgent and time is short, he may go to a supply house and directly purchase items. It is the technician's responsibility to obtain whatever is needed in the most effective manner.

Step 5: Adjust the circuit

After a circuit has been assembled, the next step is to adjust the circuit to assure that it operates. Adjustment involves checking the initial performance and making any modifications necessary. The technician is familiar with, and able to use, standard test equipment such as an oscilloscope.

Step 6: Make measurements

Through the first five steps of this illustration, an experimental circuit has been constructed and is in working order. Its characteristics now need to be determined by means of a series of precise measurements. Such measuring must be exact because broad professional decisions will be based on these measurements. It is normal for measurements of this kind to be made with some combination of commercially available test equipment (like a frequency counter) and specialized test sets designed and constructed in the organization. The technician is not required to possess a complete theoretical understanding of these sets. Nevertheless, he knows about their working in order to recognize valid from invalid data, without the necessity of making a long series of measurements only to discover ultimately that the test circuit is faulty.

Step 7: Maintain test equipment

When trouble develops in test set equipment constructed by the organization for its own use, the technician probes into the set and seeks to locate the trouble. For the technician, this task normally applies only to specialized, organization-built test sets. Standard test gear (like oscilloscopes and frequency counters) are usually maintained by personnel assigned specifically to this responsibility.

Step 8: Maintain an official notebook

The technician usually has a responsibility to keep an up-to-date official notebook for his work. All measurements are recorded directly in the notebook along with any significant observations. Other entries into the notebook may be circuit drawings, a description of difficulties that are encountered, and a listing of actions taken to overcome these difficulties. Entries are made in ink, signed, and dated. Such a notebook is essential because it constitutes a permanent detailed record to support patent applications and patent rights and the notebook contains incidental observations which may contribute to re-analyses without the need to repeat work already done.

Step 9: Assist model shop activity

At this stage it must be demonstrated that the idea which "works" in a breadboard or brassboard circuit is practicable. It is necessary to make in a model shop a working model which can be manufactured. Here, mechanics who are experienced in constructing developmental apparatus to an order construct a model. While the technician usually knows what he wants, the machinist decides what can and what cannot be done with existing machines and skills. The technician supplies whatever drawings are needed and follows through with model shop personnel to assure that the work is completed.

Step 10: Assist wiring shop activity

A relationship, similar to that between machinists and the technician in the model shop, exists between wiremen and the technician in the wiring shop. When a complex job is to be done, the work is given to a group of wiremen who are experienced, for example, in the technique of circuit hookup.

Step 11: Check out information in a library

In a small organization, a technical reference library may or may not be available. In larger organizations, there is a library usually staffed with trained librarians. With the help of librarians or on his own initiative, the technician seeks related technical information (such as new circuitry, in the illustration).

Step 12: Prepare technical memoranda

As an assignment nears completion, a report documentating the work done is prepared. The report, usually in the form of a technical memorandum, describes the circuit or piece of apparatus that has been constructed. The report is distributed to interested parties within the organization who will carry the work forward or who may be building another circuit or device which is to be incorporated in a larger system.

Step 13: Assist in preparation of drawings

The transfer of the job from the development stage to the manufacturing stage is accompanied by design information. This information may take the form of performance requirements and circuit or apparatus drawings. The technician usually makes arrangements with the drafting group for the preparation of these

[75]

drawings. Similar to the steps involving the model and wiring shops, the technician discusses the work with the draftsman and checks to assure that the drawings are correct as proposed.

Step 14: Assist in preparation of publicity material

In most cases the publication of technical memoranda describing the work done and the issuance of circuit schematics and apparatus drawings mark the completion of the job. However, if a project merits public attention, the technician may be called upon to assist in the preparation of publicity material. In this illustration, the technician may verify the technical accuracy of the work of an artist who makes a color poster showing a cutaway view of a device.

This example, an assignment to construct a single transistor amplifier, shows a range of actual duties performed by an engineering technician and serves to clarify the nature of knowledge and skills required for job performance.

EDUCATION AND TRAINING

Engineering technicians are trained in a variety of ways, ranging from the acquisition of skills and understanding through work experience to formal programs in educational institutions. Some individuals become engineering technicians after a period of work as a skilled craftsman plus specialized work experience under the guidance of a scientist or engineer. Some individuals become engineering technicians through employer in-service training programs. Some are trained in the military service as technicians in fields which have direct civilian application (such as electronics). Some are dropouts from undergraduate engineering programs. Some are graduates of formal education programs designed specifically to prepare individuals for technician positions; these programs are generally offered in post secondary schools, in technical institutes, in junior and community colleges, and in divisions of four year colleges and universities.

Employers frequently provide effective engineering technician training through on-the-job and in-service training programs; such training is geared to specific tasks of the organization. Individuals trained as engineering technicians in the military service are generally well prepared and tend to have greater flexibility than those trained by an employer. Graduates of formal technology programs are usually best equipped in fundamentals and have the most flexible background.

In addition to engineering technicians, other types of technicians are associated with scientific and engineering effort. For example, technicians who carry out specific tasks of comparatively narrow scope are sometimes called industrial technicians. Many high schools and post high school programs provide students with a background to become industrial technicians. The basic difference between the educational program of the industrial and engineering technician is the more specific job orientation and usually more limited scope of course content in the industrial program. The engineering technician is usually field-oriented (such as chemical technology), as contrasted with the industrial technician who is occupation-oriented (such as television repair). Generally, preparation for a career as an industrial technician requires less mathematics and greater manipulative skills than preparation for a career as an engineering technician. The focus of this chapter is the engineering technician.

Under Title VIII of the National Defense Education Act of 1958, federal funds were provided for area vocational education programs approved by state boards of vocational education to provide vocational and related technical training designed to fit students for useful employment as technicians or skilled workers in scientific and technical fields. By definition contained in the act, the term "area vocational education program" meant a program consisting of one or more less-than-college grade courses. Graduates of Title VIII programs filled an important role in the labor market, but generally were not educated to perform the duties of an engineering technician.

A Panel of Consultants on Vocational Education studied the national program of vocational education in 1961-62. The Panel found a great need for expanding post-secondary programs in vocational-technical education, and the Panel recommended that occupational needs should be met for all persons, regardless of occupational categories set forth in vocational education statutes which acted as limitations on the type of education which could be funded through the 1958 act.[2] Subsequently, Congress amended Title VIII of the National Defense Education Act by passage of the Vocational Education Act of 1963.

The Vocational Education Act of 1963 declared the purpose of federal grants to the states was to develop an adequate vocational education system such that persons of all ages in all communities would have ready access to vocational training or retraining of high quality. The Act broadened the scope of vocational education, for federal funding purposes, by defining vocational education as "vocational or technical training" or retraining conducted as part of a program designed either to prepare individuals for gainful employment as semiskilled or skilled workers or technicians or subprofessionals in recognized occupations and in new and emerging occupations, or to prepare individuals for enrollment in advanced technical education programs. The definition in the act specifically excluded any program to prepare individuals for employment in occupations generally considered professional or which require a baccalaureate or higher degree. Thus, federal funds could be used for programs preparing individuals for employment in a broader array of technical occupations. These programs included collegiate technical training programs not leading to a baccalaureate degree. Hence, two year collegiate engineering technology programs became eligible for funding under the act.

The Vocational Education Act of 1963 contained a provision which required the appointment of a committee to review the administration of vocational education programs and make recommendations for improvement. Accordingly, the Advisory Council on Vocational Education appointed to review and evaluate vocational education programs carried out a review of these programs. The Council reported in 1967 that technical educa-

2. Panel of Consultants on Vocational Education, *Education for a Changing World of Work,* 1964.

tion programs had been severely limited. The Council stated that electronics, drafting, and design had been stressed but that there was considerable need for programs extending over a wide range of technical occupations. Observing that the number of persons enrolled in post-secondary programs was very small, the Council stated that more experience and data were needed to evaluate achievements under the act in connection with technician occupations. The fact that state reports did not present sufficient data on the nature of the vocational education programs for which federal funds were allotted was considered a serious handicap in assessing the number of technicians trained under the act. The Council noted that significant improvements in vocational education had taken place and commented that insufficient time had passed to permit full implementation of the 1963 act. Nevertheless, the Council stated that enrollments in technical fields were "most disappointing" and recommended that a higher percent of vocational education funds be earmarked for post-secondary programs.[3]

In 1968 Congress responded to the Council's recommendations by amending the Vocational Education Act of 1963 to adapt vocational education to new manpower needs. Legislative changes which affected technical education programs funded under the act included the establishment of larger authorizations, creation of a National Advisory Council to advise the U. S. Commissioner of Education on policy concerning regulations and guidelines for vocational education programs, creation of state advisory councils to advise state boards on the development of policy related to the administration and preparation of long range and annual program plans and on evaluation of vocational education programs, research support, revised requirements for state plans, and funds for exemplary programs. The amendments, which became effective in July 1969, were thus designed to strengthen the quality and to increase the number of educational opportunities

3. Advisory Council on Vocational Education, *Vocational Education: The Bridge Between Man and his Work,* 1968.

provided by the legislation, including the education of technicians.

The National Advisory Council on Vocational Education, created by the 1968 amendments, made its first report to the Secretary of Health, Education and Welfare in July 1969. Because the Council had only recently organized, the report did not reflect a detailed appraisal of vocational education programs which is contemplated in the future. The Council recommended, however, that substantial federal funds be allocated to support curriculum development, teacher training, and pilot programs in vocational education.[4]

Data on the number of individuals trained as technicians in post-secondary programs under the Vocational Education Act of 1963, as amended, are not available. The total number of individuals trained in post-secondary programs (including adult programs) in all occupations is approximately 7% of the total enrollments in programs under the act. The legal framework for accelerating engineering technician training has been provided through the provisions of this act. However, due to such factors as budgetary limitations and a strong emphasis on other types of vocational programs, the number of technicians who have been trained under the Vocational Education Act of 1963, as amended, and who have subsequently worked with scientists and engineers is estimated to be relatively small.

Guidelines to help educators in initiating high quality technician programs or in improving existing ones were prepared and disseminated by the U. S. Office of Education in late 1968. Application of these guidelines is helping the development of larger numbers of students and graduates of programs supported by the Vocational Education Act of 1963, as amended, who will be able to work effectively with scientists and engineers.

Studies and surveys made by engineering societies, by engineering educators, and by related groups have established that college level, engineering technology programs best prepare en-

4. National Advisory Council on Vocational Education, *Annual Report,* 1969.

gineering technicians capable of working most effectively with scientists and engineers. For example, a study by the American Society for Engineering Education made in 1968 under a grant from the National Science Foundation stressed a growing recognition that high-level, full-time study, collegiate programs of at least two years duration are necessary to prepare adequately technicians who work with scientists and engineers. The kinds of duties performed by engineering technicians, the type of educational programs offered, and the qualifications of the students underscore the appropriateness of collegiate engineering technology education.

Technicians who work with scientists and engineers possess many of the same basic aptitudes and attitudes which professionals have. Thus, technicians have the ability to rationalize solutions for technical problems and to use independent thought as distinguished from routine procedures. Proficiency in communications required of technicians who work with scientists and engineers includes the ability to receive and transmit technical instructions through the spoken and written word and by means of engineering graphics with particular competence in the field of technical specialization.

While the scientist or engineer plans, the engineering technician makes and does; while the scientist or engineer creates, the technician applies. This technician often provides the liaison between the professional and the craftsman or artisan and needs to have a capacity for leadership and diplomacy in a work situation. By nature, the successful technician who works with scientists and engineers has a mature attitude toward his responsibilities in life and toward society. He is motivated by professional concepts but his interest is in the direction of application and his education is shorter with less mathematical and theoretical depth. In his work, he may take instructions of the scientist or engineer and translate them into action personally or direct their execution by other supporting personnel.

High school graduation is required for admission to curricula in engineering technology. Most institutions of higher learning

[81]

offering such programs have additional entrance requirements. These requirements generally include two or three years of mathematics, three years of English, and two years of physical science, as a minimum. Engineering technology programs are more practical in content than those leading to engineering degrees. Engineering technology programs include specialized technical subjects which make up approximately one-half of the curriculum in class time and in total student effort. These courses are integrated with related studies of college level, including mathematics, physical sciences, graphics, English, economics, industrial management, and general studies.

Students in engineering technology programs have varying intelligence quotients. An intelligence quotient score of 120 or above is not unusual for such students. However, an IQ score of 100-120 is considered a most desirable characteristic of a student who pursues the curriculum described above. Experience indicates that the individual having an I.Q. score of 100 or better is likely to succeed in this type of curriculum if he has other normal basic educational and personal qualifications.

The majority of engineering technology programs are two academic years in length. However, the number of four-year programs in engineering technology is increasing. Third and fourth year courses have been developed to fill a technical manpower gap caused, in part, by an emphasis in the four year engineering program on engineering sciences and on basic sciences and a lessening of stress upon the "art of engineering" subject matter. In particular instances, the bachelor of engineering technology degree program tends to approximate some bachelor of engineering programs of a decade ago.

Engineering technology curricula of two academic years in length generally lead to an associate degree in engineering or in applied science. Curricula of four academic years in length generally lead to a bachelor's degree in technology. When students elect to take a four-year engineering technology program, they usually attend the same campus for the four-year period; as an exception, the Capitol Campus of Pennsylvania State University has only junior and senior students (and an evening graduate program): at this institution the Engineering Technology Section offers Electrical Design, Mechanical Design, and Water Resources. Students are admitted after completion of an associate degree program at another campus or by transfer from a bachelor of engineering program.

The nature of the collegiate level curriculum in engineering technology is revealed in a series of guidelines established by a committee of the American Society for Engineering Education. This committee divided the curriculum into three major sections: (1) basic science courses, (2) non-technical courses, and (3) technical courses.[5]

With respect to basic science courses, a substantial program in mathematics and physical sciences is considered necessary to promote versatility and future technical development for engineering technology graduates. The pace at which the course proceeds, the difficulty of the problems solved, the attitude with which the material is approached, and the degree of achievement demanded of the students are such that mathematics taught is considered college level. The content of the mathematics programs, however, is essentially applied mathematics with an emphasis on problem-solving rather than on extensive theoretical concepts. Mathematics programs include selected topics from such areas as analytical geometry, differential calculus, integral calculus, differential equations, probability and statistics, vector algebra, and Boolean algebra. Observations about the role of mathematics in the engineering technology curriculum apply nearly equally to the physical sciences. The function of the physical science courses is to interrelate the technical subjects and provide the student with a foundation of scientific principles. To attain these goals, the courses emphasize the understanding, measurement, and quantitative expression of the phenomena involved.

With respect to non-technical courses, an engineering technician's education includes instruction in linguistic communication,

5. American Society for Engineering Education, *Characteristics of Excellence in Engineering Technology Education,* 1962.

[83]

humanistic-social studies, and other appropriate non-technical studies, such as industrial organization, human relations, and supervision.

With respect to technical courses, the content consists of subjects that directly and immediately pertain to the specialized occupational field. The technical skills group of courses are intended to familiarize the student with techniques and practices associated with his occupation and to develop facility in their application. The technical skills include such subjects as drafting, breadboard construction, welding, building construction practices, and manufacturing processes. Hence, the technical specialties group is made up of courses in the student's major field and other courses designed to supply the core of engineering knowledge he needs in his chosen occupation including such courses as strength of materials, machine design, semiconductors, highway design, and soil mechanics.

The Engineers Council for Professional Development administers a program of accreditation of college level, engineering technology curricula designed to prepare engineering technicians. Accreditation is voluntary and denotes that each curriculum designated as accredited by ECPD has been found satisfactory for the stated purpose it is intended to serve. The range of such curricula is wide; illustrations are aircraft electronics technology, air conditioning technology, chemical technology, civil technology, construction technology, drafting and design technology, electrical technology, electronic technology, highway engineering technology, materials engineering technology, mechanical technology, mechanical power engineering technology, nuclear engineering technology, and production engineering technology.

Individual institutions offering two-year or four-year engineering technology programs may have different goals and different subject matter emphasis in the same field of specialization. For example, in the field of civil technology, the University of Houston offers a Bachelor of Science in Technology with two separate curricula in Civil Technology (Building and Construction, Drafting); the Oregon Technical Institute offers a Bachelor of Technology degree with three optional programs in Civil Engineering Technology (Highway Engineering Technology, Structural Engineering Technology, and Surveying Engineering Technology).

The concept of cooperative education is applied to technology education programs. The plan derives its name from the fact that employers cooperate with an educational institution to provide practical experience which supplements academic study. A cooperative program for engineering technology students is usually on a twelve-month basis, divided into trimesters (fall, spring, summer). The student usually attends college the first two trimesters, then works the next trimester; thereafter, academic periods alternate with work periods. Upon completion of six trimesters of study plus intervening work periods, the student may be awarded an associate degree in the technology program in which he is enrolled. The normal time to complete the cooperative program is three full years. The requirements for admission are the same as those for a full-time student in a traditional technology program.

To an employer, the cooperative education plan offers a series of advantages: a continuing flow of talent into the organization, potential availability of graduates who have knowledge of the organization, an opportunity for scientists and engineers to be relieved of subprofessional duties so that the professional may do more professional work, and an opportunity for the employer to observe the students and to select the most able ones for full-time employment. To a student, cooperative education likewise provides advantages such as an opportunity for meaningful academic work as a result of his work experience, an understanding of the functions carried out by persons in his chosen field, a chance to test his interest and aptitude in a specific field under realistic conditions, and financial assistance in his education.

Two-year engineering technology programs are sometimes regarded as "terminal" education. However, although such education is organized to lead to meaningful, technician employment immediately after graduation, such education need not be "terminal" for those interested in continuing their education beyond the associate degree. Nevertheless, many credits obtained in a collegiate technology education program are non-transferrable, either toward completion of an associate of arts degree at another institution or toward completion of work for a bachelor's degree in engineering. Sharp inconsistencies exist among institutions. The increasing seriousness of this situation is reflected in a finding of the Engineering Manpower Commission in 1969 that 30% of associate degree technology graduates in one survey continued full-time academic study.

A prime obstacle to transfer of collegiate technology education course credits to an engineering curriculum is often the organization of mathematics programs in the two-year institution. This obstacle has been minimized in a few two-year institutions through their offering of an elective sequence in mathematics for capable students; in these institutions, students may obtain a more comprehensive mathematical background through integral calculus. In connection with student transfers, four-year institutions tend to accept at full value courses having more comprehensive material.

An educational institution offering a two-year, college level, technology program has a responsibility to offer continuing education to its graduates, especially for those who are employed in local industry. A few institutions currently offer post-graduate programs which enable two-year technology graduates to update or broaden their education. If continuing education is necessary for the scientist and the engineer, it is also necessary for technicians who work with scientists and engineers.

If increasing numbers of capable youth are to be attracted to careers as technicians, broader opportunity must be provided for the two-year graduate to continue his education at a subsequent period of time. It is important that steps be taken to increase opportunities for technicians to grow professionally in their chosen technical field, rather than out of it, Hence, progressive employers, as well as educators, assure greater opportunity for growth within the technician field through the establishment and maintenance of appropriate systems of incentives and rewards

[86]

for those technicians who successfully pursue additional formal education.

Employers often express their views on the question of adequacy of technology education programs. One method which many educational institutions use is the establishment of an advisory committee composed of employer representatives. Another method is solicitation of employer views at conferences and at special meetings. Through both methods, employers express general satisfaction with the education given to students in technology programs, particularly in collegiate engineering technology programs. In an effort to strengthen these programs, employers recently have suggested an increasing stress on mathematics, the basic sciences, and the technology specialty and a greater emphasis on specific technician needs of local industries. From the view of educators, increased stress on fundamentals is partially being provided through extension of two-year programs to four years. The economics of education do not permit the establishment of as many specialty curricula as educators would like to offer to help meet local industry needs.

SUPPLY-DEMAND RELATIONSHIPS

Many large employers, as well as many smaller ones, engaged in scientific and engineering activity have technician training programs to produce new entrants for the field. Such programs are increasing. The extent to which engineering technicians are trained by employers through the on-the-job or in-service approach is not known. Statistics on the number of individuals who become engineering technicians following either military training or dropout from a four-year engineering program are likewise not available. The number of formal education programs which develop engineering technicians is increasing, but the total number of graduates from such programs who work as engineering technicians is not known. The one series of reliable statistics available is the total number of enrollments and graduates in engineering technology programs in collegiate institutions having at least one technology curriculum accredited by the Engineers Council for Professional Development.

The total full-time student enrollment in the 61 educational institutions having at least one technology curriculum accredited by ECPD in the fall of 1968 was 23,597—a slight decline over the previous year. The only significant increase in engineering technology enrollment between fall 1967 and fall 1968 was a quadrupled enrollment for third and fourth year engineering technology students—namely from 223 (1967) to 863 (1968); the figure of 863, however, represented only 4% of the total engineering technology enrollment (23,597). The two-year associate degree enrollments were 3% lower than in 1967 despite the fact that 12 more institutions were listed in the 1968 data, as compared with 1967.[6]

Data compiled by the Engineering Manpower Commission on graduates during academic year 1968-69 from 428 schools indicated that the number of associate degrees in engineering technology was 18,406. All 46 institutions on the accredited list of ECPD represented less than 11% of the total schools covered, yet these 46 institutions granted 35% of the degrees. The figure of 18,406 engineering technology graduates for academic year 1968-69 compares with 16,920 for academic year 1967-68; however, because of data collection differences, the actual growth was 3.9%. Technology graduates from technical institutes and junior and community colleges have increased by a small percentage over the past few years but the number still amounts to approximately one-half of the current annual number of engineering graduates with a Bachelor of Science degree.[7]

The only available comparison to show national engineering technology graduate trends is made with data from institutions having at least one engineering technology curriculum accredited

6. Engineering Manpower Commission, *Engineering and Technician Enrollments: Fall 1968,* 1969.

7. Engineering Manpower Commission, *Degrees in Engineering and Industrial Technology 1968-69,* 1970.

by ECPD. Statistics of such graduates for an eleven year period are shown in Table III-2.

Table III–2

ENGINEERING TECHNOLOGY GRADUATES FROM INSTITUTIONS
HAVING AT LEAST ONE ECPD ACCREDITED ENGINEERING
TECHNOLOGY CURRICULUM

Year	Number of Institutions Reporting	Engineering Technology Graduates
1959-60	34	7,639
1960-61	33	6,284
1961-62	32	6,035
1962-63	32	5,489
1963-64	32	5,507
1964-65	33	5,695
1965-66	37	5,270
1966-67	38	6,144
1967-68	44	6,264
1968-69	46	6,536

Source: EMC study

Thus, the number of engineering technology graduates from institutions having at least one engineering technology curriculum accredited by ECPD increased by approximately 20% over the three year academic period 1965-66 to 1968-69. The number for each of the last nine years in the above ten year period failed to equal the number for the first year in the same period.

The U. S. Department of Labor completed in 1966 a comprehensive study of technician manpower in the United States. Projections to 1975, contained in the study, are considered generally valid today. Technicians are defined in the study as employees who directly or indirectly support scientists and engineers in designing, developing, producing, and maintaining the nation's machines and materials. Their work is technical in nature, but more limited in scope, than the work of scientists and engineers and has a practical rather than theoretical orientation. Specifically excluded from the study are medical and dental technicians who work with medical practitioners engaged in the care of patients.[8]

In this study, the Department of Labor classified technicians into four major occupational groups, according to the specialty or scientific discipline to which they are most closely related: (1) draftsmen, (2) engineering and physical science technicians; (3) life science technicians, and (4) "other" technicians, a miscellaneous group including industrial designers, computer programmers, and surveyors. In 1963, the base year for the study, there were approximately 845,000 technicians employed in the United States. Engineering and physical science technicians were the largest of the four groups and totaled 439,000. Draftsmen made up the second largest technician group and totaled 232,000. Life science technicians totaled about 58,000. "Other" technicians amounted to nearly 116,000.

According to the survey, manufacturing industries, primarily the electrical equipment, machinery, chemicals, fabricated metal products, and aircraft and parts industries, employed about 390,-000 technicians in 1963. In private non-manufacturing industries, large numbers of technicians were employed in engineering and architectural services (68,000), miscellaneous business services (39,000), and in the communications industry (29,000). Another large group was employed in government (170,000). Relatively few technicians were employed by colleges and universities and other nonprofit organizations. With respect to level of educational attainment, the median number of school years completed by technicians was estimated as approximately 14 years. Nearly 2 out of 3 technicians had some college education and 1 out of 10 had a bachelor's degree; younger technicians had a higher educational level than their older counterparts.

According to the Department of Labor study, approximately 90,000 persons entered the technician work force in 1963. The greatest number—estimated at about one-half of all new entrants —were upgraded from technician related jobs. Of the nearly

8. U. S. Department of Labor, *Technician Manpower: Requirements, Resources and Training Needs,* Bulletin No. 1512, 1966.

[90]

40,000 persons entering technician jobs after completing a training program designed to prepare them for technician work, more than 20,000 acquired their skills in employer training programs. Post-secondary school curriculums provided about 16,000 new graduates who entered technician jobs.

Of those new entrants to technician jobs who qualified in 1963 for their jobs through education or training received during preparation for other types of work, approximately 6,000 received training in colleges and universities, approximately one-half of whom received the bachelor's degree. The number of persons entering upon technician jobs directly after separation from U. S. Armed Forces was small, despite the large number of persons with some technician training separated from the Armed Forces; however, an unknown number of those separated entered technician jobs after receiving additional training, either in educational institutions or on-the-job.

Projections of technician requirements set forth in the study were based on a number of assumptions, including high levels of economic growth, continuation of scientific and technological advances, further increases in the complexity of industrial products and processes, and continued growth of research and development expenditures. Based on these assumptions, technician manpower requirements are expected to increase by more than three-fourths over the 1963-75 period, rising from the 845,000 workers employed in 1963 to nearly 1,500,000 required in 1975.

In addition to about 650,000 technicians needed as a result of growth in requirements, about 380,000 will be needed to replace those employed in 1963 who will leave the occupation by 1975 as a result of retirements, deaths, and transfers to other occupations. Thus, total new technician manpower needs between 1963 and 1975 are projected by the study at more than 1,025,000 or an average of nearly 86,000 each year over the period.

Underlying the projections of the future supply of technicians, as analyzed by the study, are four key assumptions: (1) that employers prefer to hire new technicians who have completed a pre-

[91]

employment training program, (2) that funds allocated under recent federal legislation to increase the facilities for technician training will be used for that purpose, (3) that current trends in the proportion of graduates of post-secondary pre-employment training programs who enter technician jobs will continue in the future, and (4) that problems of status or salary will not deter young people from entering technician jobs any more or less than they have in the recent past. Based on these assumptions, the intermediate projections of the supply of technicians indicated that approximately 830,000 workers will enter technician jobs after completing some type of specialized technician training during the 1963-75 period.

Graduates of post-secondary pre-employment curricula are expected to be the largest source of supply, with about 435,000 entering technician jobs after completing these programs. Smaller numbers of technicians will enter from government sponsored training programs, four-year college and university curricula (other than technology), and the U. S. Armed Forces.

Some individuals who enter technician occupations between 1963 and 1975 will not be in the field in 1975, the target year of the projections. For example, each year many newly trained technicians transfer to other occupations. Thus, of all new entrants over the 1963-75 period (including those from pre-employment programs and from technician-related training in colleges and universities and in the U. S. Armed Forces), the net increase in the supply in 1975 is estimated to be about 675,000 after allowance is made for deaths, retirements, and transfers.

The Department of Labor study concluded that under projected supply-demand situations, the demand for new entrants from post-secondary pre-employment technician training programs is expected to exceed the number trained.

A similar view of the Department of Labor was again reflected in the 1968-69 edition of the Occupational Outlook Handbook. This edition states that employment opportunities for technicians who work with scientists and engineers are expected to be "very good" through the 1970s. The outlook is based on the assumption that defense and space activities in the late 1970s will not be significantly different from the levels of the early and mid 1960s prior to the Vietnam buildup. Among factors underlying increased demands during the decade of the 1970s, according to the handbook, are anticipated expansion of industry, increasing complexity of modern technology, the growth in employment of scientists and engineers, a trend toward automation of industrial processes and the growth of new areas of work, and increases anticipated in research and development expenditures. The handbook adds that it is likely that more women will be trained and will find employment as engineering technicians than heretofore.[9]

In 1969 the Department of Labor issued a series of national projections of occupational requirements for 1975. The base year for these projections was 1966 employment. Technicians who work with scientists and engineers were identified in the projections in two categories: (1) science and engineering technicians and (2) draftsmen.[10]

According to the analysis, nearly 650,000 science and engineering technicians (excluding draftsmen and surveyors) were employed in 1966. Engineering technicians constituted more than one-half of the total in this category; physical science technicians constituted about one-fifth; life science technicians were about one-tenth. About three-fourths of the total number of this category were employed in private industry. Industries employing the largest numbers were electrical equipment, chemicals, machinery, and aircraft and parts. Approximately 70,000 were employed by the federal government and 60,000 by state and local governments. The remainder were employed by colleges and universities (mostly in university research institutes) and by nonprofit organizations.

---

9. U. S. Department of Labor, *Occupational Outlook Handbook,* 1968-69 edition, 1968.

10. U. S. Department of Labor, *Tomorrow's Manpower Needs,* Vol. 3, 1969.

According to Department of Labor estimates contained in the 1969 report, employment requirements for this category will increase more than one-half between 1966 and 1975 and hence rise to more than one million. One reason for the expected increase is anticipated expansion of industries employing large numbers of technicians. Another reason for the expected increase in demand is the anticipated growth in research and development. The analysis points out that the services of technicians will be used more extensively in the future as employers realize that they can better utilize scientists and engineers by providing them with additional technical support. The 1975 projection assumes that the level of defense expenditures in 1975 will not be sufficiently different from that in 1964, before the Vietnam buildup. In addition to technicians needed to fill new positions, approximately 4% of the total number employed will be needed to replace technicians who transfer to other fields, die, retire, and otherwise leave the labor force.

According to the Department of Labor analysis, approximately 260,000 technicians were employed as draftsmen in 1966. About 90% of these draftsmen were employed in private industry. Manufacturing industries employing large numbers of draftsmen are machinery, electrical equipment, fabricated metal products, and transportation equipment industries. Non-manufacturing industries employing large numbers of draftsmen are engineering and architectural consulting firms, construction companies, and public utilities. Nearly 10% of the total number of draftsmen work for federal, state, and local governments.

Employment requirements for draftsmen are expected to increase about 45% between 1966 and 1975 and thus rise to about 375,000. Among factors underlying the projected growth are continued expansion of industries employing large numbers of draftsmen and increasingly complex design problems of modern products and processes. In addition to draftsmen needed to fill new positions, about 4% of the total number employed will be required to replace draftsmen who transfer to other fields, die, retire, and otherwise leave the labor force.

[94]

In the 1969 projections study, the Department of Labor made no attempt to assess the future supply of technicians,

According to best estimates, demands for technicians are presently unfilled at each level of government. Such demands are better understood in the light of the numbers of technicians actually employed by government.

At the federal level as of October 1968, there were 65,100 technicians classified in eight civil service position categories. Table III-3 shows this classification.

Table III–3

TECHNICIANS EMPLOYED BY FEDERAL GOVERNMENT, CLASSIFIED BY JOB CATEGORY

Job Category	Numbers
Engineering technician	27,031
Electronics technician	21,702
Surveying technician	3,322
Engineering draftsman	3,185
Physical science technician	2,862
Cartographic technician	2,355
Industrial engineering technician	2,352
Meteorological technician	2,291
TOTAL	65,100

Source: CSC data

The above listing is not all-inclusive of technicians in the federal service who work with scientists and engineers.

According to a 1967 survey by the U. S. Department of Labor, state government agencies (other than educational institutions) employed approximately 50,000 technicians in four categories related to science and technology. The predominant number of such technicians were employed in highways and public works departments. A classification of employment of such technicians is presented in Table III-4.

The employment of a group of approximately 1,500 computer programmers was scattered throughout nearly all state agencies.[11]

11. E. W. Andrews and M. Moylan, "Scientific and Professional Employment by States," *Monthly Labor Review,* August 1969, pp. 40-45.

[95]

Table III–4

STATE GOVERNMENT EMPLOYMENT OF TECHNICIANS

Selected Types of Technicians	All State Agencies	Highways & Public Works Depts	Welfare Health & Depts	Agriculture & Conservation Depts	Other Depts
Draftsmen	7,080	6,580	30	280	180
Surveyors	7,810	7,590	—	170	50
Engineering Technicians	33,050	32,390	200	250	210
Physical Science Technicians	2,460	1,670	440	220	130
Total	50,300	48,230	670	920	570

Source: Dept. of Labor Survey

Although precise data are not available on the numbers of technicians who work with scientists and engineers and who are employed by local government, it is conservatively estimated that approximately 45,000 individuals are so employed.

In addition to current vacancies at all levels of government, the needs at each level—especially at state and local government levels—are rising as increasingly larger appropriations implement a series of intergovernmental programs having a science or engineering content.

An impressive "package" of federal programs which involve science and technology and which provide financial assistance to state and local governments have been developed during the past few years. Significant numbers of competent engineering technicians will be in demand to work as state and local government employees as these program objectives are met. The list of selected programs presented below indicates the varied nature of the "package" of programs:

DEPARTMENT OF TRANSPORTATION
Primary and secondary highway systems and urban extensions
High speed ground transportation
Appalachian development highway system
Landscaping and scenic enhancement

[96]

Economic development facilities
Industrial and commercial development
Technical and planning assistance
Economic development districts and centers

DEPARTMENT OF HEALTH, EDUCATION AND WELFARE
Construction aid for education
Air pollution prevention and control
Environmental engineering and sanitation
Solid waste disposal

DEPARTMENT OF HOUSING AND URBAN DEVELOPMENT
Community facilities programs
Low rent public housing
Urban planning
Urban renewal

DEPARTMENT OF THE INTERIOR
Water pollution control
Saline water research and development
Irrigation projects
Strip and surface mining

State and local governments participate voluntarily in these federal programs. In some instances, state and local governments have already entered into agreements with the Federal Government to participate and are presently engaged in program implementation, including recruiting and employing engineering technicians. In other instances, state and local governments are preparing to participate or federal officials are engaged in activities preparatory to inviting them to participate.

The extent of employment of engineering technicians in government programs varies sharply, both at early and later stages of individual programs. Because of the current status of state and local participation, the impact of many of these federal programs has not yet appreciably involved engineering technicians. However, there is no doubt that engineering technicians are already playing a key role in the public service and will continue to do so in the future. Preference is generally for engineering technology graduates who can supply a high degree of technical competence.

From the viewpoint of total needs for engineering technicians, in both public and private endeavors, it is apparent that the education and training of such technicians is not progressing at a pace sufficient to meet current or future demands in particular specialized fields. Lack of adequate accurate data and inadequacies in survey methodology cast limitations on the value of literal figures in any estimates of current or prospective technician needs. Evidence does seem conclusive, however, that the present sources are failing, by far, to produce sufficient numbers of qualified engineering technicians to meet even the most conservative estimates.

To the extent that demands for qualified engineering technicians are not met, adverse results are observable. In some instances, professional personnel perform technician duties and thus underutilize their own professional talent, often in short supply. In other cases, unqualified persons carry out technician duties: employment of unqualified technicians results in poor workmanship, loss of material, delay in meeting deadlines, and antagonized scientists and engineers. In identifiable instances, essential scientific and engineering activity is not undertaken or is postponed because of lack of qualified technicians. The consequences of not undertaking or postponing a particular scientific or engineering activity can be so serious as to jeopardize the national interest.

Further confirmation of the short supply of adequately educated technicians is evidence that beginning salaries for graduates of engineering technology programs have continued to rise during the past several years, at a rate faster than salaries of comparable types of personnel. Employers report that the competition for qualified graduates from engineering technology programs equals, and in some areas surpasses, the competition for qualified engineering graduates with baccalaureate degrees. One institution reported that the average beginning salary (12 months, 40 hour week) for its forty-three graduates obtaining a Bachelor's Degree in technology in June 1969 was $9,613.

[98]

It is estimated that the desirable technician support for scientists and engineers, in the aggregate, should be between one and four technicians to each scientist or engineer. This variation depends to a large extent upon the type of work involved and the experience and ability of the individual scientist, engineer, and technician. Recent evidence continues to show that the national ratio of technicians to scientists and engineers remains approximately 0.7 to 1. Figures derived from a ratio approach cannot be regarded as conclusive, but they are considered generally indicative of large, unfilled technician requirements. The need for more and better educated technicians is as critical—if not more so—than the need for manpower at professional levels.

STEPS TO INCREASE SUPPLY

IMPEDIMENTS

Three factors which constitute serious impediments to increasing the number of qualified engineering technicians are a shortage of students, a shortage of competent faculty, and inadequate counseling.

There is a shortage of students pursuing engineering technology education programs. One aspect of the lack of progressive growth in engineering technology enrollment is a popular notion that, to be successful, a student must pursue an academic program which results in the immediate attainment of a traditional baccalaureate degree, regardless of his specific skills and aptitudes. Furthermore, a very large number of high school students do not learn of employment opportunities for qualified technology graduates. Some high school graduates who did not select the proper science and mathematics courses required for admission to a collegiate engineering technology program face a decision to take additional courses or to pursue a different area of interest. With increasing numbers of high school graduates interested in continuing their formal education, institutions offering engineering technology programs should be capable not only of meeting current employer needs for technology graduates but also of helping to alleviate the deficit in future numbers of such graduates. However, although the number of students in higher education has increased steadily during the past few years, this increase has not been reflected proportionately in enrollments in college level, engineering technology programs.

There is a shortage of competent faculty to teach technical subjects in all types of educational institutions offering technology education programs. Institutions offering engineering technology programs indicate a particularly acute need for faculty members having a scientific or engineering background or orientation. Preferably, approximately one-half of the faculty teaching in engineering technology should be graduate and experienced scientists or engineers. Part of the shortage is the result of misunderstanding of the proper role of engineering technology education and a misconception that teaching engineering technology programs is participating in second rate education for students not otherwise capable of continuing their education. A contributing condition to a shortage in particular geographical areas is a comparatively low salary schedule for faculty in technical subject matter, in comparison with other types of positions which prospective faculty members may obtain elsewhere in and outside of the field of education. Furthermore, many prospective faculty members are not fully aware of the opportunities which in fact exist in this type of education.

Individuals who have had successful work experience as technicians are especially valuable as faculty, provided they are also qualified for teaching. Another portion of the faculty in institutions offering technology programs should be properly qualified in other disciplines, such as the humanities and communication. All faculty members should have a comprehensive knowledge of the objectives of engineering technology education and its place in the broad spectrum of education. Educators generally agree that a realistic expansion of quality engineering technology education depends upon meaningful action to increase the supply and to sharpen the abilities and knowledge of individuals already teaching in these programs.

With respect to inadequate counseling, high school counselors as a group are not sufficiently knowledgeable about engineering technology education, including information on the precise nature of this type of education, specific academic requirements, the kinds of work which graduates of this type of education actually perform, and the range of their earnings. Many college counselors also appear to be inadequately informed in this area. The majority of counselors have an educational background in the liberal arts and through their own experiences usually have not obtained a clear understanding of the work of engineering technicians. Pressures of daily work of counselors often make it difficult for them to take the time to acquire direct knowledge of the work of such technicians. When counselors do seek out engineering technician career data, they often are unable to find sufficient current information. Constructive efforts are being made to improve counselor understanding of this type of education. However, the rate of expansion of the number of counselors and the rate of turnover among counselors are relatively high. From a numerical viewpoint, present programs for imparting useful information only partially meet counselor needs. When counselors are more fully informed of the role of engineering technicians, counselors will play a larger part in interpreting opportunities in engineering technology education.

SUGGESTED ACTIONS

With respect to each of these three impediments, a series of actions are hereby suggested for consideration by those having appropriate responsibility.

To reduce the incidence of the current student shortage, the following recommendations are offered:

1. The use of pretechnical education programs to overcome an individual's earlier educational deficiences should be expanded. Pretechnical programs are offered in a summer period prior to the beginning of a regular academic year or during a regular academic year as a prerequisite to particular technology courses. Increasing the number of both types of offerings will increase stu-

dent competency and enlarge the flow of students likely to complete satisfactorily technology programs.

2. The responsibility of educational institutions to help their graduates to locate initial technician employment or to enter an advanced higher educational institution should be more clearly recognized. College placement services of some institutions do not appear to be attuned to assisting graduates in a meaningful way to make an effective transition to their first technician position or to their immediate continuation to advanced higher education. Greater recognition of this responsibility on the part of educational institutions reduces the loss of graduates who through inability to make a proper transition fail to enter technician employment.

3. Employers should participate in larger numbers in career programs to spotlight technician work opportunities. Aggregate participation by employers in career programs which outline professional opportunities greatly overshadow similar efforts to portray the nature of technician opportunities. Either as a separate feature at a career night or as a distinguishable part of a total career night program or at student assemblies of educational institutions, employers can profitably participate more actively in explaining and illustrating technician employment opportunities.

4. Summer technician-oriented student employment should be linked to an individual's continuance as a student in technology education. Employers often provide technician-oriented summer work opportunities without regard to the formal education programs of students thus employed. Furthermore, students sometimes decide to forego the rest of their formal education after a summertime work experience and to continue in employment with the same employer. One way to stimulate students to complete their formal education program is for employers to consider the technician education accomplishments and goals of the student as an important employment factor when employers select students for technically-oriented summer jobs. Employers should also urge these students to resume their formal education at the expiration of the summer employment.

5. The Department of Defense should provide more meaningful information on technician employment opportunities to servicemen about to be discharged. Through efforts, such as Project Transition, servicemen returning to civilian life are provided career information. Details concerning technician employment opportunities in the civilian sector are particularly relevant because many servicemen have already received excellent technical training and experience directly applicable to civilian technician employment.

6. The public should be made more aware of the shortages of qualified technicians together with basic information on educational requirements for becoming a technician. Segments of this public, such as parents and friends, exert an influence upon career selections by youth. Because of general public misunderstanding, efforts to provide public information on the role of the technician also tends to improve the status of the technician occupation.

To reduce the incidence of the faculty shortage, the following recommendations are offered:

1. Programs to assist experienced technical personnel to become full time teachers in the technician field should be developed. Early retirement and/or a subsequent desire to teach frequently induces experienced technical personnel to want to become faculty members in technician education. Such persons willing to undergo educational experiences which qualify them to become competent teachers often do not find such experiences available. Greater effort to set up more programs to provide transitional education experiences designed to qualify such individuals as teachers has value as a faculty recruiting device.

2. Some technical students should be motivated to consider becoming teachers while these students are still pursuing their technician education. Some students who desire to become technicians also have the basic ability to become technical education teachers. Faculty in technical programs can identify these individuals and can encourage them to pursue appropriate courses

and programs which will lead to their ultimate development as faculty members.

3. Specific measures of the need for technical faculty should be frequently projected on a national basis and continuously updated. Although technical faculty needs of individual educational institutions and, sometimes, of all of the educational institutions in a state are determined, generally detailed projections are not made on any systematic national basis. Information on aggregate faculty needs, classified by type of faculty and qualifications necessary, would be useful not only as a target toward which policy and programs could be directed but also as a stimulator for career decision-making because of the span of opportunities noted.

4. Education programs specifically designed to develop teachers for engineering technology education should be expanded. A few current technical faculty development programs are very effective; in addition, experimental projects are underway to devise new methods to develop such faculty. The basic limitation, however, is the relatively small number of such programs. A sharp increase in the number of these types of programs is necessary.

5. State higher education planning should be strengthened to assure participation on the part of all types of institutions which offer engineering technology education. State higher education planning sometimes tends to ignore particular types of institutions such as technical institutes which offer such education. In these cases, identification of faculty needs and preparation of actions to meet these needs may not realistically represent the total needs or the related actions of the state. The nature of the faculty shortage is such as to require institutional participation on as broad a base as possible.

6. Qualified military retirees should be better informed on teaching opportunities in engineering technology education. Such individuals often decide to embark upon a second career. The extensive use of science and technology in the military service provides rich experience which is translatable, in some instances,

to effective technical teaching in civilian life. The desirability of calling technology education faculty opportunities to the attention of qualified military retirees merits much greater attention than is being given to this source of faculty recruitment.

7. The assignment of qualified technical personnel in industry or government to temporary or part-time technology education positions should be given greater encouragement. Such an approach not only adds to the total number of faculty available but also offers an experience which may result in a decision by the individual to become a full-time faculty member after retirement from his industrial or government position.

To reduce the incidence of inadequate counseling, the following recommendations are offered:

1. Greater opportunities should be provided for counselors to become acquainted with major types of engineering technician positions, including the types characteristic of employers in their geographical area. The wide spectrum of duties performed by technicians means that individual counselors usually do not have familiarity with all types of positions. They may strive, however, to obtain an understanding of the major types as well as all types used by local employers. Counselors acquire this knowledge through opportunities such as counseling seminars and employer visitations.

2. Specific material on engineering technician employment opportunities should be included in all summer and academic year institutes for counselors. Granted that these institutes are concerned with numerous aspects of counseling, these institutes offer an excellent vehicle for the dissemination of data about technology education and technician employment opportunities. An additional approach is the use of special lecturers during the institute period to discuss current and future technician employment trends.

3. Career experiences should be arranged for counselors to become better acquainted through actual work observation with the range of duties of engineering technicians in the world of

work. Employers can arrange useful tours and exhibits for counselors. Furthermore, counselors can be employed in industry or government for limited periods to provide better counselor understanding while at the same time they contribute useful service to employers.

4. Written materials on the role of engineering technicians should be developed for use by all types of educators, not solely by counselors. Counselors constitute an essential, but not exclusive, influence upon the career decision-making process. In the school setting, classroom teachers, administrators, and librarians, for examples, also have an influence. It is not enough for guidance material to be prepared solely for counselor usage; other educators need access to explanatory career data to carry out their collateral counseling responsibilities.

5. Career information on the role of engineering technicians should be included on local, state, and national programs of counseling societies and groups. Organizations of counselors at the local, state, and national levels are in a unique position to transmit career data to their membership through use of such avenues as organization publications (including bibliographical sections of such publications) and meetings of the organization. More than dissemination of career literature is contemplated by this suggestion, however; graduates of technology programs and supervisors of engineering technicians should be featured at panel sessions as well as at pertinent parts of general sessions in order to provide clear understanding of this type of education and work experiences.

6. A technician guide should be developed to include a comprehensive listing of formal technology education programs together with the names of specific institutions offering such programs. Currently, material available on such programs and institutions are illustrative rather than being fully definitive. Use of the guide proposed would provide sufficient information to enable interested students to make direct application to the proper educational institution offering the precise type of education desired by the students.

[106]

OBSTACLES TO MORE EFFECTIVE USE

Analysis of the role of engineering technicians indicates several obstacles to the effective use of technicians. A brief review of key obstacles and suggestions for minimizing these obstacles follows.

A sizeable segment of managerial personnel does not appear to understand the proper place of the technician. One suggestion for improving management understanding is the use of work analysis studies to identify technician jobs: the resultant identification may suggest upgrading of certain positions or employees to the professional level and downgrading other positions or employees to the nonprofessional technical level. Other suggestions to improve management understanding are the inclusion of material on the proper place of technicians in the executive development program of the organization, the participation of managers on educational advisory committees which would provide greater insight into curricula offered, and visits by managers to other companies and agencies successfully employing technicians with the objective of obtaining accurate, firsthand information about the role of technicians in these organizations.

Some supervisory scientists and engineers are reluctant to accept the technician as an integral part of scientific and engineering activity. Many professional persons have been trained to perform varying degrees of manual work and have difficulty in changing their accustomed work patterns. Suggestions to reduce this reluctance include the establishment of in-plant training programs to orient professional supervisory personnel in the potential use of technicians, the creation by management of an adequate number of billets with necessary funds to permit the appointment of needed technicians, and the use of incentives for scientists and engineers who are in a supervisory capacity to make successful use of technicians. Programs of professional societies also may be used as a means of overcoming reluctance on the part of the professional employee. From a longer range viewpoint, new concepts in engineering education at the collegiate level which portray the proper role of the technician are helping to improve this condition.

A practice of considering the engineering technician as an engineer-in-training gives a transitional character to the technician's work and minimizes the unitary role of a technician. This practice is somewhat understandable because the technician is often associated with an engineer. Thus, the technician's normal line of promotion may seem to be through the engineering classification. It is strongly suggested, however, that the advancement of the technician should be more properly considered within the framework of his own education and ability. Methods already mentioned above to overcome previously cited obstacles (such as an emphasis on the proper place of the technician and work analysis studies to differentiate professional and non-professional technical work) are also recommended.

Some individuals classified as technicians are inadequately trained to perform the duties reasonably expected of engineering technicians. One solution is the raising of selection standards by educational institutions. Another is improvement in curricula to provide a closer relationship between the knowledge and skills of graduates and particular requirements of employers. Employers may exert positive influence in this direction through participation on educational advisory committees and through maintenance of close contacts with educational institutions. Improved selection standards used by employers is also advocated. The establishment of in-service training programs for technicians which stress application of subject matter to specific employer work operations and the creation of updating programs for technicians are highly encouraged.

A shortage of specific types of technicians exists in particular geographical areas. It is suggested that managers assure maximum use of the knowledge and skills of technicians already on their payrolls by ascertaining that these technicians are performing bona fide technician duties. In some cases, the hiring of clerks, artisans, and other types of employees is necessary to relieve technicians of non-technical duties. Active personal interest and support on the part of employers in engineering technology education are also recommended as a means of reducing shortages. Recommendations to overcome student shortages have been set forth in the preceding section.

A practice of combining technicians with general non-professional personnel of an organization for personnel policy and personnel program purposes tends to blunt the type of personnel staff service required to facilitate the proper use of technician manpower. The establishment of a separate set of personnel policies and procedures applicable specifically to technicians as a key group of employees in an organization is desirable. Proposed policies and programs would be similar in some respects, but not identical, to personnel policies and programs applicable to scientific and engineering personnel. This approach means the creation and application of carefully considered and specially devised personnel policies and methods for technicians to embrace such functions as recruitment, selection, compensation, training, promotion, and recognition. Some individuals insist that the most effective use of technicians requires special treatment of technicians, personnel-wise, as distinguished from the personnel treatment accorded rank-and-file, non-professional workers.

NEED FOR STATUS

The prestige of engineering technology education is increasing but more progress is still to be made before the degree of status which both the engineering technology education and the graduate of this type of education deserve will be attained. Engineering technology education is sometimes regarded as having been designed exclusively for the student who is academically inferior to his four-year college associates or who fails undergraduate engineering courses. Such attitudes are erroneous. Although complete acceptance of the vital role of the engineering technology graduate has not yet been achieved, the image of engineering technology education as second rate education and of the graduate as a second rate citizen is largely the result of misunderstanding of the role of engineering technology by some parents, counselors, college faculty and college administrators, employers, and employees.

A remedy for such misconceptions is the promotion of an understanding of the true role of the technician and of the significance of his skills and aptitudes, an understanding effectively developed through education of the public. Helping the public form a proper perspective of engineering technology education and of the graduate of this type of education is a task for government, industry, professional and technical societies, educators, and scientists and engineers, as well as for technicians themselves.

To provide recognition of the importance of the role of engineering technicians and to enhance the status of technicians, the National Society of Professional Engineers created in 1961 the Institute for the Certification of Engineering Technicians. The Institute carries out the following objectives: to elevate performance standards of engineering technicians as an essential part of the engineering team, to determine the competence of engineering technicians through investigation and examination, to issue certificates to engineering technicians who voluntarily apply and qualify for certification, and to maintain a registry of holders of such certificates. The Institute is administered by a Board of Trustees composed of four professional engineers and four senior engineering technicians, each serving without pay. The Institute acts as a national certifying body, similar to state registration boards which provide for the registration of professional engineers. Although certification is voluntary and not based on authority provided by law, certification is recognized by employers as a type of achievement. An engineering technician who has been certified is eligible to become a member of the American Society of Certified Engineering Technicians.

An individual who believes his work brings him under the purview of the definition of an engineering technician as set forth by the Institute is eligible to apply for certification to the Board. The applicant provides relevant personal information and a detailed chronological summary of his work assignments, in addition to statements describing the degree of responsibilities involved. After review by the Board, eligibility and the grade of certification are determined on the basis of requirements set forth in Table III-5.

An engineering technician certified in one of the lower grades can be upgraded by submitting evidence that he has met the requirement of the next higher grade. Through the three level system of certification, incentive for self-development is provided. An increasing number of employers have converted their position classification system for engineering technicians to conform to the Institute pattern. Certification has thus become a factor in promotion as well as in employment. As of January 1970, there were an estimated 15,500 active certificate holders. Of this total, 4,178 were in the grade of junior engineering technician, 7,750 in the grade of engineer technician, and 3,572 in the grade of senior engineering technician.

Table III–5

MINIMUM REQUIREMENTS FOR CERTIFICATION

Grade	Age	Education and/or Experience	Qualifications
Senior Engineering Technician	No maximum— 35 years minimum	Graduation from an ECPD accredited program in engineering technology plus 15 years engineering technician experience under the direction of a professional engineer or equivalent or 17 years engineering technician experience under the direction of a professional engineer or equivalent.	Demonstrated high qualifications, knowledge of detailed technical character. Responsible performance. Endorsements from three professional engineers or equivalents.
Engineering Technician	No maximum— 25 years minimum	Graduation from an ECPD accredited program in engineering technology plus 5 years engineering technician experience under the direction of a professional engineer or equivalent. or	Demonstrated technical knowledge plus satisfactory completion of an examination (which may be waived by the Board)

[111]

Table III–5 (Continued)

Grade	Age	Education and/or Experience	Qualifications
		7 years engineering technician experience under the direction of a professional engineer or equivalent.	Endosements from two professional engineers or equivalents.
Junior Engineering Technician	No maximum No maximum	Graduation from an ECPD accredited program in engineering technology.	Elementary technical ability.
		or	
		Examination to be determined by the board after a review of the applicants educational resume.	Endorsement from one professional engineer or equivalent.
		or	
		Two years engineering technician experience under direction of a professional engineer or equivalent.	

Source: ICET data

PARTNERSHIP RELATIONSHIP

Some employers have learned from experience that the employment of engineering technicians constitutes a practical method of optimizing the utilization of scientific and engineering manpower on ther payrolls. The extent of the relationship of the engineering technician as a partner in scientific and technical effort is already increasing. If engineering technicans currently available are themselves employed properly and if larger numbers of qualified technicians to work with scientists and engineers can be trained for such a relationship, much improvement in the utilization of scientific and engineering personnel will be realized.

IV

BROADENING THE ROLE OF
CONTINUING EDUCATION

•

NATURE OF CONTINUING EDUCATION

In view of the rapidly changing pace of science and technology, individuals initially educated in these fields must periodically obtain additional education if optimum utilization is to be approached. Scientists and engineers must take affirmative steps to acquire knowledge in new fields or to keep up-to-date in their own or related fields: otherwise, these individuals may soon become obsolete. The formal education in science or engineering which an individual once received does not equip him to cope indefinitely with challenges in these fields. The extent to which the scientist or engineer can effectively handle today's—and tomorrow's—assignments depends upon the recency of his initial formal education and the amount of additional education he has received during the intervening period.

In some cases, the recency of his initial education is such that little additional education in his field may be needed. In other cases, the same degree of recency may require much additional education because the individual is about to embark upon an area of science or technology for which he was not specifically educated. In still other cases, merely the passage of time since acquisition of his initial formal education requires him to pursue additional education, either to learn refresher material or to obtain an understanding not previously acquired.

The terms "updating" or "retraining" or "continuing studies" are often used to denote activity on the part of an individual to acquire new knowledge and skills. A differentiation between "advanced degree education" and "continuing studies" is sometimes made, but this differentiation is difficult, if not impossible, to make in specific situations. A practice has developed to apply the term "continuing education" to a broad concept which embraces professional education and training acquired at any time after the completion of one's initial formal collegiate education. Initial formal collegiate education refers to the period of time during which an individual pursues full-time collegiate education on a continuous basis and receives one or more degrees. Under the concept, the content of continuing education may be repetitious of one's earlier education or may be actually new to the individual. For a scientist or engineer without a degree in either of these fields, the term applies to education and training acquired any time after he begins his initial regular job assignment in science or engineering.

The question of continuing education for scientific and engineering personnel has been given much attention during the past few years. Constructive efforts have been undertaken to offer continuing education opportunities for increasing numbers of scientists and engineers, not only through federal assistance but also through numerous non-federal programs. However, within the context of the total education and training effort in the United States, relatively little sustained effort has been consciously directed to provide continuing education specifically for scientists and engineers.

Many responsible persons believe that the challenge of providing continuing education opportunities for scientists and engineers is significantly different in several aspects from that posed by non-professionals. The defense of the nation depends to an extraordinary degree upon the continued competency of the scientific and engineering personnel of the nation. Very large federal expenditures, particularly for research and development, require the highest quality of scientific and engineering manpower for effective results. The federal government is already expending undetermined amounts of money for continuing education for scientists and engineers, but without clear knowledge of the overall results of such expenditures. Continuing education for scientists and engineers is sharply restricted under some general updating programs. The administration of key programs related to continuing education for scientists and engineers is diffused among several federal agencies. The incidence of "obsolescent" scientists and engineers—one result of the absence of continuing education opportunities—has been seriously felt in geographical areas of the nation where employers have reduced their scientific and engineering staffs.

A comprehensive picture of the details of continuing education for scientists and engineers is not now available for several reasons:

1. With respect to individual programs, records of numbers and types of participants and precise program patterns are often unavailable because some employers do not maintain such records. Furthermore, continuing education activities are usually so decentralized to individual field units of large organizations that special studies on the part of central administrative offices of these organizations are required if even approximations of pertinent details of the organization's programs are to be ascertained.

2. Some scientists and engineers engage in continuing education activities, independent of their employers. Contact with individual scientists and engineers through special questionnaires becomes the only method of obtaining data involving self-directed continuing education efforts independent of the industrial or academic environment. Up to the present time, this approach has not been commonly used.

3. Courses and programs leading to undergraduate degrees for some individuals are sometimes, concurrently, continuing education opportunities for other individuals. Hence, it is often difficult, if not impossible, for purpose of analysis, to separate continuing education activity from "first exposure" education.

4. Continuing education opportunities for scientists and engineers are occasionally only part of a course or program attended by personnel other than scientists and engineers. Because of the nature of records maintained, it is often impossible to

identify the portion of such a group who are scientists and engineers.

In spite of limitations of data, sufficient information is available to permit a description of essential features of continuing education for scientists and engineers as it is carried on presently, to provide some measurement data, to examine a series of issues related to such education, and to raise policy questions.

ROLE OF INDIVIDUAL SCIENTISTS
AND ENGINEERS

Until a relatively few years ago, formal education and professional work in science and technology were regarded as distinctly separate stages in the life of a scientist or engineer. Experience during the work phase was considered the basis for orderly advancement. This approach fitted an accepted pattern. The student pursued specialized education in one or more related phases of his field. Subsequently, on entering employment, the individual mastered the special science or technology of the activity, product or service with which he found himself engaged.

Today, acceleration of science and technology necessitates a different approach. Such acceleration is accompanied by a necessity for changing education concepts. The pace of science and technology leads to obsolescence of those individuals with only an earlier education background unless in some way the individual adds substantially to his former education by experience and by further development. Continuing work in science and technology and continuing education are now regarded as concurrent factors.

It is the basic responsibility of the individual to keep up-to-date in a professional field. He must decide the field and level of competence to set for himself. This goal changes at different stages in his career. To be a contributor to his profession, the scientist or engineer must be alert throughout his whole career to changes in science and/or technology which may have a serious impact on his place on the competency scale. He must take the initiative and determine his own response to scientific and en-

[116]

gineering change. His response may be negative and in effect he may coast into oblivion, or his reaction may be to pursue courses or programs or self-study in which he re-acquaints himself with earlier concepts which have been forgotten or familiarizes himself with new knowledge. In any event, he needs to prepare himself to meet the competition of more recent and better-trained graduates if he is to survive professionally. The results of his initiative may cause him to incorporate new knowledge into his current work. On the other hand, he may deliberately take action designed to lead to a new career in a different and expanding area of science or technology. In any event, he needs to avoid letting his technical understanding deteriorate to the point where scientific or technical obsolescence makes his return to the world of new ideas extremely difficult, if not impossible.

Much can be accomplished by the individual after he considers, and begins to respond to, the range of educational opportunities available. Some of his most important decisions are the selection from the total mass of ideas those ideas which are meaningful for him, the courses of action he should follow, and the priority he should give these ideas in a very complex world. His employer, educational institutions, professional and technical societies, and the Federal Government may, and often do, provide assistance to enable him to maintain and expand his professional competence. Nevertheless, action begins with the individual.

The nature of the continuing education problem is such that the individual must engage in careful planning in order to maintain a degree of continuous learning. One of the main aspects of such planning is to recognize the continuity of scientific and technological growth. As one scientific or technological area grows out of another and as further proliferation takes place, it is difficult for one to capitalize on his scientific or technical background unless he charts a firm course to keep abreast of subsequent developments.

To remain competent, today's scientist or engineer must be willing to read and study regularly on his own time and even pay for continuing education costs out of his own pocket, if necessary,

[117]

in the expectation that this experience will help him to progress professionally. A concept of the professional "half life-time" has been set forth: this concept refers to the approximate point in time at which the professional competency of the individual has been reduced about fifty percent from his earlier maximum competency unless further education has been undertaken. It has been estimated that an engineer's "half life-time" is about ten years. Under this concept, engineers who graduated in 1960, for example, and who have not kept-up-to-date do not now have an adequate technical background to enable them to work in many problem areas. In many instances, engineering curricula prior to 1960 did not include a sufficient amount of fundamental science; instead, the curricula tended to emphasize technology. The "half life-time" concept also has been applied to scientists but with the time determinant usually more than ten years.

Continuing education efforts involve collaboration among individual scientists or engineers, employers, educational institutions, professional and technical societies, and the Federal Government. For example, a scientist may participate in an in-service program established by his employer, or an employer may provide an off-campus engineering education program on his premises in conjunction with an educational institution. In this chapter, an analysis of the role of each of these groups is presented separately; however, it must be understood that close interrelationships among these sectors do exist in particular continuing education situations.

FINDINGS OF STUDIES

A series of studies during the past few years provides an understanding of individual participation in, and attitudes toward, continuing education.

Pennsylvania State University Study

A landmark study related to continuing education of engineers was conducted in 1963 by Pennsylvania State University. The study is significant because of the nature of the data derived and because Pennsylvania State University officials today believe

[118]

that current educational needs of engineers are comparable to the findings of the 1963 study.[1]

The objective of the study was to determine the educational needs of individual engineers employed in industries of Pennsylvania who received their bachelor's degrees five or more years previous to the study and to recommend methods for providing educational programs for updating engineers in Pennsylvania. A sample of 2,090 engineers employed in 176 companies was used. Highlights of findings are summarized in the following tables.

A comparison of the rank of undergraduate fields, shown in Table IV-1, with the rank of fields of work at the time of the survey, shown in Table IV-2, indicates considerable shifting of fields among engineers.

Table IV–1

UNDERGRADUATE FIELDS OF ENGINEERING OF RESPONDENTS

Fields	Rank	Number of Respondents
Mechanical Engineering	1	536
Civil Engineering	2	292
Electrical—Power	3	262
Chemical Engineering	4	261
Electrical—Electronics	5	208
Industrial Engineering	6	125

Source: PSU study

Table IV–2

FIELDS OF WORK OF RESPONDENTS

Fields	Rank	Number of Respondents
Mechanical Engineering	1	322
Engineering—General	2	266
Other Fields	3	197
Electrical—Electronics	4	186
Civil Engineering	5	180
Electrical—Power	6	145

Source: PSU study

1. Pennsylvania State University, *Continuing Professional Education for Engineers in Pennsylvania,* 1965.

[119]

Respondents were grouped into age brackets (Table IV-3). When the first three ranks are added together, a total of 1,285 or 62% of the respondents were in the age group of 30 to 44. This fact suggests a long work span ahead for the majority of the engineers in the survey.

Table IV–3

AGES OF RESPONDENTS

Rank	Age Group	Number of Respondents	Percentage of Respondents in Age Groups
1	35-39	533	26
2	40-44	395	19
3	30-34	357	17
4	25-29	223	11

Source: PSU study

Respondents were classified on the basis of selected work activities (Table IV-4). The first eight activities are primarily administrative in nature and collectively occupied approximately 66% of the time of the respondents. In these areas undergraduate training is often not provided. To perform the cited work activities effectively, technical knowledge as well as administrative knowledge is essential.

Table IV–4

FREQUENCY OF SELECTED WORK ACTIVITIES

Activities	Rank	Number of Respondents
Conferences	1	1,775
Correspondence	2	1,521
Planning and Organization	3	1,421
Supervision	4	1,391
Coordination	5	1,197
Technical Report Writing	6	1,028
Consulting	7	957
Economic Evaluation	8	929
Non-Routine Technical Calculations	9	878
Field Work	10	833
Self-Development	11	792

[120]

Table IV–4 (Continued)

Activities	Rank	Number of Respondents
Professional Study	12	532
Laboratory Work	13	475
Drafting	14	430
Research	15	408

Source: PSU study

Tables IV-5, IV-6, and IV-7 are self-explanatory and help place data in better perspective. Attention is called particularly to the second ranked educational activity in Table IV-7: approximately one-third (726) respondents stated they had engaged in no educational activity (other than possible formal degree courses) during the previous four years.

Table IV–5

SOURCES OF INFORMATION USED TO KEEP UP-TO-DATE

Source of Information	Rank	Number of Respondents
Scientific and Technical Journals	1	2,012
Technical Books and Reports	2	1,900
Manufacturer's Literature	3	1,856
Lectures and Conferences	4	1,655

Source: PSU study

Table IV–6

YEAR OF RECEIPT OF B.S. DEGREE

Year	Rank	Number of Respondents
1950-54	1	569
1955-58	2	412
1945-49	3	366
1940-44	4	226
1935-39	5	160
1920-29	6	153
1930-34	7	115
1910-19	8	9

Source: PSU study

Table IV–7

EDUCATIONAL ACTIVITIES OTHER THAN FORMAL DEGREE
COURSES IN WHICH RESPONDENTS PARTICIPATED DURING
PREVIOUS FOUR YEARS

Activity	Rank	Number of Respondents
Engineering Lectures and Seminars	1	822
None	2	726
In-Service Training Courses	3	588
Management Workshop or Courses	4	500
Special Training Courses	5	480
Short Courses by Professional Societies	6	295
Short Refresher Courses	7	292
Liberal Arts and Humanities Workshop	8	98
Student-Teacher Conferences	9	75

Source: PSU study

Pennsylvania State University officials responsible for this survey concluded that the results underscored increasing needs for continuing education and undertook action to enhance the opportunities in the state to fulfill such needs. As a result of the study, forty changes were made in the engineering program of Pennsylvania State University in 1966 and 1967. The study led to the development of a series of informal courses, workshops, and seminars throughout the state. Partly as a result of the study, a graduate center was established outside of Philadelphia to fill engineering needs within that geographical area. During academic year 1968-69, a total of 241 seminars based on findings of the study were offered by the University.

National Society of Professional Engineers Study

Significant information on participation by professional engineers (i.e., those licensed by states) in continuing education activities was revealed in a study conducted in 1965 by the National Society of Professional Engineers. The report of the study

[122]

was based on 2,528 member returns on a detailed questionnaire sent to 5,000 NSPE members.[2]

Respondents represented a varied background as described by employment level, major areas of work effort, highest degree held, length of engineering employment, and extent of formal education. The average respondent was a professional engineer employed as a project manager in a manufacturing phase of industry who had received a bachelor's degree some time after 1941 and who had been employed as an engineer for fifteen years or more in a firm employing one to twenty engineers.

Respondents were asked about the extent of their participation in continuing education programs including the duration and number of the programs in which they participated. Analysis of these replies indicated that:

1. Approximately 55% of the engineers who participated in the survey had taken and had completed some type of formally organized continuing education program during the five-year period 1960 to 1965.

2. Most of the costs incurred were personal to the individual engineer, with the average out-of-pocket expenses totaling slightly over 60% of the total cost; on the average, however, each man received 21 credits toward a second or a third degree in higher education.

3. Programs organized and conducted by colleges or universities were as well attended as programs organized and conducted by the respondents' employers; the percentage of participation in programs organized and conducted by professional and technical societies was low probably because fewer programs were offered by them.

4. Programs running for twelve weeks or more ranked highest where respondents pursued continuing education programs conducted by colleges or universities; where programs were offered by employers or professional and technical societies, the short courses running from one to three weeks ranked highest.

---

2. National Society of Professional Engineers, *Continuing Education of Professional Engineers,* 1966.

5. Technical programs were pursued by more engineers (67%) than any other type of program offered by colleges or universities, employers, and professional and technical societies; managerial programs, however, reflected a large percentage of participation (38%).

With respect to reasons for participation and non-participation, engineers replied that they participated in formally organized continuing education programs primarily because they wished to broaden their technological backgrounds for their own satisfaction, because they wanted to advance their knowledge in specialty fields, and because they felt additional training would help them receive a raise or promotion. Other reasons included to keep up-to-date with advancing technology, to fulfilling company requirements, to do a better job, and to broaden their nontechnical backgrounds. Engineers who did not participate in formally organized continuing education programs indicated that their major reasons for not doing so were that the courses offered or subject matter covered were not within their interests, that they did not feel that an advanced degree would be of any value to them, and that they did not believe that additional training would help them receive a pay increase or promotion. Other reasons included lack of time to participate, a lack of programs in their geographical area, a lack of financial assistance from employers, and the intense pressure of work which made such participation an impossibility.

From the viewpoint of cross tabulation of results, the survey also produced information on relationships among identifiable factors:

1. Little relationship of any significance was found between company size and extent of participation; 25% of the engineers employed by companies having engineering staffs of over 1,000 participated in continuing education programs while 24% of those employed by companies with engineering staffs of from one to twenty also attended some type of formally organized continuing education program.

2. 52% of the respondents who were in supervisory positions participated in some type of formally organized continuing education program in the five-year period 1960 to 1965; more technical programs, organized by colleges or universities or by employers and conducted for a period of from one to three weeks, were taken by supervisors than any other type of program.

3. 68% of the nonsupervisory level engineers in this survey participated in some type of formally organized continuing education program during the period 1960 to 1965; more technical programs, sponsored by employers and conducted for a period of twelve weeks or more, were taken by non-supervisory engineers than any other type of program.

4. Engineers who spent the greatest part of their work effort in sales attended and completed twice as many managerial programs as technical programs; with few exceptions, however, the greatest number of respondents participated in technical programs.

5. 63% of the respondents employed as engineers for less than five years participated in some type of formally organized continuing education program, primarily programs sponsored by colleges or universities.

6. 64% of the respondents employed as engineers for five to fifteen years participated in some type of formally organized continuing education program, primarily programs sponsored by colleges or universities.

7. 49% of the respondents employed as engineers for over fifteen years participated in some type of formally organized continuing education programs, primarily programs sponsored by employers, although college or university sponsored programs were a close second.

The results of the NSPE study subsequently stimulated activity by NSPE and educational organizations to change attitudes and habits of professional engineers which were revealed in the study.

Stanford Research Institute Study
An appreciation, on the part of individual scientists and re-

[125]

search managers, of the role of continuing education is illustrated by a study of work activities and attitudes which was conducted by the Stanford Research Institute in 1965.[3] During this study, questionnaires executed by chemists, mathematicians, physicists, and biologists provided data on a series of specified factors related to work requirements. The first three mentioned groups of professional employees contributed approximately two-thirds of the total returned questionnaires: usable returns were received from 3,075 chemists, mathematicians, and physicists and from 1,680 biologists. One of the two factors rated most important of all the factors related to their work was the opportunity to keep up-to-date on scientific developments. Out of a total of 3,691 individuals responding to this factor, ninety-six percent rated the factor "extremely or quite important."

The attitude of research managers on the significance of this factor was even more pronounced than that of the scientists themselves. Ninety-eight percent of 1,060 research managers stated that keeping up-to-date on scientific developments was "extremely or quite important." The attitudes expressed in the SRI study are consistent with views expressed in similar surveys involving both scientists and engineers.

University of Delaware Study

The Pennsylvania State University study served as a model for a similar study undertaken by the University of Delaware in 1967.[4] This latter study focused on the role of the University in meeting continuing education needs of scientists and engineers employed by the chemical industry in New Castle County, Delaware, and surrounding areas. Specific objectives of the study were to survey needs for continuing education in the physical sciences (including mathematics) and engineering on the part of employees whose educational background and/or current job assignment were in these areas, to determine how these needs

---

3. Stanford Research Institute, *Work Activities and Attitudes of Scientists and Research Managers*, 1965.

4. University of Delaware, *Continuing Technical Education Needs of Scientists and Engineers in Northern Delaware*, 1969.

could best be met by the University, and to determine the extent to which individuals were motivated to continue their formal education.

A twelve page, pretested questionnaire used by the University of Delaware included a listing of 187 specific courses that might be offered. For each course, the respondent was asked to choose one of three answers: "should have," "could use," and "don't really need." Additional spaces were provided for "write-in" courses. The remaining questions solicited data about the respondents and about types of courses which respondents would be interested in taking. A 20% sample from each of five companies was sought through the distribution of 780 questionnaires. A total of 558 employees or approximately 72% of those contacted returned questionnaires.

Analysis of the data indicated that 32% of the respondents worked in research; 33% in development, design, consulting, and economic evaluation; 21% in manufacturing, marketing, construction, and maintenance; and 14% in miscellaneous functions. With respect to courses taken for university credit, replies revealed the following data:

1. 12% had taken science or engineering courses during the two year period preceding the survey.

2. 8% had taken courses in business administration or other nontechnical areas during the two year period.

3. 10% had taken no courses during the previous two years but had plans to pursue credit work in science or engineering.

4. 13% had taken no courses but had plans to pursue credit work in business administration or other nontechnical fields.

5. 57% had taken no work during the previous two years and had no plans to take credit courses in the future.

With respect to other types of courses, data indicated diverse participation as follows:

1. 11% attended university short courses during the previous two year period.

[127]

2. 65% attended technical lectures, seminars or training courses offered by the company.

3. 18% attended short courses offered by professional societies.

4. 25% did not attend any of the above.

Concerning employee perception of employer attitudes toward continuing education, respondents had contrasting beliefs, as follows:

1. 78% believed the company encouraged them to attend company training.

2. 67% believed the company encouraged them to enroll for advanced work.

3. 48% indicated their immediate supervisor encouraged them to update their knowledge.

Respondents provided a range of views on the need for additional continuing education, as follows:

1. 73% indicated an interest in enrolling in either a full semester or a short course in at least one of 187 technical subjects listed in the questionnaire.

2. 50% indicated they would take four full semester courses or short courses in scientific and engineering subjects during the next two years if courses of the appropriate level and type were offered by the University at a convenient time.

3. 67% of the potential enrollments were for short courses.

4. 33% of the potential enrollments were for full semester courses.

5. The largest number of potential enrollments were registered in the following academic areas: chemistry; statistics and computer science; engineering design, analysis, and systems; engineering sciences; and mathematics and physics.

The University of Delaware study concluded that continuing education opportunities offered in the immediate geographical area were not sufficient to meet the needs of scientists and engineers employed in the area. The study suggested initiation of a series of short courses based upon the needs revealed in the survey and a review of full semester course offerings to ascertain specific subject matter needs of industry which were not being met. The study also pointed out that scientists and engineers face a motivational problem and stressed that the relationship between continuing education and advancement must be made clear to each scientist and engineer by his employer. Subsequently, the University, as a result of the study, initiated steps to broaden the range of pertinent continuing education courses. Thus, recommendations in the report served as the basis for planning evening credit course offerings and non-credit courses (such as courses in rheology and instrumentation) for academic year 1969-70.

NSF Funded Study

In a study conducted under contract for the National Science Foundation, information on the need for, and use of, continuing education activities of R&D scientists and engineers was obtained.[5] The data were collected during 1966 and 1967 from 17 large industrial and government R&D laboratories. All of the laboratories (9 industrial and 8 government) had an annual R&D budget of at least $10 million, a work force of at least 250 R&D scientists and engineers (of whom not less than 25% were research scientists), and a continuing education program for at least the three years preceding the study. Sources of data were: 95 interviews with chief R&D line executives and personnel and training executives in the 17 laboratories; 205 interviews with scientists and engineers, including 54 supervisors in 10 of the 17 laboratories; 394 questionnaires in the same 10 laboratories; and 71 academic persons in 24 colleges and universities in the same or nearby community as were the 17 laboratories.

Comparison of participation by scientists and engineers during the previous two year period in six types of continuing education activities reveals (Table IV-8) that more scientists than engineers

---

5. National Science Foundation, *Continuing Education for R&D Careers,* 1969.

attended professional meetings and took leaves of absence with pay, that more engineers than scientists attended short courses, and that more scientists than engineers attended in-lab lectures or seminars.

Table IV–8

COMPARISON OF PARTICIPATION IN TYPES OF
CONTINUING EDUCATION ACTIVITIES

Types	Percentage of Participation by Scientists N=231	Percentage of Participation by Engineers N=163	Percentage of Participation by Scientists and Engineers N=394
Professional meetings	75	49	64
University credit courses	28	31	29
Short intensive courses	17	28	22
Educational leave (with pay)	10	4	8
In-lab formal courses (non-credit)	35	33	34
In-lab lectures or seminars	87	66	78

Source: NSF funded study

A comparison of participation of scientists and engineers during the same two year period in nine types of continuing education activities (the above six types, plus reading scientific and technical literature, attending workshops on specific subjects, and engaging in discussion with outside consultants) shows (Table IV-9) that 15% of the scientists reported using none, one or two of the types, as compared with 37% of the engineers. Also, 79% of the scientists reported using three to six of these types, as compared with 59% of the engineers.

From among seven types of continuing education activities, R&D scientists and engineers selected those types regarded as first or second in importance to them. Reading scientific and technical literature was clearly the most important and most used of the seven types. Selection of types, together with the extent of use of these types, is shown in Table IV-10.

[130]

Table IV–9

COMPARISON OF FREQUENCY OF PARTICIPATION IN
CONTINUING EDUCATION ACTIVITIES

Number of Activities reported	Percentage of Participation by Scientists N=231	Percentage of Participation by Engineers N=163
None	3	7
One	6	10
Two	6	20
Three	17	15
Four	26	21
Five	21	15
Six	15	8
Seven	4	2
Eight	1	1
Nine	0.5	0
Total	99%*	99%*

*Percentages do not add to 100 because of loss in rounding.

Source: NSF funded study

Table IV–10

RELATIVE IMPORTANCE OF TYPES OF CONTINUING
EDUCATION ACTIVITES

Types	Percentage of Participation by Scientists and Engineers N=394	Percentage of Users Ranking Activity First or Second
Reading scientific & technical literature	98	85
Professional meetings	77	44
University credit courses	36	44
Short intensive courses	22	41
Educational leaves with pay	14	21
In-lab formal courses (non-credit)	40	20
In-lab lectures or seminars	81	28

Source: NSF funded study

R&D scientists and engineers indicated their opinions on other needs associated with continuing education activities (Table IV-11). Among needs expressed by the majority of respondents, more in-lab courses, in-lab lectures, and paid education leave were most frequently cited.

[131]

Table IV–11

EXPRESSED NEEDS ASSOCIATED WITH CONTINUING EDUCATION

Needs Cited	Percentage of respondents N=394
In-lab courses	17
In-lab lectures	12
Paid educational leaves	11
Supervisory encouragement	8
Outside short intensive courses	6
University credit courses	6
Expenses to professional meetings	5
Tuition refunds for non-credit courses	4
Workshops on specific topics	4
On-the-job reading time	4
Improved university programs	4
Communication exchanges of information within laboratory	4

Source: NSF funded study

Almost one-fourth of the respondents (23%) stated that no additional activity was needed and that existing programs were adequate for these respondents.

ANALYSIS OF INDIVIDUAL PARTICIPATION

A key obstacle to individual participation in continuing education is the cost, both in terms of money and in time. Attempts to measure the value of continuing education, in terms of costs borne by the individual, have met with very limited success. Evidence indicates that scientists and engineers who keep up-to-date tend to produce more patents and professional papers—and presumably are more valuable—than those who do not do so. It is also clear that employers generally prefer scientific and engineering personnel who have maintained or enhanced their competence through continuing education. Such personnel tend to be promoted faster, with accompanying increased monetary rewards. Preference for the updated person becomes economically meaningful when it is realized that success usually depends on the organization's ability to stay abreast of a science or technology or to keep ahead in the scientific or technical area in which the organization makes a product or renders a service.

A negative aspect of cost is ascertainable by study of work records of scientists and engineers who cannot be placed on new or augmented projects because these individuals have been by-passed by subsequent developments in their fields of science and engineering. There seems to be a meaningful positive correlation between the incidence of continuing education and comparability of salaries.

The cost to the individual who fails to invest effort and time to keep himself reasonably abreast of such changes may be roughly estimated. Loss in potential earning power to the individual is an intangible factor since no one can be sure of the amount of his annual salary, had his preparation and opportunity been different from actuality. Through application of median salary data for engineers as related to years after completion of college, an official of a large corporation estimated that loss of $50,000 to $60,000 gross earnings is incurred over a fifteen year period by a scientist or engineer who does not maintain a normal rate of professional growth. Should the individual be forced to seek a new field, the effect on his total earning power is estimated to be much greater. Although the amount of "lost" salary, due to obsolescense of an individual scientist or engineer depends upon several hard-to-measure variables, the monetary loss to the individual during the second half of an "average" length career is placed as high as $6,000 annually.

Other reasons why some scientists and engineers do not participate in continuing education activities are identifiable. Chief among these reasons are the following:

1. Lack of sufficient desire, on the part of some long-time employees, to want to be updated,

2. Alleged lack of educator interest in individuals seeking continuing education but not matriculating for a graduate degree,

3. Impossibility of being away from daily assignment in order to participate,

4. Non-availability of continuing education opportunities at a time personally convenient to the individual,

5. Reluctance on the part of older scientists and engineers to compete academically with their juniors who may be strong competitors or even surpassers in a formal learning situation,

6. Changes in curricula which may require older persons to pass new undergraduate prerequisites before they can take desired graduate courses.

Non-participative attitudes and inaction on the part of some scientists and engineers are in sharp contrast to a series of actions which other scientists and engineers pursue in order to keep up-to-date. Those persons who wish to avoid personal obsolescence usually select one or more of the following positive steps:

1. Pursue in-house training aggressively, as the opportunity arises,

2. Act alert to the impact of job changes and react accordingly,

3. Explore the range of continuing education opportunities afforded through the total educational facilities in their geographical area and take full advantage of such opportunities,

4. Consider new assignments with a view toward future development,

5. Seek job opportunities consistent with individual abilities and skills,

6. Aim to advance out of "dead end" assignments,

7. Work closely with supervisors to take advantage of their experience and know-how,

8. Accept the challenge, when available, to apply knowledge to new fields,

9. Establish and maintain contacts with library staffs of the employer and of the community,

10. Be responsive to organization program changes affecting the rate of obsolescence of current knowledge and skills.

[134]

Scientists and engineers realize with greater frequency that graduation from college is no longer sufficient to sustain them through twenty or thirty years of professional life. Hence, continuing education in science and engineering is as critical as the development of newer technologies themselves. Courses offered on the employer's time provide evidence of management's interest in the individual's growth, but, without individual motivation, such courses cannot attain their objectives. Achieving professional growth through continuing education is, in fact, a part of a professional man's responsibility. Fulfillment of this responsibility by the professional may be blocked at a particular point in time, but, without individual acceptance of his basic responsibility for keeping up-to-date, continuing education efforts usually meet with very little success.

ROLE OF EMPLOYERS

The employer is regarded as one of the partners in the continuing education process. The role of the employer is considered to be that of appreciating the need on the part of his scientists and engineers for continuing education, offering encouragement and opportunities to such employees to enable them to maintain currency in one or more of their fields, and providing appropriate recognition to those who do keep up-to-date.

The types of continuing education opportunities provided by employers are varied. Many employers make available courses of study or sessions dealing with new developments in science and engineering. These courses may be offered in the formal academic framework at a college or off-campus or in-service. In terms of time, such opportunities vary from a one-time meeting to a full academic or calendar year program. In some cases, continuing education opportunities are on a part-time but continuous basis. Some employers pay full or partial costs incurred by their employees for this purpose.

The establishment of educational loan programs represents another phase of employer participation. Official time for pursuing basic research of an individual's choice and the granting of a leave of absence for the purpose of broadening knowledge may be sanctioned by employers. Employees who participate in an outstanding manner in continuing education may be given special employer recognition through more responsible assignments, salary increases, and augmented indirect benefits.

Appreciating the importance of continuing education, offering courses at partial or full employer expense, providing loans, and extending individual recognition, however, do not constitute the full contribution of the progressive employer. A working environment that encourages continuing education may also be provided. Furthermore, a high priority for the role of continuing education must be demonstrated by management. For example, minimum standards on the amount of development dollars and time to be devoted to continuing education may be set and pursued in an organization, regardless of temporary changes in economic conditions. Continuing education as part of the preparation necessary for advancement is appropriately recognized by employers. Official time for study in connection with specific continuing education projects may be provided. Continuing education programs may be occasionally favored over project demands which involve overtime or out-of-town trips.

SURVEYS OF ACTIVITIES

The diversity of continuing education needs among scientists and engineers means that an individual continuing education program sponsored by an employer is best geared to the specific requirements of the group to be served. Thus, although there are common elements, there is no fixed program of continuing education applicable to every employer. However, an understanding of the nature of a continuing education program of a progressive employer may be obtained from a review of elements of the program of a company currently engaged in a highly competitive field and employing approximately 3,300 scientists and engineers. The program involves several aspects: career development courses, advanced technology seminars, short courses, technical meetings and symposia, educational leaves of absence, integration of faculty and recognized authorities with scientific and engineering staff of the company, and a graduate work-study program.

In the program of this company, a variety of career development courses are held in-house each quarter: some courses are held during working hours but the majority are held after work. Advanced technology seminars are held monthly and supplement specialized monthly programs of local technical societies. Participation in short courses takes place at three universities; in addition, a new short course is introduced in-house approximately every month. Technical meetings and seminars are held at frequent intervals. Educational leaves of absence are encouraged, provided the individual's development program is related to the company's interests. There is periodic integration of faculty of various universities and recognized authorities from outside the company with scientific and engineering staff of the company; depending upon their background, these persons serve as consultants, temporary employees, and instructors. Graduate courses are given on company premises by faculty from a nearby campus. An honors program which permits time off for course attendance provides 100% tuition reimbursement at full pay.

This company believes that its continuing education program has resulted in distinctly better trained scientists and engineers and more effective utilization of them. Awareness of the company's interest and recognition of continuing education promotes an atmosphere of high morale and motivation and results in low turnover. The frequent contact with faculty of the nearby campus and scientists and engineers of the company tends to contribute to the shaping of the institution's graduate curriculum and benefits both the industry and the educational institution. The program, in the opinion of company officials, educators, and scientists and engineers, has produced a scientific and engineering staff whose efforts reveal very effective manpower utilization.

Relatively little statistical information is available on the extent of continuing education activities on the part of employers. One comprehensive effort was a formal, nation-wide survey of

[137]

continuing education activities conducted by companies for their own scientific and engineering personnel in 1963.[6] Analysis of replies from 96 companies employing in the aggregate 22,000 scientists and engineers is contained in Table IV-12.

Table IV–12

PARTICIPATION IN EMPLOYER SPONSORED
CONTINUING EDUCATION ACTIVITIES, BY TYPE

Types	Percentage of Participation by Respondents	Average Number of Scientists and Engineers per Company Engaged in Activities	Mean Time (Hours per Year) per Scientist and Engineer Devoted to Such Activities
Tuition Refund Plan	90	404	169
Technical Society Meetings	67	324	44
Technical Lectures (Outside Plant)	62	116	61
In-Plant Scientific and Technical Courses and Lectures	57	843	78
Educational Leave Plan	37	40	314
Research or Teaching by Employees	30	25	195
Postdoctoral Training	6	—	—

Source: Special survey

In the above project, employers reported that scientists and engineers employed by respondents devoted sharply differing periods of time to the type of continuing education activities offered during the same year, as shown in Table IV-13.

Table IV–13

PARTICIPATION IN EMPLOYER SPONSORED CONTINUING
EDUCATION ACTIVITIES, BY TIME PERIOD

Man-Days per year	Number of Scientists and Engineers	Percentage of Total Participation
1-10	12,274	55.4
11-30	7,443	33.6
31-90	1,388	6.3
91-180	890	4.0
181-360	140	.7

Source: Special survey

6. W. G. Torpey, "Company Investment in Continuing Education for Scientists and Engineers," *Educational Record,* Vol. 45, 1964, pp. 408-413.

Each of the 96 companies participating in the previous survey had to have an above-average interest in continuing education as a prerequisite to selection for survey participation. Hence, the extent of participation of these companies in continuing education is believed to have been greater than that of the average company.

Recent informal recheck with several of the major companies in the above survey indicates that essential findings related to types of continuing education are still valid but that the mean time (Table IV-12) and numbers of scientists and engineers participating (Table IV-13) have increased approximately fifteen and twenty percent, respectively, since 1963.

In a NSF funded survey of continuing education for R&D scientists and engineers, data for which were collected in 1966 and 1967, analysis of employer sponsored programs of continuing education in nine large industrial laboratories showed that in most cases three types of activities were provided—tuition refund courses, expenses paid to meetings, and inside laboratory lectures.[7] Table IV-14 is a summary of these programs.

Table IV–14

TYPES OF ACTIVITIES IN EMPLOYER SPONSORED PROGRAMS

Specific Industrial Laboratory	Expenses Paid to Meetings	Courses with Tuition Refund	Paid Sabbatical Leaves	Outside Short Courses	Lectures Inside Lab.	Courses Inside Lab.	Major Conferences Inside Lab.
#1	x	x		x	x		x
#2	x	x	x		x		x
#3	x	x		x	x	x	
#4	x	x	x		x	x	
#5	x	x	x		x	x	
#6	x	x	x		x		
#7	x	x	x		x		
#8	x	x					x
#9		x					
Totals 9	8	9	5	2	7	3	3

Source: NSF funded study

7. National Science Foundation, *Continuing Education for R&D Careers*, 1969.

[139]

Participation of 213 R&D scientists and engineers in continuing education opportunities provided by the nine industrial laboratories during the previous two year period indicated the predominance of in-lab lectures and seminars and attendance at professional meetings. Such participation is shown in Table IV-15.

Table IV–15

PARTICIPATION IN TYPES OF CONTINUING
EDUCATION ACTIVITIES

Types	Percentage of participation
In-lab lectures and seminars	78
Professional meetings	62
In-lab formal courses (non-credit)	35
University credit courses	25
Short intensive courses	21
Educational leave with pay	2

Source: NSF funded study

The NSF funded survey reported an intensity of conviction, on the part of almost all of the 95 top managers interviewed, toward the need for continuing education. One top manager was quoted as stating that it is a question, not of how continuing education benefits a laboratory, but what happens to a laboratory if continuing education is not supported.

An unusual approach made by employers to provide continuing education for scientists and engineers is employment of college and university faculty during a summer period with the objectives of their assessing the status of obsolescence among individual scientists and engineers in their organization and of helping the latter to update themselves. Under this approach, the major assignment of the faculty member is to talk with scientists and engineers and their supervisors in order to evaluate scientific and technical capabilities and continuing education needs. Such faculty member also recommends a program for improvement, where needed, in order that a high level of scientific and technical capability of staff may be maintained during the years ahead. A conclusion from these analyses is that positive motivation and convenient periods for further study are not sufficient to provide all scientists and engineers with necessary continuing education opportunities. Part of the follow-through of the evaluation is often the design of a series of courses to develop and to help maintain the particular level of scientific and technical competence desired. In this approach, employers make the continuing education program an integral part of the assigned program of work for each scientist and engineer. Since the program helps to minimize or eliminate professional obsolescence, the cost of the program is considered a beneficial investment.

EMPLOYER COSTS

Employers may be motivated to invest a portion of their funds in providing continuing education for their scientists and engineers because of such factors as economic competition to produce better or new products or services, shortages of scientists and engineers in a particular area, continuing education opportunities afforded by competitors, and plans for reassignment of scientists and engineers within the organization.

"Hard" figures on employer costs of continuing education are very scarce. One detailed survey was made in 1963 to obtain a reasonable estimate of the extent of employer financial involvement in such education.[8] Cost data obtained from the 96 companies on their continuing education activities for their scientists and engineers are shown in Table IV-16.

Recent rechecking with several of the major companies which participated in the above survey suggests that direct company cost per individual scientist or engineer who is the beneficiary of employer sponsored continuing education activities has increased approximately forty-five percent over the cited figures.

8. W. G. Torpey, "Company Investment in Continuing Education for Scientists and Engineers, *Educational Record,* Vol. 45, 1964, pp. 408-413.

Table IV–16

DIRECT COMPANY COSTS OF TYPES OF CONTINUING EDUCATION ACTIVITIES

Types of Activities	Direct Company Cost Per Individual Scientist or Engineer Participant
Education Leave Plan	$1,871
Research or Teaching by Employees	1,270
Technical Lectures (Outside Plant)	500
In-plant Scientific and Technical Courses and Lectures	353
Attendance at Annual Professional & Technical Society Meetings	192
Tuition Refund Plan	105

Source: Special survey

Total employer costs—both direct and indirect—for providing individual types of continuing education opportunities cannot be compiled on a meaningful basis because of the highly variable range of factors used in compiling costs. However, rough estimates of current employer costs have been made for two types: the tuition refund plan and the short course program. Under the tuition refund plan by which a scientist or engineer obtains a master's degree on a part-time basis, current tuition costs for a master's degree are variable but approximate $3,000 to $3,500. In addition, there are costs of transportation, books, and incidentals. Where an employer reimburses the scientist or engineer for all expenses incurred by the employee and the employer adds a value for released time, the total cost to the employer reaches as high as $6,600 per man. In a short course program, total employer cost of the attendance of a scientist or engineer at a one week course offered off the premises of the employer (including registration fee, transportation, incidentals, and the value of released time) approaches $1,400 per man.

A significant number of employers show a keen appreciation of the value of continuing education for their scientists and engineers. This appreciation is reflected in the financial support which employers give to such programs. However, other employers do not choose to participate in continuing education activity. These latter employers often have a traditional attitude that scientists and engineers are exclusively responsible for keeping abreast of scientific and engineering developments. Sometimes these employers believe that a young scientist or engineer recently graduated from college brings more overall benefit than does the updating of an experienced scientist or engineer. Furthermore, the cost of continuing education is a major factor for nonparticipation by employers.

OBSERVATIONS

Review of data on employer participation in continuing education for scientists and engineers leads to the following observations:

1. Relatively few employers maintain detailed records which show specific financial involvement in their continuing education activities. In formal surveys and informal reviews, as many as one-half of employer respondents state such information cannot be compiled from their financial records. A special analysis on the part of an employer is often necessary if he is to prepare any useful data on such costs.

2. Where costs are determined, the factors used to compute employer costs of continuing education activities are so diverse as to make employer-to-employer and employer-to-norm comparisons very difficult. With respect to tuition refund, for example, some employers calculate only costs of reimbursement to the individual scientist or engineer for all or a portion of the tuition paid; other employers compute costs based on tuition refunds, on books, on incidental employee expenditures such as meals and transportation, on time away from the job, and on the salary of a substitute to perform work while the regular employee is away attending a continuing education activity. It is necessary to determine uniform cost components before valid comparisons can be drawn.

3. Specific types of continuing education activities chosen by employers to facilitate the dissemination of scientific and engi-

neering knowledge and skill to their scientists and engineers vary sharply, not only on the basis of large and small organizations, but also on the basis of different types of employers. The predominant techniques pursued by the majority of employers providing continuing education is the tuition refund plan; by contrast, postdoctoral training programs receive very little employer support.

4. Insufficient attention appears to be given by employers to the quality of continuing education activities. Employer complacency sometimes results where emphasis is placed primarily on specific amounts of money spent for this purpose and on particular numbers of personnel involved, without regard to the subsequent results attributable to participation in such programs. The absence of refined employer evaluations of continuing education activities is a weakness which should be overcome.

5. Absence of a priority designation for continuing education programs has a very adverse effect on such programs in time of retrenchment. Employers often do not give a priority designation to such programs to reflect deep concern for the worth of continuing education as a regular phase of doing business. Employers who regard continuing education as an integral part of operations give such education a priority which, in time of retrenchment, imposes only a proportionate budgetary cut upon such programs.

6. Where employers concur in the principle that continuing education is a necessary and continuous employer responsibility, there is sometimes lack of translation of the principle into the top decision-making processes of the organization. The establishment of an appropriate administrative policy reflecting top management concern assures that adequate funds and ceiling points are provided for use in updating efforts on a continuing basis. Such an arrangement enables incumbent scientists and engineers to participate in a continuing education program, as necessary, and permits the acquisition of temporary replacement personnel as needed. This arrangement assures continuation of

operations while regular incumbents are engaged in continuing education activity either on a part-time or full-time basis.

ROLE OF EDUCATORS

The majority of educational institutions have already made curriculum changes designed to minimize early obsolescence of graduates in science and technology. Earlier types of curricula have been succeeded by courses which strengthen fundamental concepts as well as present new information on the frontiers of science and technology. Institutions show an increasing alertness to the danger of inadequate professional preparation and seek ways to relate curricula to a meaningful preparation for scientific and engineering work. Some schools are studying improved means to present courses more effectively and to help the student attain continued professional competence. Nevertheless, the final report of the Goals Committee of the American Society for Engineering Education, published in 1968, recommended that engineering schools cooperate to a much greater extent with industry, government, and professional and technical societies in programs of continuing education in order to achieve maximum benefit for students and to strive for maximum utilization of teaching resources.[9] Similar recommendations have been contained also in science education studies.[10]

TYPES OF OFFERINGS

Continuing education programs administered by educational institutions include a variety of types of offerings. The more common types may be summarized as follows:

1. On-campus graduate study—Institutions provide full-time on-campus graduate study usually leading to advanced degrees in science and engineering. Employees sometimes receive a job assignment to pursue a graduate course on a full-time basis and the employee may receive full salary and other employee bene-

9. American Society for Engineering Education, *Final Report of the Goals Committee*, 1968.

10. National Academy of Sciences, *The Mathematical Sciences*, 1968.

fits; in some cases the employer pays only tuition and related fees. Scientific and engineering personnel usually apply for admission to this type of program on a competitive basis. Course and university selection is usually the responsibility of the employee, with educational advice provided by the educational institution and sometimes by employer counselors.

2. Off-campus graduate degree programs—Such programs leading to advanced degrees in science and engineering are offered by an educational institution at an employer's request. Acceptance in the program is entirely dependent upon the qualifications of a scientist or engineer in relation to the requirements of the educational institution. Instruction is by full-time or part-time faculty members of the educational institution. Courses are taught both on the employer's time and on the individual's time. The choice of time depends upon such factors as the nature of the course, its relation to the work of an organization, and the availability of instructors and classrooms. An employer may provide facilities and other costs of the program.

3. Advanced Studies—Such studies cover basic subject matter or highly specialized scientific and technical material. Courses are generally for persons already having at least one degree in science or engineering and some experience. The content is designed to broaden an understanding of regular course offerings and/or to acquire new knowledge. A range of individual courses, as well as programs integrating several related courses, are offered. Advanced studies may parallel regular courses offered to the general student body or studies may be tailored to the work of a particular type of organization. Such studies are aimed at professional growth on present and future job assignments and usually do not lead to an advanced degree.

4. Seminars and colloquia—Seminars and colloquia supplement formal educational courses offered by educational institutions. Lectures are conducted on scientific and technical subjects of a general nature. Topics are primarily concerned with current developments in science and engineering and with other

selected subjects. When such programs are under institutional auspices, speakers are usually academic staff, but occasionally outside specialists lecture on topics of their particular competency:

5. Correspondence courses—The part played by correspondence education in providing continuing education for scientists and engineers is increasing even though the percentage of such personnel taking correspondence courses is still relatively small. Several colleges and universities recognize the quality of science and engineering offerings extended through correspondence courses by granting college credits for correspondence study administered by the Armed Services, by institutions of higher education, and by private home study schools. Examples of correspondence courses available to scientists and engineers are numerical control, fortran, vibration control, and electronics. There are several unique advantages of the correspondence method for continuing education purposes: there is no need for an interruption in study if a scientist or engineer is transferred to another geographical location; the material is readily available for individual study; the individual can pursue the material at a time and place of his convenience; an individual can select an instructional program tailored to his specific needs; and the use of brief texts provides helpful flexibility. On the other hand, lack of personal contact with the instructor and lack of class discussion and of group interaction are handicaps for some learners. Correspondence education supplements other types of continuing education and constitutes an integral part of the total continuing education spectrum.

It is not possible to separate many of the current continuing education efforts of educational institutions for scientists and engineers from the total scientific and engineering education programs of such institutions. Hence, statistics on total numbers of course offerings or on total attendance at classes do not necessarily measure continuing education participation of scientists and engineers. Analysis indicating a partial measure of institutional activities related to continuing education for scientists and engineers is contained in the sections on the role of scientists and engineers and on the role of employers.

From one viewpoint, scientists and engineers who seek continuing education through educational institutions may be placed into two categories: (1) scientists and engineers who seek advanced degrees and (2) scientists and engineers who seek new knowledge and skills but who are not degree candidates. It is estimated that the number of individuals in the second category exceeds those in the first by a ratio of approximately 3:1. However, the vocal demand for continuing education opportunities often comes from, or on behalf of, those in the first category. As a result, the continuing education response of educational institutions has frequently concentrated upon formal degree courses instead of upon other types of continuing education. The needs of scientists and engineers in both categories should be met in a realistic institutional program.

SELECTED PROGRAMS

A unique approach to continuing education is followed by the Center for Advanced Engineering Study of the Massachusetts Institute of Technology. The Center was established in 1963 to provide ways to help experienced scientists and engineers maintain a high level of competence needed for continued leadership. The Practicing Engineer Advanced Study Program enables experienced applied scientists and engineers to work in depth in technological areas pertinent to their professions. Under the program, participants spend one or more academic terms on the MIT campus in academic research and other special activity most relevant to their present and future needs. Each participant formulates his own program in consultation with MIT faculty. Some participants enroll in formal classroom courses; others pursue emerging technology in the light of its relevance to their home organizations with no limitation on methods of acquisition of knowledge or on subject matter. In addition to regular MIT courses, the Center offers a number of special programs designed to meet particular needs of participants. During the first four years of program operation, 120 individuals completed the program. Fifty were in residence in 1969. In addition to the Practicing Engineer Advanced Study Program, the Center offers five to ten week programs in specialized areas of science and engineering and interdisciplinary projects which are concerned with potential contributions of new and advanced technology. The Center also is developing new educational systems for on-the-job continuing education of experienced engineers.

Carnegie-Mellon University has a special program of professional education aimed at combating the growing problem of technical obsolescence in industry. The University, with the cooperation of companies in the Pittsburgh area, offers high-level scientific and technical programs for scientists and engineers working in industry. This program differs from usual continuing education programs in that academic officials work with a formal industrial committee to find industry's needs in order that custom-built courses and seminars can be constructed. Furthermore, only high-level technical courses are conducted and, to the extent possible, are offered after normal company hours in order to avoid the expense to industry of released time for executives. One part of the program consists of a "package" of integrated courses available to scientists and engineers who need training in depth in modern courses offered to present day undergraduates (for example, numerical analysis). A second part provides intensive noncredit seminars and courses for scientists and engineers who wish to increase their competency in their own field or to gain breadth by exploring recent advances in other fields (for example, advanced heat transfer).

Another aspect of the responsibility of educational institutions in continuing education is provision for support for continuing education opportunities for their own faculty members who are scientists and engineers. A review of summer opportunities in continuing education available for engineering faculty members sponsored by the Ford Foundation contained a series of recommendations for individuals interested in continuing edu-

[149]

cation for faculty members. Key recommendations were that steps should be taken to publicize in many ways opportunities available, that action be taken to bring before the administrative officers of engineering schools the urgent need for their taking a more active part in encouraging their faculty to engage in activities which are professionally worthwhile, that institutional funds should be budgeted for this purpose, that recognition to faculty participants in such activities should be given, and that steps should be taken to explore the possibility of increasing stipends and travel allowances for faculty members so involved. The study group also stated that employers who engage faculty members under a continuing education plan should raise significantly the technical level of work in which faculty members engage while they are in the temporary employment of the company.

A significant number of present day faculty members in science and engineering have little experience in aspects other than research and teaching. To keep research and teaching pertinent to the needs of employers, the faculty member often needs an updated understanding of the scope of his professional field. Continuing education opportunities which provide practice in his profession enable the faculty member to obtain greater insights of his field and to become a more effective teacher. Under the Program of Residencies in Engineering Practice, sponsored by the American Society for Engineering Education and the Ford Foundation, young engineering faculty members called residents obtain experience in professional practice at levels of engineering decision-making in industrial or consulting firms or in government agencies. The residents are under the guidance of experienced engineers in the organization who are called preceptors. The resident occupies a position as a paid employee who works for a continuous period of from twelve to fifteen months. Under this program, the employer of the resident accepts the fact that the resident comes primarily to gain an educational experience. This experience motivates the resident upon his return to his teaching position to innovate in both course content and teaching methods, consistent with his newly acquired insights and understanding.

An experimental five year joint program of the University of Illinois and of the University of Colorado is another approach to provide continuing education opportunities for science and engineering faculty. The program starting in 1964 and related to engineering faculty consisted of six parts: (1) visiting exchange professorships between these schools, (2) faculty leaves of absence for advanced study which allowed many faculty members without advanced degrees to attend the other school and work on their advanced degrees, (3) joint and cooperative research programs which provided an opportunity for research investigators of both schools to meet and work on mutual problems and to collaborate on joint publications or reports, (4) graduate student exchanges which afforded the opportunity for students from each of the schools to attend the other school and take advantage of any exceptional facilities, (5) joint conferences and seminars which included specialized, high-level conferences attended by a few people from both schools interested in specific technical subjects, and distinguished individuals from various parts of the nation, and (6) short-term exchanges which gave faculty an opportunity to broaden their horizons by permitting inter-university visits for the purpose of increasing their familiarity with laboratory techniques and research facilities. During the five year period ending in 1969, the following events had taken place: 12 curriculum conferences, 9 technical conferences, more than 100 faculty seminars, 12 short term faculty exchanges, 7 long term faculty exchanges, 8 graduate student exchanges, 7 teaching associate appointments, 40 cooperative research projects, and 18 course and laboratory development projects. Both institutions feel that the program was a success and enabled faculty of both institutions to expedite the development of their technical knowledge and skills.

USE OF EDUCATIONAL TECHNOLOGY

An emerging dimension of the role of educators in continuing education is the increasing use of educational technology in the

[151]

continuing education process. It is difficult to separate the use of educational technology approaches in continuing education for scientists and engineers from the use of such approaches in basic education in science and engineering. Nevertheless, there is a growing recognition of the vital part which educational technology can play in continuing education for scientists and engineers. Educational technology for continuing education purposes is also used by employers and by professional and technical societies.

At his place of employment, an engineer goes to a terminal of a computer which is located nearby or at a distant point. The engineer informs the computer of his identity and of his desire to participate in a specific continuing education program stored in the computer. The computer administers a diagnostic test to the engineer to ascertain his present level of performance in the subject area of the program involved. If the engineer's performance meets certain criteria, he is phased out of the program; if not, he is given an appropriate test to determine whether remedial instruction is required. The computer scans the engineer's response history and presents him with media appropriate for his particular learning task. The computer establishes a conversational interaction with the engineer and shapes his responses to resemble those of desired goals. Thus, the engineer gains new technical knowledge. The foregoing description does not reflect current practice. Nevertheless, this situation, posed at a recent meeting of the American Society for Engineering Education, represents a potential inherent in the application of the computer to continuing education for scientists and engineers.

Educational technology used in continuing education for scientists and engineers involves increasing use of the following devices: electro-writer (sometimes called telewriter), audio tape, programed learning, computers, closed circuit television, and video tape.

The electro-writer activated by an instructor at one location uses telephone lines to transmit blackboard drawings and schematics to a class at another location. The impressions on the blackboard follow the traces of the electro-mechanical pen of the instructor as he supplements his oral presentation which is simultaneously being transmitted to the same class. The drawings and schematics constitute "live" data for those participating in a continuing education program. This approach is used, for example, by Auburn University in its program at Huntsville, Alabama, and by Cornell University in its program at Towanda, Pa.

Audio tutorial instruction uses an audio tape recording to present instructional material. The method has the advantage of permitting a scientist or engineer who seeks updating to listen to a pertinent tape at his convenience and at a relatively inexpensive cost. The individual adjusts the flow of ideas by stopping the audio tape recorded when he wishes to do so. Audio tape (such as cassettes) permits supplementation of basic informational material at critical subject matter points. For laboratory instruction, for example, audio tutorial instruction may replace traditional mimeographed notes and laboratory preparation sessions. This approach is especially useful where the educational objective is to develop particular types of skills or to have the information repeated whenever desirable.

In programed learning, subject matter is presented to scientists and engineers in a series of steps called frames. The steps begin with relatively simple concepts and proceed through more difficult principles. Each step requires a response from the scientist or engineer who usually answers a question or completes a statement. Review material may be presented periodically in the series to provide reinforcement of basic ideas. Under a linear program, the scientist or engineer progresses step by step through the subject matter whether his individual responses are correct or incorrect. Under a branching program, the scientist or engineer is provided an alternate sequence which depends upon a correct or incorrect response. A branching program is more intricate and usually requires the use of an automated device, such as a computer. In programed learning, the subject matter is pursued at a rate related to the capacity of the scientist or engineer to proceed and at a time of his convenience. A programed learning course can be used as a refresher course, as a supplementary course to a regular textbook-oriented course, or as a basic introduction to a scientific or engineering subject.

By means of a computer, learning experiences may be presented at an appropriate rate (as rapidly as the scientist or engineer can assimilate), at a proper level (within the response capability of the scientist or engineer), at a propitious time (the scientist or engineer successfully completes one level before attempting the next), and with specified behavioral outcomes (the scientist or engineer knows what he must be able to do at the end of the instructional sequence). The use of computers in continuing education for scientists and engineers—separate from courses related specifically to computer theory and practice—is increasing. Computers are used, for example, for carrying out class assignments and for completing outside class assignments—especially at the graduate level. A few graduate engineering courses require extensive use of both digital and analogue computers. Computers are sometimes used in connection with closed circuit TV for graduate education. However, the total usage of computers in continuing education courses for scientists and engineers is presently on a relatively small scale due primarily to the cost of equipment involved and lack of technical knowledge on the part of potential users.

As an illustration of the use of a computer in continuing education, in a particular one-week university short course for engineers employed in industry, the instructor uses a remote terminal that connects with a digital computer. Engineers must learn complex statistical techniques and use them in the course. Students are taught how to converse with a computer terminal: this learning is accomplished, in part, during special evening tutorial sessions by means of the remote terminal. The remote terminal then serves as a substitute for regular engineering processes. To provide realistic problems, certain engineering operations are simulated and placed in the computer. Employing techniques learned earlier in the week, students then manipulate operating variables through use of the terminal and improve upon plant performance through the learning situation, which has been assisted by the computer.

Among the forms of educational technology used for continuing education of scientists and engineers, greatest attention appears to be given to closed circuit television. Under closed circuit television instruction, two or more educational centers are interconnected by coaxial cable or by microwave transmitter and receivers to provide instruction in specialized courses to students who are scientists and engineers. By this approach, an instructor at any point in the network may originate a course that may be taken at any or all centers in the network. This method is used generally to teach highly specialized, low enrollment courses or to provide courses in situations where the only available faculty member is separated from a student body by a long distance or to permit an outstanding instructor or guest lecturer to share his talents concurrently with students elsewhere.

There is usually a control console and one or more class rooms prepared for TV use at each center. Each classroom has at least two monitor TV receivers and two cameras, one for covering the instructor and one for close-up shots of details such as blackboard diagrams or charts. The instructor stands at a lecturn or sits at a desk. Students usually sit at tables equipped with microphones. One monitor carries the program originating in the classroom with the instructor while another monitor shows students in the classroom located at another educational center. Two-way sound communication continues at all times. Through this arrangement, students ask questions of the instructor during the lecture, and all students at all locations hear all questions and all answers. Visual aids which supplement a presentation include slides, films, models, film strips, and charts. The closed circuit television approach also enables the taping of classes for delayed or repeat showing.

In order to maximize availability of programs, this approach allows an individual employer to tap the network and provide an in-house receiving point for such courses. Under these circumstances, scientists and engineers can be released at any time during the day to attend courses without excessive loss of time away from duty. This arrangement increases course availability, allows the educational institution to make more efficient use of its network, and permits enrollment of individuals who otherwise might be excluded from organized instruction.

In 1963 the Graduate Engineering Education System (GENE-SYS) of the College of Engineering, University of Florida, pioneered in the closed circuit approach for meeting continuing education needs of scientists and engineers employed at different locations in Florida. The GENESYS system includes five operating facilities: Orlando, Cape Kennedy, Daytona Beach, West Palm Beach, and the University campus at Gainesville. At each location, much of the instruction is performed by "live" instructors in the conventional classroom approach; in addition, closed circuit television is used.

The GENESYS network extending from Orlando to Cape Kennedy passes directly over the Merritt Island Launch Area. NASA has tapped the network at that point to provide TV course receiving facilities directly at the MILA location. This approach brings courses to NASA scientists and engineers who otherwise would not be able to take such courses. The Air Force also taps the TV network to provide course reception facilities at the Patrick Air Force Base. There is also a reception facility at a naval base at Orlando.

The College of Engineering of the University of Florida offers three graduate degrees to resident students on the Gainesville campus—the Master of Engineering, Master of Science, and Doctor of Philosophy. Because GENESYS is a part of the resident campus, all three degrees currently available in Gainesville are also available through GENESYS in all subject areas and under circumstances applicable to Gainesville. For the Ph. D. degree, GENESYS students must spend a minimum of three academic quarters at the Gainesville campus. The GENESYS plan anticipates that post-baccalaureate, non-degree programs aimed at professional improvement of scientists and engineers will be provided.

[156]

The Association for Graduate Education and Research (TA-GER), a group of seven educational institutions in Texas, created in 1967 an educational television network equipped with a two-way audio/one way video circuit for graduate study. The TAGER network under the leadership of Southern Methodist University consists of two major educational television studios: one at Southern Methodist University in Dallas and one at Texas Christian University in Fort Worth. Fourteen television class-rooms are located in various industrial and educational centers in the geographical area. This program concurrently permits the resident student to attend class on campus and the employed scientist and engineer to attend class in his own company, usually during working hours. Through this method, a seminar in aero-space design, for example, orients on-campus engineering students toward the use of their acquired disciplines in the aeronautics field and concurrently broadens the knowledge of engineers in industry. Subject matter emphasis of TAGER is on science and engineering.

The TAGAR system differs from regular educational television in that the purpose of TAGAR is to provide a large number of courses to a relatively small number of students in small class-rooms, all classes are conducted "live", and all courses must en-roll students in the studio classroom before the course is made available for remote reception via the network.

Another illustration of closed circuit television instruction ap-plied to continuing education was a program carried on during academic year 1968-69 by Pennsylvania State University and in-volving the University Park campus and the Capitol campus near Harrisburg. Instructors from the main campus went to the off-campus facility for the first and last class meetings of a class series in order to establish rapport with class members. The program was discontinued for the academic year 1969-70 because of the cost of toll charges for the microwave connection in relation to the relatively small number of classes using the facility.

Pennsylvania State University experience indicated that the cost of this type of instruction—based on fixed charges for equipment, on micro-wave service, and on technical production personnel and through planned scheduling of 4-5 hours per day— totaled approximately $60-75 per hour in the classroom. If no costs of original instruction were assigned to the TV facility, the cost of a class of 25 students enrolled in a three hour course at the off-campus facility was calculated to be $42 per student credit hour. This figure is comparable to the cost of resident campus instruction, calculated by the university to be $40 per student credit hour. It is anticipated that the Pennsylvania State University program will again become operational when a larger number of classes at the Capitol campus is ready to use the facility.

The use of video tape for continuing education of scientists and engineers is illustrated by two programs of Colorado State University. In 1967, the College of Engineering of the University, in cooperation with seven industrial firms in the state, initiated Project SURGE (State University Research in Graduate Education). The primary function of SURGE is to provide advanced and post-graduate courses in engineering and related sciences to employees of Colorado industry. Regular classrooms at the University are equipped with television cameras and monitors to permit "live" lecture situations to be recorded on video tape. The tapes are sent to industrial areas where scientists and engineers employed in industry view the tapes. In the fall of 1969, twenty courses were thus offered to approximately 400 employees at seventeen industrial locations.

A related program also under the leadership of the School of Engineering of Colorado State University is Project CO-TIE (Cooperation via Televised Instruction in Education) which involves the University and six junior colleges within the state. Although aimed primarily at courses in preprofessional engineering, this program, initiated in 1968 and involving the use of video tapes, also offers opportunity to college faculty members in science and engineering fields to obtain new technical information and to take courses leading to advanced degrees. College instructors may obtain video tapes of single lectures or sets of lectures, of seminars, and of graduate courses in such subjects as mathematics and computer sciences. The network has experimentally offered short courses, such as computer programming.

There are several barriers to the greater use of educational technology for continuing education for scientists and engineers. An enumeration of such barriers and suggested actions to minimize these barriers are hereby described.

1. Priority of hardware-software versus programming—Some educators maintain that electronic and mechanical devices and their operating systems should be made available before large-scale content programs are prepared on a meaningful basis. Other educators believe that programed courses should be developed first after which time equipment manufacturers can examine content materials and determine specifications for needed equipment. Long term development requires adherence to a flexible approach which avoids the rigidity of either extreme. Research on this problem for the purpose of developing practical guidelines would be helpful.

2. Lack of experience in constructing appropriate criteria for evaluating individual participation in courses involving the use of educational technology—The usual end-of-term achievement examination does not fully measure the yield from individualized technology-assisted instruction. In traditional instruction, grades are usually based upon the learner's scale position relative to all other learners who were exposed to the same information. In an individualized course of instruction in which gaps in the learner's knowledge are filled by means of diagnostic and remedial steps, it seems inappropriate to ask the learner to prove mastery of content by the usual standard. Research and experimentation are required to devise accomplishment standards which will permit evaluation of individual achievement in some learning situations aided by educational technology.

3. The relatively large amount of time required to prepare a course of instruction for presentation—The instructor using an educational technology device usually spends more time than normal in the preparation for his presentation. The more sophisticated the program, the more faculty preparation is required.

The establishment of rewards for faculty members who successfully employ educational technology for continuing education acts as an incentive to faculty members to spend the amount of time needed for proper preparation.

4. Lack of knowledge concerning the appropriate "mix" of instruction provided by educational technology and instruction provided by "live" teaching—The ideal degree of intermingling these types of instruction appears to depend on such factors as content, methodology, individual qualifications of the instructor, and individual learning abilities. Through research and experimentation, fundamental guidelines for a proper "mix" may be established although it is currently believed that each teaching situation is a separate entity in its own right. Thus, the proportion of knowledge and skills to be learned via instruction provided by educational technology or via "live" instruction will vary according to the particular teaching situation being experienced.

5. Lack of compatibility between systems—This condition tends to retard the free exchange of programs of instruction of different laboratories and curriculum centers. Major systems in use today accomplish similar purposes, yet operationally each system is usually an independent unit, not susceptible to "tie in" with other major systems. Competition seems to be gradually forcing the development of more compatible systems.

6. Lack of funds—The development and use of educational technology devices is a relatively expensive undertaking. Greater availability of funds, especially in development and initial use stages, is a requirement. The availability of funds for such purposes is increasing but not at a rate sufficient to meet worthwhile proposals. A spur to the availability of larger amounts of public funds is completion and dissemination of data showing specific values already accruing from the use of educational technology in continuing education.

7. Inertia of faculty members—Sometimes, faculty members are disinterested in considering the use of educational technology because they are opposed to change or have a lack of understanding of the value of educational technology. Realistic en-

couragement and incentives by education administrators is helpful in arousing faculty curiosity in the potential of this approach and in faculty efforts to employ tested devices.

8. Need for information on the use of educational technology— It is often difficult for faculty and administrators to obtain objective data on which to base judgments related to adoption of various methods. The preparation of case studies on successes and failures in individual situations, regional demonstrations of equipment and devices, and orientation seminars for faculty and administrators are steps which develop practical information about the use of educational technology.

The essential element in employing forms of educational technology to provide continuing education opportunities for scientists and engineers is to insure effective transfer of knowledge and skills to those individuals participating in such a program. In any plan to use educational technology, the actual assistance provided by this approach to the individual scientist and engineer to help him acquire the knowledge and skills which he seeks is paramount.

Basic Issues

A group of issues related to continuing education for scientists and engineers call for careful consideration by educators. Resolution of these issues, in whole or in part, will influence the future of continuing education for scientists and engineers. These issues are as follows:

1. What should be the basic nature of a graduate degree course which is a means for continuing education for experienced scientists and engineers? These scientists and engineers often find return to the rigors of formal graduate study very difficult because of their long absence from the formal class system. Hence, participation of such individuals in a traditional graduate course is often "shock treatment" to which the mature scientist or engineer may respond negatively. The course content of traditional graduate courses is often geared to the young professionals who have recently been disciplined in fundamentals. The experienced

scientist or engineer may have forgotten or may never have learned these fundamentals. Wtih respect to faculty relationships with graduate students, the young scientist or engineer may have much to gain by pursuing class projects which reflect the instructor's interests while the experienced scientist or engineer having a different perspective may have little respect for the specific views of the instructor. This attitude of the mature scientist or engineer may be based on mental blindness developed through experience or on access to specialized knowledge not possessed by the instructor. In view of such difficulties as long absence from the formal class system, course content, and faculty relationships, the question may be raised whether the traditional nature of the graduate degree course should be modified to accommodate experienced scientists and engineers and, if so, in what manner would the accommodation best be accomplished.

2. Should academic requirements be modified for experienced scientists and engineers who seek continuing education through a graduate degree program? Such programs sometimes seem to be characterized by a series of fixed academic requirements with which the experienced scientist and engineer as a graduate student must comply without deviation. Language requirements, for example, may have outlived their usefulness. A conflict arises when experienced scientists and engineers believe that particular academic requirements for advance degrees are artificial, theoretical, and unrealistic while, at the same time, educators feel that mature scientists and engineers want a "watered-down," applied program. At issue is the appropriate degree of flexibility of present academic requirements which are designed to maintain quality standards but which tend to deny continuing education opportunity to some scientists and engineers who have the greatest need for academic assistance.

3. Should a new branch of an educational institution be created to provide for the totality of continuing education needs of scientists and engineers? The inability of fragmented continuing education offerings available in specific geographical areas to meet all of the continuing education needs of scientists and

engineers may be solved by the establishment of a new branch of the institution. This branch could recognize the short and long range needs for continuous professional updating and plan for a variety of continuing education experiences which in the aggregate would serve to keep individual scientists and engineers up-to-date on a career basis. Such a branch could be developed by blending the talents and experiences of professional and technical societies, employers, and several units within the university structure. Instead of choosing from a large array of courses and, in effect, relying upon chance to supply an integrated program for the individual, scientists and engineers would benefit from a broadly conceived and cooperatively developed continuing education program. It is possible for a university extension division to serve this objective but, in many cases, the influence of regular university departments preoccupied with other educational objectives dominates the activity of extension divisions. Unless university extension divisions can become a more independent university unit and arrange for totality of fulfillment contemplated by this proposal, the creation of a new branch of an educational institution to accomplish this purpose merits consideration.

If continuing education for scientists and engineers is to meet the array of realistic needs, educators must be willing to demonstrate positive leadership, to provide significant learning opportunities related to particular needs of scientists and engineers and offered at convenient locations and time, to use newer and most effective teaching methods and techniques, and to give sympathetic administrative support to this type of education.

ROLE OF PROFESSIONAL AND TECHNICAL SOCIETIES

One reason for the existence of professional and technical societies is to provide for the dissemination of new ideas and concepts to their members through meetings, seminars, publications, and committee activities. Although these societies do not usually perform a teaching function, they stimulate an awareness of the need for continuing education and often provide for transfer of knowledge. Several national societies have established formal committees to enlarge society understanding and action in the area of continuing education. In this respect, societies may act individually or in concert.

TYPES OF ACTIVITIES

One of the common methods by which professional and technical societies stimulate continuing education for member scientists and engineers is the holding of sessions at the local, state, and national levels, designed to provide for the exchange of new scientific and technical information. Another beneficial method is the featuring of articles containing such information in society publications.

A society may form a committee to ascertain the extent of membership participation in continuing education activities and to ascertain needs of the membership for continuing education opportunities. In such a case, a questionnaire is usually prepared and distributed to the membership. Based upon returns, the society may establish or strengthen its own continuing education program or seek to stimulate other societies, organizations or institutions to fill continuing education needs of its membership. This approach is the chief role in continuing education for many societies.

The National Society of Professional Engineers created a special committee in 1965 to conduct a survey of the continuing education activities of its membership. The survey was significant, not only because it provided useful data on engineer participation in such activities but also because the survey provided stimulus for a broad continuing education program subsequently established by the Society.

As a result of the survey, NSPE established in 1966 a committee to study the feasibility of developing and establishing a broad continuing education program for its members. Subsequently, in 1967, NSPE adopted a continuing education plan to be implemented specifically at all three levels of the society. Local chapters were given responsibility to initiate or to support

[164]

the compilation and distribution of listings of continuing education opportunities available to members in the geographical area served by the chapter, to use a specific occasion at which the matter of personal planning for continuing education would be a topic of principal concern on the occasion, and to organize or participate in the organizing and conduct of additional continuing education opportunities. State societies were given responsibility to provide for activities and services to stimulate continuing education at the chapter level and to report to the headquarters organization on needs for additional continuing education material and policies. National headquarters was given responsibility to inform the entire membership of six courses in program instruction then available through the headquarters and to make agreements with publishers for specific promotion of selected course materials.

Since 1967, the continuing education program of NSPE has experienced a continual upswing in member participation. The series of programed learning courses has increased to twenty courses and covers such subject matter areas as application of reliability techniques, PERT for managers, application of value analysis, analytic trigonometry, and the language of algebra. By January 1970 more than 3,000 individual sales of such courses were made to members. Furthermore, on a pilot basis, national seminars have been held in Washington since 1968 on such subjects as quality control and economics of air pollution control; plans for offering similar seminars at other geographical locations are underway. In connection with a 1969 national meeting of the Society, a seminar on motivation and discipline was offered. In addition to participation in programed learning courses, members have taken greater advantage of continuing education opportunities offered through state society and local chapter activities. As an example, several state societies and local chapters incorporate seminars providing continuing education in their regular meeting programs; these seminars are popularly attended.

[165]

The American Chemical Society conducted a survey in 1964 and subsequently created a broad program in continuing education in a different manner. A study of the problem of technical obsolescence among society members showed that:

1. 29% of the respondents believed that technical obsolescence was then a threat to them,

2. 28% believed that such obsolescence was not a threat to them at that time but would be so in ten years,

3. 43% stated that such obsolescence was not a threat to them at that time nor would obsolescence be a threat to them subsquently.

Nevertheless, 81% of the respondents believed that the Society should initiate a program of continuing education. The recommendation of the study that the society initiate new programs in continuing education was adopted in 1965. A continuing education program has evolved until it presently embraces short courses, films, packaged courses, and lectures on tape.

ACS short courses were initially offered at national meetings of the Society in 1965. Because attendance at these courses depended upon attendance at national meetings, the vast number of members were unable to participate. As a result, a program of short courses offered at many locations was started. Short courses have been continued at national meetings but the majority of short courses have been given at local section meetings. Total enrollment in short courses for 1969 approximated 4,200. Short courses varying from one to three days in length are available on more than twenty-five subjects. The trend is to offer courses of wide appeal and at places where the concentration of chemists is high and hence to assure that the program is financially self-sufficient through collection of attendance fees. Illustrations of such courses are applied polymer science, chemical microscopy, and organic photochemistry.

ACS film courses began in 1968 with a film on the interpretation of infrared sprectra, a course of four, one-half hour reels. A chart book containing reproductions of the charts is available for purchase for each viewer. The heavy demand for the film has caused the Society to obtain a total of eighteen prints for simultaneous distribution.

ACS packaged courses begun in 1969 are short courses sent to employers who buy the course and provide and manage the facility incident to the actual offering of the course by Society teaching staff. The Society makes the course available at a lower price per registrant under this method. The list of packaged courses reached twenty during 1969.

ACS lectures on tape began in 1969. Tapes are twenty to twenty-five minutes in length and are accompanied with text materials. Tapes deal with such topics as inorganic chemistry, xenon compounds, and molecular nitrogen. Colleges and industrial companies find particular use for these lectures.

The continuing education programs of NSPE and ACS typify a kind of direct and useful contribution which additional professional and technical societies can make to meet continuing education needs of their membership.

One function of professional and technical societies is to identify new concepts in science and engineering, to determine the implications of each development for science or engineering education, and to devise effective means of modifying the educational program to incorporate these new concepts. In accordance with this function, individual societies have established new committees to deal with such topics as biomedical engineering and energy conversion. The work of these committees is ultimately reflected in the content of on-campus and off-campus programs. As a further aid in bringing new developments to the attention of society members, a professional or technical society may invite officials of other professional or technical societies (including the chairmen of such societies and members of education committees) to attend annual meetings. Meetings of the American Society for Engineering Education illustrate this method.

Another method is for a society, through designated members, to review broad aspects of education including continuing education. This method is illustrated by a three-year national survey of engineering school curricula and of the range of engineer responsibility in government and in industry. The survey supported by the National Science Foundation was undertaken by the American Society for Engineering Education and directed by the Goals Committee appointed by the Society. With respect to continuing education, one phase of this project was the design of a graduate program to satisfy both the practical requirements of professional engineers who return to study additional subjects pertinent to their jobs and the academic needs of resident students whose emphasis is on research.

The Goals Committee report stressed the need for currency of knowledge on the part of all engineers regardless of year of graduation and regardless of the degree level at which the individual enters engineering employment. The committee recommended that engineering schools recognize more fully the place of continuing education as a distinct category in the spectrum of education and that, wherever possible, engineering schools provide additional leadership in the planning and offering of continuing education as part of normal institutional activity.

Another method is for a society, either singly or in cooperation with other societies or organizations, to assess and evaluate continuing education opportunities as the exclusive objective of a study. For example, the Joint Advisory Committee on Continuing Engineering Studies was set up by the Engineers Council for Professional Development, in association with the Engineers Joint Council, the American Society for Engineering Education, and the National Society of Professional Engineers, as a multisociety effort. The objective of this group was to catalogue, clarify, and evaluate alternate methods by which engineers could update their technical competence and be effectively informed on new technology. Four task forces set up by the Committee dealt with continuing education problems of industry, education, professional and technical societies, and government. In its report in 1965 the Committee stated that the future of engineering depends to a considerable extent on the competence of individual engineers to make maximum use of the latest scientific and technical knowl-

[168]

edge. The Committee observed that large numbers of earlier graduates need updating because they possess much know-how which is no longer applicable and because they lack currently essential background. Recent graduates possess much more sophistication but they may need to develop a know-how for applying this knowledge effectively. The Committee offered three general recommendations: (1) a national agency of high prestige should assume leadership for a coordinated effort to deal with the national problem of continuing engineering studies, (2) problems of continuing engineering studies are so complex that individuals and groups of exceptional technical competence should be called upon to assist in the development of suitable programs, and (3) a central agency should be identified to develop and maintain a reference list of course material and to make available basic materials for continuing engineering studies.[11]

A society may offer staff assistance on a regular basis to its members, or to other scientists and engineers for a fee, in order to promote greater participation in continuing education activities. Thus, the Engineers Joint Council, with support from the Office of State Technical Services of the U. S. Department of Commerce, operates a Learning Resources Information Center to provide current information about continuing education opportunities. The Center exemplifies the fulfillment of one of the general recommendations contained in the report of the Joint Advisory Committee on Continuing Engineering Studies. The basic service of the Center is the publication of a directory which is a compilation of essential information on courses, conferences, seminars, workshops, and other educational activities. The directory, published three times a year and available by subscription, lists programs from several sources such as educational institutions, professional and technical societies, government, and industry. Furthermore, corporate subscribers to the directory may consult with the Center about specific continuing education problems related to the content of the directory. The Center

11. Engineers Council for Professional Development, *Continuing Education Studies: A Report of the Joint Advisory Committee*, 1965.

plans to identify and obtain information about correspondence courses, programed learning materials, films, and video tapes in order to provide a selective alerting service on specific subjects.

Employee Associations

Another type of society of scientists and engineers is the association composed of scientists and engineers who work for a particular employer. This type of society has also been actively concerned with continuing education. In some cases associations have persuaded employers to initiate a shared cost plan under which scientists and engineers are reimbursed for all or for a portion of costs for continuing education. In a few instances, these associations have developed and offered to their membership technical courses for updating purposes.

Illustrative of pioneer association action was a program of the Association of Scientists and Professional Engineering Personnel, whose membership is composed of scientists and engineers employed by RCA in Camden, New Jersey. A pilot updating program was initiated in 1963 when courses in six science and technology areas were offered at night for fifteen weeks in a local high school under Association sponsorship. Approximately 300 members of the Association participated in the two programs conducted during the academic year 1963-64. A more formalized study program was administered during the academic year 1964-65 when approximately 200 members of the Association participated; thirteen different courses were offered in such areas as digital computers, applied transistor circuit analysis, theory of control systems and solid state masers. A special course in plasma physics was offered during the summer of 1965. Individuals paid a moderate fee ($20 per course per semester) which constituted the income to operate the training program. Faculty generally were volunteer members of the Association. Subsequently, the ASPEP program was terminated when broader continuing education opportunities became available through employer sponsorship.

[170]

Another association, the Seattle Professional Engineering Employees Association, developed a proposed program of continuing education and offered it for university implementation. The Association is composed of scientists and engineers employed by the Boeing Company and Continental Can Company in Seattle and Renton, Washington. A few years ago, the Association sponsored a study of continuing education needs of working engineers in the Seattle area. Two approaches were proposed in the report of the Association: course option I, an offering with a broad background for an engineer who wanted graduate level exposure to the whole spectrum of science and engineering and course option II, consisting of a series of five specific subjects designed for the engineer who wanted exposure to new developments in a few areas of study. The curriculum subjects were the same under both options, but more time was allocated to specific topics under course option II. The proposals in the study served as a basis for discussion and analysis among employers, engineers, and educational institutions. In 1965 the Association proposed to the University of Washington that the plan be adopted. The University committee which studied the plan concluded that it was unworkable in its original form but agreed there was a definite need to improve continuing engineering education opportunities in that geographical area. As a result, the University modified and expanded its continuing engineering education program which is pursued today by association members and other engineers. The Association also sponsors seminars on technical subjects with the objective of presenting current material by specialists who are usually members of the Association. These seminars are not intended to be a coordinated course of study; they are individual technical information sessions at which open discussion of the topic follows the formal presentation.

The TVA Engineers Association, an independent group representing scientists and engineers who are employees of the Tennessee Valley Authority, has entered into an arrangement with the International Correspondence School whereby association members can purchase its courses at a discount rate.

ROLE OF FEDERAL GOVERNMENT:
POLICIES AND PROGRAMS

The Federal Government—as promoter of the general welfare of the nation, as civilian employer, and as guardian of national defense—has a vital share in continuing education for scientific and engineering personnel. In this section, the role of the Federal Government as policy maker and program administrator for the general welfare will be described. In succeeding sections, the roles of the Federal Government as civilian and military employer will be reviewed.

Federal responsibility for the general welfare involves policies and programs which rely on the effective utilization of scientific and engineering manpower. Economic growth, for example, depends greatly upon technological progress and innovation: the latter are related to the effective utilization of scientists and engineers. The Federal Government, as a partner in science and technology, provides assistance to improve the quality of scientific and engineering personnel through continuing education.

MULTIPLE AGENCY PROGRAMS

Several federal agencies administer similar programs to carry out a concern of the Federal Government for continuing education for scientists and engineers. Multiple agency programs in support of continuing education are found predominantly in the following areas:

1. Education of senior faculty and scholars—The Federal Government provides continuing education opportunities to senior personnel in the form of fellowships and specialized seminars. Fellowships usually provide stipends and expenses for an extended period and thus allow the pursuit of advanced training for professional growth. Specialized seminars are usually limited to a relatively short time period. The Public Health Service, the National Institutes of Health, the Atomic Energy Commission,

and the National Science Foundation have such programs. The Public Health Service and the National Institutes of Health provide postdoctoral fellowships for advanced study in certain physical sciences. The Atomic Energy Commission provides a limited number of post-doctoral fellowships in fields associated with atomic energy. The National Science Foundation provides broad support for post-doctoral study.

2. Support of graduate students at the predoctoral level—Programs at the predoctoral graduate student level are designed to provide stipends and expenses to individuals who are enrolled in graduate study programs leading to a doctorate in science or engineering. A significant number of graduate students are supported through fellowships and training grants sponsored by federal agencies. Such stipends may be awarded for study in specific areas, such as nuclear engineering or biological oceanography, or in science generally. The latter type are awarded without government restriction to a particular area. Among the federal agencies administering such programs are the National Science Foundation, the National Institutes of Health, the Atomic Energy Commission, the U. S. Office of Education, and the National Aeronautics and Space Administration. Graduate students are also supported through federal programs which finance research projects relating to their graduate education.

3. Upgrading college faculty in science and engineering— Major programs are known as research participation, summer institutes, short courses, academic year institutes, in-service seminars, and advanced science seminars. Under a research participation program, college faculty members, who usually have a master's degree as a minimum requirement for participation, gain research experience at both predoctoral and postdoctoral levels. A summer institute program offers work at an advanced level in courses that are often designed for individual participants; the institute offers a faculty member an opportunity to pursue a particular subject in depth. A short course program involves a specialized, short term plan covering advances in selected scientific and engineering areas. The academic year institute program

[173]

enables a faculty member to attend lectures, engage in laboratory work, take courses, and participate in seminars during a regular academic year. Under an in-service seminar program, professional development of a faculty member who must work full time at his institution is provided through attendance at special sessions which do not conflict with his teaching schedule. An advanced science seminar supplements graduate school curricula and permits participants to pursue subjects in depth; some advanced science seminars are held on college campuses while others are held at special locations for field training. The principal agencies engaged in the support of these programs are the National Science Foundation, the Atomic Energy Commission, and the U. S. Office of Education.

4. Programs to provide educational facilities and equipment— Adequate facilities and equipment are essential for continuing education programs. Federal programs provide funds for the construction of laboratories and classrooms; for laboratory, audio-visual and closed circuit television equipment; and other special items of equipment which may be used in continuing education programs. Funds for facilities and equipment are provided by the U. S. Office of Education, the National Science Foundation, the National Institutes of Health, and the National Aeronautics and Space Administration.

SELECTED SINGLE AGENCY PROGRAMS

In addition to multiple agency programs, individual federal agencies administer special programs which involve, in whole or in part, continuing education opportunities for scientists and engineers.

The question of Federal Government reimbursement to private employers for costs of continuing education of scientific and engineering personnel on contractor payrolls arises in connection with cost-plus-fixed-fee type contracts made by the Department of Defense. According to Armed Services Procurement Regulations, certain costs of part-time education at the undergraduate or graduate level which are related to the job requirements of bona fide employees are allowable. Such costs include those for training materials, textbooks, fees and tuition at an educational institution, and straight-line compensation of the employee for time spent attending classes during working hours. For full-time education at the graduate level which is related to job requirements of bona fide employees, costs of tuition, fees, training materials, and textbooks are allowable under the regulations. The extent of reimbursable costs in the individual case depends upon the precise nature of the cost, as applied to the regulations. In practice, the Department of Defense as a contractor facilitates continuing education for scientists and engineers by providing for reimbursement for such education under prescribed circumstances intended to assure a direct relationship between the continuing education approved and contract performance. Unfortunately, statistics on the number of scientists and engineers so involved are not maintained. Costs of continuing education for contractor scientists and engineers are usually construed as an element of overhead for which a composite rate is determined. Use of a composite rate in such a case makes impossible the identification of a single element such as continuing education.

The Department of Labor is authorized to provide for continuing education for scientists and engineers in connection with its administration of the Manpower Training and Development Act of 1962, as amended. In a change in the act in 1965, Congress declared that many professional employees who have become unemployed because of the specialized nature of their previous employment are in need of brief refresher or reorientation educational courses in order to become qualified for other employment in their professions. The administration of the original act provided for occupational training for other than professional personnel. The effect of the 1965 amendment was to permit incorporation of scientists and engineers in the scope of the MDTA coverage. However, no project providing specifically for continuing education for scientists and engineers has been approved by MDTA because of a higher priority placed on other groups in need of training and limitations on the amount of available funds.

Through the Higher Education Act of 1965, funds are provided for the purpose of assisting in the solution of community problems such as housing, government, recreation, employment, youth opportunities, transportation, health, and land use. To accomplish this purpose, the U. S. Commissioner of Education makes grants to states to strengthen community service programs of colleges and universities defined as education programs, activities or services. A state wishing to receive its allotment of federal funds for this purpose designates or creates a state agency or institution which has qualifications especially fitting it for assisting in the solution of community problems. The state agency or institution is broadly representative of the institutions of higher education in the state which are competent to offer community service programs. The state submits its state plan through the agency or institution designated to the Commissioner. Under the act, a state may use its allotment in accordance with its approved state plan to provide expanded or improved continuing education activities and services designed to assist in the solution of problems faced by communities. These activities and services involve professional level refresher programs for professional personnel, including scientists and engineers.

Under the State Technical Services program, the Department of Commerce joins with state governments, universities, and non-profit institutions to translate scientific and technical information, in a useful form, for use of private industry. The act aims to increase employment through development of new business, improved processes and products, and new services that flow from the exploitation of technology. These objectives are accomplished by providing technical services designed to encourage a more effective application of science and technology. A state designates an institution or agency to administer and coordinate the program and to prepare and submit plans to the Secretary of Commerce for approval under the act. Programs to implement a plan are submitted by states each year to qualify for federal funds. This program does not support scientific research; instead, the program promotes wider use of results of research. Technical services, as defined by the act, means activities or programs designed to enable business, commerce, and industry to acquire and use scientific and engineering information more effectively through such means as preparing and disseminating technical reports; providing a reference service to identify sources of scientific and engineering expertise; and sponsoring seminars, training programs, extension courses, demonstrations, and field visits designed to encourage more effective application of scientific and technical information. The program provides for an application of the university extension concept and is implemented through such methods as seminars, conferences, short courses, and task forces. Scientists and engineers are among those individuals benefited. An illustration of special concern for continuing education is a report of a task force on continuing professional studies, appointed by the Director of the Office of State Technical Services. The chief recommendation of this task force was that the Office support a program of study in depth to suggest organized approaches toward more effective methods of dissemination and use of technical knowledge.

A federal agency may share its facilities on an organized basis with an educational institution in a geographical area in order to provide continuing education for scientists and engineers. Such a relationship is illustrated by the NASA-ASEE summer faculty fellowship program.

A program of summer institutes is held at NASA centers in association with appropriate nearby educational institutions to provide educational and research experience for young engineering faculty members. Fellows are selected competitively on the basis of several criteria, including scholarly credentials, experience record, degree of prior involvement in space sciences, and anticipated adaptability to on-going NASA research or design programs. Such programs have been conducted, for example, with Ames Research Center and Stanford University, with Langley Research Center and Old Dominion College, with the Jet Propulsion Laboratory and California Institute of Technology, with Goddard Space Flight Center and Catholic University and the

University of Maryland, and with Lewis Research Center and Case Western Reserve University. Individual programs have had as many as thirty fellows in attendances at one time. The NASA-Case program of course work in chemical rocket technology and research participation for the summer period typifies the NASA-ASEE approach. Both the fundamentals and the engineering art of chemical rocket technology are covered in a manner to provide a background for continuing professional participation in the aerospace field. Each engineering professor who participates in the program is assigned a research project, selected with a view to participation in an established on-going program or working on a task of important but limited scope such that the task can be handled with some completeness during the summer period. The multi-million dollar research laboratory facilities at the Lewis Research Center made available to provide faculty experiences cannot be duplicated at an education institution.

Federal concern for the role of continuing education extends to United States international policy. The Agency for International Development has a contract with the National Science Foundation, the objective of which is to establish a national program for improving the teaching of science and engineering in India. The contract assists the development of an organizational framework capable of carrying on the Indian national program when United States assistance to India is terminated. Since 1963, institutes directed to the development of new approaches in teaching mathematics, chemistry, physics, and engineering have been held regularly. As an example of faculty participation, of a total of 25,000 college teachers of science in India, approximately 40% have been involved in summer institutes under the program. Phaseout of the program is planned for 1971. The Agency for International Development also has a contract with the Educational Development Center under which a consortium of eleven American universities are developing the engineering faculty at Kabul University, Afghanistan, in four fields of engineering. It is anticipated that a viable engineering faculty will become an increasing component in Afghanistan's economic and industrial development. The number of Kabul University faculty updated or to be updated in this program over a ten year period (1963-1973) ranges from eight during 1964 to a projected forty-four during 1973. The majority of these faculty members are experienced teachers.

FEDERAL POLICY QUESTIONS

Review of current continuing education activities suggests a series of federal policy questions. Specifically:

1. Should some portion of federal funds be earmarked for continuing education opportunities for scientists and engineers? Federal funds for continuing education are usually an unsegregated portion of federal funds for training or other purposes; in this respect, continuing education programs compete with other programs for support. Is it desirable to set aside a certain amount of federal funds specifically for continuing education of scientists and engineers?

2. To what extent should industrial costs of providing continuing education for scientific and engineering personnel working on government contracts be paid by the government? Industrial employers have urged greater flexibility on the part of government contract officers in allowing costs to a company to upgrade their personnel. Does government have a responsibility to allow a specific share of the costs for such activity? Should a certain portion of contract costs be allocated to continuing education or a fixed override on all contracts be used to finance continuing education as well as other adjustments?

3. To what extent should the Federal Government encourage scientists and engineers to seek continuing education or stimulate the establishment of an environment conducive to continuing education efforts? Granted that the responsibility for continuing education is basically a matter for the individual, does government have an obligation to promote better understanding of the role of continuing education and voluntary follow-up action on the part of other sectors of society?

[179]

4. Should the Federal Government assess the extent of its involvement in continuing education of scientists and engineers and determine a practical level of federal involvement? For non-federal scientists and engineers, government programs support several types of continuing education opportunities. What is the precise extent of total federal involvement? What is the extent of federal expenditures for continuing education? How do these expenditures compare with the industry's share for its own personnel? What should be the proportionate level of federal contribution?

5. To what extent should federal assistance be provided for continuing education of non-government scientists and engineers in areas of national manpower needs, before anticipated job displacement occurs? Impairment of scientific and engineering knowledge and skills by obsolescence can be identified. Continuing education in particular geographical areas or in particular occupational areas of declining importance can be set up in advance of employment loss. Certain federal programs already extend help to semi-skilled and skilled employees in the labor force. Federal legislation permits the inclusion of professional personnel in development programs. A practical consideration is the amount of time and money involved in continuing education for professional personnel. Under the circumstances, to what degree is federal sponsorship of continuing education for scientific and engineering personnel on an "anticipatory" basis feasible?

6. Should federal tax credit be extended to employers who provide their funds for continuing education for their scientists and engineers? Employers often comment that they would provide more opportunities for their personnel if funds were available. Is there a sufficient public interest in the maintenance of an up-to-date corps of industrial scientists and engineers to warrant such a federal subsidy as a tax credit? Furthermore, the individual tax-payer under certain circumstances may deduct, for federal tax purposes, educational costs necessary to retain his present position. To encourage greater individual expenditure for

continuing education, is it desirable to amend federal tax regulations to permit the individual scientist and engineer a tax deduction to the full or partial extent of his out-of-pocket continuing education costs, a deduction independent of the concept of need to know to retain one's present position?

7. From the viewpoint of mobilization readiness, should active consideration be given to the degree of currency of scientific and engineering knowledge and skills possessed by the nation's pool of scientists and engineers and applicable to the defense posture of the nation? To what extent are scientists and engineers, in a period of national emergency, competent to move from non-defense work to defense assignments requiring knowledge of the latest scientific and engineering techniques having military application? What types of continuing education are essential for such movement, what plans are prepared for use of such methods, and what time elements are involved? Attention has been given to the conversion of scientific and engineering effort from defense to civil technology projects; should concurrent attention be given to the reverse process so that scientific and engineering manpower can be rapidly and effectively devoted to defense purposes as changes in national security consideration dictate? What guidelines can be established to implement decisions reached now regarding mobilization aspects of continuing education?

The Federal Government is faced with alternatives with respect to its concern for continuing education for scientists and engineers. From a practical viewpoint, the Federal Government may maintain the status quo in providing continuing education for such personnel; in effect, this alternative suggests continuance of uncoordinated, fluctuating support on the part of the Federal Government for a miscellaneous series of activities. Another alternative, designed to strengthen government and non-government continuing education policies and programs, involves a series of positive actions ranging from the establishment of a series of new and revised policies and programs aimed at recognizing the importance of continuing education to broader federal conduct or sponsorship of studies related to better coordination of continuing education efforts. The choice of alternatives plays a large part in the determination of the utilization of this nation's scientific and engineering manpower in the decade ahead.

ROLE OF FEDERAL GOVERNMENT: AS CIVILIAN EMPLOYER

The Federal Government as civilian employer has been particularly sensitive to the needs of its scientists and engineers for continuing education. In response to such needs, the government has established a series of programs, participation in which is part of the official activity of many of these employees.

ELEMENTS OF CONTINUING EDUCATION

Major elements of continuing education for federal scientists and engineers include the following:

1. Graduate study centers—More than 100 graduate study centers have been set up in government laboratories throughout the nation. These centers are normally joint efforts between universities and federal agencies and provide close-by facilities for graduate courses and for seminars and short courses in special fields of interest. Numerous government field agencies have cooperated with nearby colleges and universities to provide continuing education opportunities for scientists and engineers.

2. Non-government facilities for federal employees—The Government Employees Training Act contains broad authority for the use of non-government educational resources. The act contains specific limitations on training through non-government facilities: no more than 1% of total agency salaries may be paid to persons undergoing training in non-government facilities; no employee may undergo such training during his first year of employment (unless the head of the agency determines it is in the public interest); no more than one year in each ten years of government service may be spent in non-government training; and

training can not be authorized solely for the purpose of obtaining an academic degree.

Under the terms of the act, the Civil Service Commission has the authority to waive any or all of the first three of these restrictions. The Commission has exercised its authority by permiting agencies to send scientists and engineers for up to two years for each ten years of government service to pursue training in nongovernment facilities. With respect to the prohibition against training solely for the purpose of obtaining an academic degree, the Civil Service Commission feels that training should be authorized to meet specific purposes. If the meeting of these purposes also, incidentally, results in fulfillment of the academic requirements for a degree, the Commission believes acceptance of the degree is not in contravention of the interest of the act and, in fact, actually results in an additional benefit to the agency, the individual, and the government. None of the limitations contained in the act constitutes a barrier to effective use of nongovernment facilities by federal employees. Collegiate instruction carried on under authority of the act is an important factor in federal employee continuing education efforts.

3. Employment of college faculty—Civil Service Commission regulations allow agencies to employ college faculty members in scientific or professional positions for up to one year without regard to rosters of eligibles or usual appointment procedures. By interspersing carefully selected faculty members among career scientists and engineers, government laboratory personnel are exposed to the insight of new professional perspectives. In addition, use of this authority allows faculty members who seek a first-hand knowledge of government operations to obtain it for constructive use in their academic work upon return to a university campus.

4. Attendance at professional meetings—Professional meetings and conferences are among effective means of enabling federal scientific and engineering personnel to keep abreast of significant developments in their fields of interest. In addition, participation in such meetings helps create a working atmosphere con-

ducive to attracting and retaining top-flight personnel. The Government Employees Training Act authorizes departments to spend "expense-of-travel" money for attendance at meetings related to departmental activities but there is a wide variance between agencies in the use of this authority. A Civil Service Commission policy statement on attendance at scientific and professional meetings urges agencies to review their policies at frequent intervals and to take steps to obtain maximum yield from attendance at such meetings, both as a source of information and as a vehicle for professional development.

5. Fellowship awards—Federal scientists and engineers are affirmatively informed of nation-wide fellowship opportunities which provide continuing education and are encouraged to compete with non-government personnel. Scientific and engineering personnel from several agencies have been successful in competition. For example, NSF senior fellowships as well as post-doctoral fellowships have been awarded to government scientists and engineers.

6. Interagency training programs—Training conferences and institutes are held to respond to specific needs of federal scientists and engineers. Interagency programs focus upon professional development in scientific, engineering, and administrative knowledge and skills; information on government plans, operations, and proposals in the research and development field; more adequate comprehension of the basic structure and techniques of management operations within the government; relationships within scientific, technical, and academic fields relevant to development of career and laboratory objectives; better utilization of personnel; and improved communications among scientists, engineers, administrators, and the public.

Furthermore, an inventory of interagency training, including interagency training in science and engineering, is published and disseminated by the Civil Service Commission central office. In addition, regional offices of the Commission publish similar bulletins to call attention to continuing education opportunities in the region. Additional assistance is provided when a regional office of the Commission lists, for federal agency use, available laboratory facilities and personnel competent to train in specialized scientific and engineering areas; such facilities and personnel are available for use in the development of training programs in particular competencies when needed by interested agencies.

ASSESSMENT OF ACTIVITIES

A comprehensive assessment was made in 1965 of continuing education activities conducted by federal agencies which employ engineers.[12] Sixty-nine federal laboratories and other federal facilities, each employing at least 25 civilian engineers, provided meaningful data. The total number of engineers employed by the 69 federal units (26,382) represented approximately one-third of the total population of federal civil service engineers. The total number of continuing education opportunities provided by the 69 units was 30,913. With a total of 26,382 engineers, each federal engineer in the reporting units had a theoretical average of 1.17 opportunities for continuing engineering education through his employer's efforts during the year. Management of these units believed that 78% of the total continuing engineering education requirements were met by the continuing engineering education opportunities offered by these units; the same management indicated that it should provide 85% of these requirements. Since there are other methods beside those provided by employers by which engineers are updated, management opinion indicating that it provide for the 100% requirements would have been unrealistic. Table IV-17 indicates types of continuing engineering education activities offered by responding federal units.

Recent recontact with a sample of federal agencies involved in the 1965 assessment reveals a series of current views: the nature and extent of continuing engineering education in individual federal agencies is still very diverse; overall, the percentage of engineers engaged in formal continuing education has risen to

12. W. G. Torpey, "Federal Government Investment in Continuing Education for Engineers," *Educational Record*, Vol. 46, 1965, pp. 412-415.

approximately 1.40 opportunities per year (as contrasted with 1.17 found in 1965); and the total continuing engineering education opportunities provided by management should be increased to meet current needs of engineers. Respondents reported that a very adverse effect upon continuing education opportunities for both scientists and engineers was caused by strict budgetary and ceiling limitations during fiscal years 1969 and 1970. Other obstacles cited are the use of lump-sum allotments by agency administrators to favor expenditures for general travel over expenditures for continuing education and an emphasis on recruitment of scientists and engineers at the expense of providing adequate funds for continuing education purposes.

Table IV–17

TYPES OF ACTIVITIES CONDUCTED BY
RESPONDING FEDERAL UNITS

Types	Number of Units Providing Type N=69
Attendance at Technical Society Meetings	63
In-house Lectures	60
Technical Lectures Outside Agency	68
Tuition Refund Program	53
Job-related Teaching	45
Educational Leave Program	33
Job-related Research	40
Other	28
Post-doctoral training	18

Source: Special survey

In a NSF funded survey of continuing education for R&D scientists and engineers, data for which were collected in 1966 and 1967, a summary of programs of continuing education in eight government laboratories surveyed showed that five types of activities were carried on in the majority of instances.[13] A summary of these activities is shown in Table IV-18.

13. National Science Foundation, *Continuing Education for R&D Careers,* 1969.

Table IV–18

TYPES OF ACTIVITIES IN LABORATORY SPONSORED PROGRAMS

Types	Number of Laboratories
Outside laboratory	
Expenses paid to meetings	8
Courses with tuition refund	8
Sabbatical leaves with pay	7
Outside short courses	5
Inside laboratory	
Lectures	7
Courses	4
Major conferences	3

Source: NSF funded study

Participation of 181 R&D scientists and engineers in continuing education opportunities provided by eight government laboratories during the previous two year period indicated the predominace of in-lab lectures and seminars and attendance at professional meetings. Participation is shown in Table IV-19.

Table IV–19

PARTICIPATION IN TYPES OF CONTINUING
EDUCATION ACTIVITIES

Types	Percentage of Participation
Professional meetings	67
University credit courses	34
Short intensive courses	23
Educational leave with pay	14
In-lab formal courses (non-credit)	33
In-lab lectures and seminars	80

Source: NSF funded study

The Department of Defense has a policy of providing, when possible, continuing education opportunities for civilian employees (including scientists and engineers) adversely affected by a reduction or termination of work at defense installations. The objective of the policy is to help prepare such personnel for employment in other installations if their present capabilities cannot be utilized. Authority to waive unduly restrictive formal qualification requirements and to enter into continuing education agreements with the Civil Service Commission has been established. Application of such authority to scientists and engineers involved in layoffs, however, has been very minimal.

ROLE OF FEDERAL GOVERNMENT: MILITARY

Continuing education opportunities in science and engineering are afforded military personnel who have primary duties in scientific and engineering fields. Such opportunities are provided at civilian and military schools, with industry, and at specialized conferences and seminars. Career patterns of scientific and engineering officers, together with incentives, encourage military officers to keep abreast of developments in scientific and engineering fields.

TYPES OF PROGRAMS

The military services provide several types of continuing education activities for scientists and engineers who are officers. The services offer participation in programs which lead to advanced academic degrees. These programs have been established to meet specific requirements within the service involved. The services have different magnitudes and types of programs to meet their scientific and engineering requirements. Advanced degree programs within the military services are provided by civilian institutions and by service-operated educational facilities. The Naval Post Graduate School at Monterey, California, and the Air Force Institute of Technology at Wright-Patterson Air Force Base in Dayton, Ohio, grant degrees upon completion of approved curriculum. Advanced degrees in science are awarded in such fields as physics, mathematics, environmental sciences, and operations research. Advanced degrees in engineering are awarded in such branches as civil, electrical, electronics, aeronautical, and nuclear.

[188]

Training-in-industry programs provide selected military officers with on-the-job training from nine to twelve months at various industrial concerns. These officers pursue programs by which they gain knowledge of industrial operations in support of the defense effort. The purpose of such programs is to provide knowledge not available elsewhere in the services. Engineering, including techniques and methods related thereto, is among the subjects featured in these programs.

In addition to advanced degree programs and training-in-industry courses, the services use locally funded and controlled measures as a means to assure that scientific and engineering officers have the opportunity to acquire current knowledge as needed. These measures include short course training, full tuition support of off-duty education, and attendance at technical conferences, seminars, and symposia.

Short course training in each service is often conducted in conjunction with receipt of new equipment. In these courses, contractor engineers are engaged to instruct military engineers until self-sufficiency in a system is attained by the military. Often the training of military engineers is conducted at the contractor's facilities where, for example, a team of military engineers is trained by a contractor on the technical details of operation of equipment. This team may subsequently be responsible for the test and evaluation phase of a defense system.

Other short courses provide updating or familiarization for military engineers to prepare them for specific military duties. Generally, these local command programs are individually established as current operating conditions dictate. Examples of titles of short courses are Engineering Programing, Engineering Statistics, Linear Programing and Theory of Games, Recent Mathematical Advance in Operations Research, Research and Research Management Program, Soils Engineering, and Electronic Information Display Systems.

Full tuition support is provided for off-duty continuing education for officers who take specifically approved courses related to their current duties. Examples of such courses are physics of

[189]

upper atmosphere and higher mathematics for engineers. Many officers attend conferences and seminars as a result of local command decisions. The funding for such attendance is usually controlled at the local level. In addition, many officers attend continuing education activities on their own time. A large number of scientists and engineers in the service belong to one or more professional and technical societies, membership in these societies involves receiving scientific and engineering publications, additional sources of self-development.

CAREER DEVELOPMENT PATTERNS

Each of the three services has specific career development patterns established by personnel management directives. When an officer with a scientific or engineering academic background is identified as primarily qualified in the basically line officer category, his career progression is related to the overall career plan. This plan requires that the officer first becomes well grounded in the tactics, techniques, and professional or technical requirements of his basic service. This phase extends to approximately the eighth year of commissioned service. Beyond that point, provisions are made for periodic attendance at military service schools, specialized education courses, and assignments of increasing responsibility throughout a career of military service.

All three services have specific career development patterns for officers whose primary identification is related to science and engineering. Examples of such patterns are research and development in the Army, meteorology in the Navy, and aerospace science in the Air Force. Special career development areas provide for the orderly progression of military officers through the successive grades and years of service.

Within the Department of Defense, there are many systems and methods of collecting, evaluating, and disseminating scientific and technical information that help to keep military scientific and engineering personnel up-to-date. All services maintain technical libraries ranging from the large scientific and technical libraries in a headquarter's office to small libraries maintained on a naval vessel. Extensive efforts are also carried on to produce and disseminate scientific and technical periodicals, bulletins, newsletters, and reading lists. Correspondence courses and off-duty study programs provide further means of enabling military manpower to keep scientifically and technically current.

A military career is often the first step in a two-step career. Retirement for officers usually comes after twenty to thirty years of service. The knowledge and skills learned by many officers are readily transferable to the civilian field. This transferability is especially pertinent to practicing military scientists and engineers. Although much of the knowledge and many of the skills gained through military continuing education programs are ultimately lost to the military organization, these attributes are not necessarily lost to the nation as a whole. The fact is that continuing education programs in the military enrich the nation's scientific and engineering manpower resources.

PRESENT STATUS OF CONTINUING EDUCATION

The practical programs included in this chapter furnish evidence of endeavors to promote maximum utilization of scientific and engineering manpower by keeping knowledge and skills up-to-date. However, careful analysis of all data indicate that available continuing education opportunities, in the aggregate, do not meet the needs of scientists and engineers as a total group. Quantity-wise, although statistics on total coverage of continuing education do not exist, it is estimated that current opportunities (excluding sporadic, personal reading) are pursued annually by approximately thirty percent of the scientists and engineers in the United States at present. Quality-wise, although objective measures are lacking, it is estimated that approximately one-half of the total current continuing education opportunities are not fully responsive to the needs which these opportunities purport to serve.

Fulfillment of visible, continuing education needs requires efforts by all sectors of society involved, to a much greater extent than already expended. For examples, colleges and universities should offer additional tailor-made programs where unmet needs exist or are anticipated. Industry should give greater recognition and financial support. Professional and technical societies should assert greater positiveness in identifying and in helping to fulfill the continuing education needs of their members and of the profession in general. The Federal Government should provide effective, coordinated leadership buttressed by appropriate research and analysis and should attain a greater degree of program balance. Scientists and engineers themselves should take more advantage of current opportunities related to their needs.

The strength of the nation's science and technology depends upon scientists and engineers whose competencies should be reasonably current at all times. Continuing education as an aspect of optimizing the utilization of scientific and engineering manpower deserves higher priority attention and more intensive follow-through action if this objective is to be realized.

V

FACILITATING THE RETRIEVAL
OF INFORMATION

·

INCREASING FLOW OF DOCUMENTS

The utilization of scientific and engineering manpower is increased when scientists and engineers tap the largest possible knowledge base in the least amount of time.

Scientists and engineers need to know scientific and technical results which their colleagues have found or are finding in specific subject matter fields. Over one million scientists and engineers regularly make assignment and program determinations which require the use of scientific and technical information as a basis for decision-making. With a proper amount of information at their disposal, scientists and engineers can make reasonable judgments. Without such information, they may be oblivious of some essential ideas already available or duplicate needlessly what is already known and reported. Scientific and technical analysis involves the often tedious task of locating particular data related to the assignment at hand. Countless hours, days, weeks, and even months of time are spent annually by individual scientists and engineers in searching for data.

Documentary data, as contrasted with oral data, are not used to the same extent by all scientists and engineers because of the nature of their tasks. For example, scientists engaged in research tend to rely on documentary information to a greater extent than engineers engaged in systems development. However, documentary information in varying degrees is essential to the work of the overwhelming majority of scientists and engineers.

The need to seek out and use scientific and technical data beyond those available from traditional sources is not always appreciated. The full range of scientific and technical information available in document form is often not used. Scientists and engineers, as highly trained individuals, sometimes feel that their informal contacts, the publications which accompany their membership in professional and technical societies, and a collection of books and journals routinely accessioned and maintained in a local library are adequate sources of information input for them. This attitude shows a lack of understanding of the inadequacies of traditional methods as the way to use the increasing reservoir of data continuously being generated by scientific and engineering efforts and recorded in documentary form.

Many scientists and engineers who desire to make full use of available documents lack knowledge of existing scientific and technical information services. Neither the formal education nor the experience of many scientists and engineers has equipped them to know the range of information services available now nor the mechanics pertaining to their use. Unfortunately, for some major fields of science and technology, a comprehensive inventory of information services providing detailed orientation for potential users is not available.

The challenge to scientists and engineers is to search out and obtain, within the most economical time frame possible, scientific and technical information from the widest possible array of sources inside and outside of their organizations.

An appreciation of the flow of information may be obtained from consideration of a few statistics. National expenditures for research and development, public and private, exceed $27 billion per year in the United States alone. Information thus produced is an essential input to new research and development as well as to the application of the results of research and development. These data in documentary form are diverse in nature and are the concern of different scientific and technical audiences. Volume-wise, approximately one million individual scientific and technical articles were published in 1960; now, a decade later, approximately two million articles are published annually. New scientific and technical information becomes available at the rate of approximately 65,000 words per minute. It is estimated that it would take a scientist or engineer, reading 24 hours a day, 400 years to review the scientific and technical data which have been added to the fund of knowledge during the past six years alone.

Factors which are increasing the flow of such information in documentary form include the large growth of scientific and technical activity, greater emphasis on thorough documentation of scientific and technical work through written reports, a sharp increase in scientific and technical periodicals, a plethora of specialized documents such as technical conference proceedings, methods which permit the printing and reproducing of small quantities of a document the printing of which would not otherwise be feasible, increasingly complex concepts requiring new relationships among disciplines, and greater demands for the rapid application of scientific and technical data.

To be responsive to this growth, technology has been applied in such forms as computers, microphotography, and related devices to design and operate methods and systems which promote efficiency and economy of information storage and retrieval. For example, application of the computer results in the storage of banks of data representing large collections of documents and in machine searching as a retrieval action which produces document identification.

Effective methods for storage, display, and transmission of printed matter have been devised. Videotape, microfilm, and microfiche are useful ways for storing information even though the use of microform readers and similar devices has not yet been fully accepted by scientists and engineers. Facsimile transmission of scientific and technical documents from remote information centers is often more acceptable to scientists and engineers: in this instance, the display of documents stored in microform, together with availability of selective printouts, provides a comparatively easy method of retrieval.

Advanced concepts for documentary information handling have been developed. Review of traditional library subject-classification methods has resulted in more effective methods of index-

[195]

ing large collections of documents. Reappraisal of traditional formats for information, such as a report or a book, has brought changes in publication media. Scientific and technical reports themselves have been examined from the viewpoint of providing for the storage of data; for example, tabulations and graphs, heretofor regarded as report material, are being stored through computers or on microfilms to conserve large amounts of space and to provide quick access to such information.

The use of scientific and technical information systems has increased during the past decade. Such a system has been defined as the combination of a body of scientific and technical documents, an index to the body, a method or mechanism for producing the index, a method or mechanism for searching the index, and a method for printing out or otherwise displaying the results of the searches or other index manipulations. A National Science Foundation funded study of scientific and technical information systems in use in 1966 revealed 175 such systems, of which number 87 were industrial.[1] To be included in this analysis, the system had to be based on the use of either mechanical or electronic means of index manipulation or some unusual indexing system. Of the 175 systems, 118 or 67% were computer systems. The growth of these systems nearly doubled in the four year period since 1962, the date of the previous comparable NSF funded study. It is estimated that there are now approximately 400 such systems in use.

IN-HOUSE SCIENTIFIC AND TECHNICAL INFORMATION FACILITY

An effective in-house scientific and technical information facility operated by professional staff is very helpful in conserving the time of scientists and engineers. The in-house information facility may be a scientific and technical library maintained by an organization or a specialized center with computer facilities. The nature of scientific and technical information services provided

---

1. National Science Foundation, *Nonconventional Scientific and Technical information Systems in Current Use*, 1966.

in-house varies and may include alerting, literature searching, making state of the art reviews, and consulting. As minimal documents, in-house information facilities include internal reports and other written material generated by the organization, open literature such as books and periodicals generally available, and classified data acquired through the restricted dissemination by such groups as trade associations and research bureaus.

An effective in-house scientific and technical information facility makes use of abstracting and indexing services. These services are essential to provide scientists and engineers with a current awareness of subject matter developments in fields of specialization. From the point of view of content, abstracts can be classified into three types: (1) those listing the publication and stating only essential library index card details; (2) those providing a synopsis of subject matter of the publication, in addition to library index card details; and (3) those reviewing and evaluating the contents of the publication. Chief forms of indexing used by abstracting and indexing services are the descriptive cataloguing index which uses library index card elements, the alphabetic subject index which uses the alphabet to arrange subjects, and the keywood index which uses principal words of the title or abstract. The development of thesauri for use in indexing and retrieval is increasing.

The publication of abstracts covers a range of formats. For example, a traditionally printed publication of abstracts may contain a variety of abstracts classified in broad subject matter categories such as the Technical Abstracts Bulletin. The publication of abstracts may be computer-produced in which case the abstracts are placed on magnetic tape such as the Compendex of Engineering Index. Illustrations of currently available abstract publications prepared by non-government organizations for use of scientists and engineers and available for in-house facilities are set forth in Table V-1.

In small organizations, a formalized information facility may not be feasible but the time saved in medium-sized and large organizations through the assistance provided by such service justifies the cost of the service. Information on the development of in-house information services is available from the American Documentation Institute, the Special Libraries Association, and the Industrial Research Institute.

Table V–1

SELECTED NON-GOVERNMENT ABSTRACTING AND
INDEXING SERVICES

Name of Publication	Publisher
Applied Mechanics Review	American Society of Mechanical Engineers
Chemical Abstracts	Chemical Abstracts Service
Engineering Index	Engineering Index, Inc.
Mathematical Reviews	American Mathematical Society
Meteorological and Geoastrophysical Abstracts	American Meteorological Society
Review of Metal Literature	American Society of Metals
Solid State Abstracts	Cambridge Communications, Inc.

Source: Society data

Costs involved in the information acquisition process may be realistically viewed when one realizes the employer cost of the time which a scientist or engineer spends in search and retrieval. As a simple illustration, a scientist whose salary is $20,000 per year may spend the equivalent of five weeks in search and retrieval effort during the year at a pro-rated cost of approximately $2,000. If there are 20 scientists having the same time expenditure in the organization, the total pro-rated costs of the 20 scientists approximate $40,000. If a particular scientific and technical information service costs an employer $10,000 a year, the service would approximately pay for itself in the year if the service saved one-quarter of the total search and retrieval time of the 20 scientists.

One large, nationally-known company has recently established an in-house scientific and technical information facility which combines continuous internal and external assistance for its scientists and engineers. The program consists of two parts: a

[198]

technical abstract service and an alerting service. Through the technical abstract service, the company with the aid of computer technology prepares and issues a monthly publication which contains abstracts of such data as engineering memoranda and technical reports prepared by company personnel, technical papers obtained from outside sources, and information on new patents obtained by company personnel. The classification system used in the publication contains thirty-five titles. Distribution of the publication is to approximately 500 engineer supervisors who in turn forward the publication to their own subordinates.

Through the alerting service in this company, an outside information distribution organization provides under contract magnetic tapes which contain library index card information describing articles appearing in scientific and technical literature, in addition to technical descriptors. Company scientists and engineers who wish to use the alerting service prepare a profile of their interest areas. A profile may represent an individual's interest or a group's interest. Profiles are matched regularly with the incoming tapes, and the individual scientist or engineer receives a printout of items corresponding to his interest profile. To obtain the full article, the scientist or engineer uses the first part of a two part card: he sends the first part to the company library to request the periodical or other format in which the article appears; he retains the second part of the card as an addition to his personal library file. The company coordinates its total library holdings located in various organizational units and at different locations of the company to permit maximum use of the resources of the company's individual libraries.

Another large research-oriented company has an information system under which selective distribution of internal science reports in mathematics and computer sciences is made to approximately 1,500 scientist staff members. Computer comparison of interest profiles of individual scientists has sharply improved the dissemination over the previous program under which internal scientific reports were disseminated to a much smaller audience by means of an author-prepared list.

[199]

An example of an advanced in-house information facility is the RECON (Remote Console) system administered by NASA. To achieve speed and precision in retrieving information maintained by the organization, NASA places scientists and engineers seeking information in direct contact with a computer. By means of its RECON system, NASA scientists and engineers at a remote console conduct their own literature searches through a dialogue with the computer. Basic elements in the RECON system are a keyboard, a computer, television screen, and automatic printer.

A scientist or engineer starts the process by using the keyboard to tell the computer located at the NASA Scientific and Technical Information Facility at College Park, Maryland, the subject in which he is interested. Letters on the keyboard are arranged as they are on a standard typewriter. The computer contains bibliographic data about every one of more than 550,000 documents in the NASA scientific and technical information system. Users of RECON have immediate access, for example, to the collection of documents that are announced in the semimonthly journals STAR and IAA as well as in periodic issues of C-STAR and Aerospace Medicine and Biology. Another collection in the system comprises NASA Research Resumes, based on current research and development activities. The RECON system does not store or transmit classified information.

Under the RECON system, a television screen is the computer's means of communicating with the scientist or engineer. On the screen is displayed, in printed words, answers to the user's requests and questions. In response to the user's request, the computer shows a list of indexing terms alphabetically surrounding the subject, together with numbers of documents indexed to these terms. After the scientist or engineer selects from the list an indexing term that seems to be close to his area of interest, the computer assigns an identifying number to the particular group of related reports and displays a citation from it. After a narrowing of related groups of reports to the precise subject matter area of concern to the scientist or engineer, the computer finally shows a list of report accession numbers of pertinent reports.

An automatic printer gives a printout of the end result of the user's literature search, generally in the form of a list of report citations responsive to the user's needs. The printer also delivers a printed record of the request-question-response sequence which the user keeps to guide him through future searches in the same subject matter area. With the computer-provided list, the user goes to a nearby document collection or requests his local NASA library to obtain the documents cited. Since the total time of the literature search is usually less than an hour, the time of the user in locating appropriate material is much less than the time involved through traditional literature search methods.

Under the RECON system, begun in 1969, consoles are located in the libraries at NASA Headquarters, Washington, D. C.; at the Langley Research Center; at the Electronics Research Center; at the Lewis Research Center; and at the NASA Scientific and Technical Information Facility. It is planned to extend RECON to include all NASA centers and other selected points. At present, RECON terminals are fixed and connected to the computer, but the use of completely portable console units is anticipated in the near future.

SCIENTIFIC AND TECHNICAL
INFORMATION CENTERS

The scientific and technical information center is a service-oriented information handling unit which assists scientists and engineers seeking data. The operation of a center provides accessibility to large amounts of written data in the form of reports and other documentary material. The overall types of service provided by these centers are referral, document repository, and information analysis.

With respect to the referral type of service, scientists and engineers who desire specific information contact a center providing referral service and are directed to particular sources for information, depending upon the nature of the data they seek. This type of service is in contrast to the traditional method by which scientists and engineers desiring data from outside of their organization ferret out for themselves potential sources and contact those sources most likely to have data related to their particular interests. The center providing referral service maintains current data on the identity of information sources and the characteristics of each source. Characteristics include the nature of the information covered by the individual source, the format in which information is obtained, qualifications of the user, cost of the service to the user, procedures to be followed to obtain information, and the usual time span for servicing requests. The center uses these data to answer requests from scientists and engineers who seek the identification of sources of data for their specific questions or problems. Referral service is provided, for example, by the National Referral Center for Science and Technology of the Library of Congress and the Science Information Exchange of the Smithsonian Institution.

The National Referral Center for Science and Technology collects data on scientific and technical information sources and, upon request of individual scientists and engineers, refers them, without charge, to pertinent sources of information. Scientists and engineers then seek the subject matter data they desire directly from suggested sources. The Center transmits requests for reference material—as contrasted with requests for referral service—to other divisions of the Library of Congress, such as the Science and Technology Division. However, the Center does furnish titles of abstract journals, indexes, and directories when they are relevant to the inquiry. Approximately ninety days after answering a request, the Center follows up with the inquirer to ascertain whether he obtained the information needed, which sources were most helpful, and whether any source failed to provide the services described by the Center.

The Science Information Exchange receives annually approximately 100,000 one-page records of basic and applied research projects that are planned or in progress. The information obtained by the records consists of unclassified, unpublished descriptions of research funded by all sources of support. The information, updated annually, describes who supports the individual project, who carries out the project, where, and when, together with a technical summary of the planned work. Since the collection covers research in life and social sciences, as well as the physical sciences and engineering, interdisciplinary relationships are given special emphasis. Information obtained is processed into a computerized data bank. In response to inquiries from scientists and engineers, the Exchange provides answers in terms of the input items cited above. Answers are also provided for any combination of these items, such as projects on which individual scientists are engaged or projects reported by a particular organization. A service fee applies to Exchange users.

With respect to the document repository type of service, scientific and technical documents not published in open literature are obtained, indexed, stored, and distributed. The center providing this service usually acquires reports prepared under specific kinds of scientific and technical programs such as atomic energy projects. The center uses relatively sophisticated indexing methods and generally publishes and distributes periodic abstract indexes. In response to individual requests, the center makes a search of its collection of documents and provides a compilation of document titles as well as copies of specific documents desired. The responsibility for evaluating the significance of the document rests wholly with the user scientist and engineer.

Document repository service is provided, for example, by the Defense Documentation Center, by the Clearinghouse for Federal Scientific and Technical Information, and by NASA.

The Defense Documentation Center, an activity of the Defense Supply Agency, is the central facility of the Department of Defense for the secondary distribution of scientific and technical reports generated by DOD funded efforts in research and development. The Center acquires, processes, stores, announces, and provides copies of scientific and technical reports to organizations within the federal research and development community. For this purpose, the community refers to federal agencies, their con-

[203]

tractors, subcontractors, and grantees. The services of the Center are available to eligible organizations which are registered for the service. Approximately 6,000 organizations are registered. If classified information is requested by any organization other than a unit of the Department of Defense, approval depends upon verification that the facilities of the requesting organization are proper to protect the classified documents desired. Potential defense contractors may also use the service of the Center through individual programs established by the three military services.

The scientific and technical report collection of the Center consists of approximately 900,000 titles. Approximately 50,000 documents are added each year. The reports, both unclassified and classified, vary in length from a few pages to hundreds of pages and range in content from concept formulation to final development studies.

The Center receives documents directly from Department of Defense agencies or from industrial, educational, and nonprofit organizations which have DOD contracts and grants. By regulation, each DOD agency contractor, subcontractor, and grantee is required to provide to the Center twenty copies of scientific and technical reports which formally record results of research, development, testing, and engineering efforts. Upon arrival at the Center, these reports are reviewed to ascertain that they contain information of scientific and technical value and that any limitation on distribution is properly worded. Each report is also given a control number. One copy is photographed for microfiche storage. If additional copies are needed, they are reproduced from microfiche.

The Center classifies reports into twenty-two major subject fields as follows:

Aeronautics
Agriculture
Astronomy and Astrophysics
Atmospheric Sciences
Behaviorial and Social Sciences
Biological and Medical Sciences

Chemistry
Earth Sciences and Oceanography
Electronics and Electrical Engineering
Energy Conversion (non-propulsive)
Materials
Mathematical Sciences
Mechanical, Industrial, Civil and Marine Engineering
Methods and Equipment
Military Sciences
Missile Technology
Navigation, Communications, Detection and Countermeasures
Nuclear Sciences and Technology
Ordnance
Physics
Propulsion and Fuels
Space Technology

The major subject fields are further divided into a total of 188 subject groups.

Classified reports and unclassified reports having a distribution limitation are announced in a semimonthly Center publication titled "DDC Technical Abstract Bulletin." Unclassified reports having no distribution limitation are announced in a semimonthly Clearinghouse for Federal Science and Technical Information publication titled "U.S. Government Research and Development Reports." Companion index volumes are available with each issue.

Registered user organizations request either a full-size hard copy (for which there is a service charge) or a microform copy (for which there is no service charge) of reports by recording the control number of the report on punch cards provided by the Center. If a user organization does not have the identification number of a document which it believes should be in the collection of the Center, the user organization notifies the Center which will undertake a search to locate and provide a copy of the report to the requesting organization if it is eligible to receive the report.

Requests for reports are computer processed. The average document request processing time varies from two days (when

[205]

the report is in stock) to five days (when the report is reproduced). Approximately one-fourth of the requests are for copies
of documents in microfiche form. The size of the sheet film is
four by six inches and permits up to fifty-eight page microimages
to be stored on the first sheet of microfiche and up to seventy
microimages on succeeding sheets. By use of microfiche, a
scientist or engineer can maintain a personal library of thousands
of reference documents in his desk drawer. A microform reader
needed to use the microfiche may be a compact-sized desk ac-
cessory.

The two announcement publications cited permit a user organization to learn of the existence of a current accession. A
bibliography service provided by the Center furnishes listings
which describe available scientific and technical reports relating
to specific subject matter areas. One type of bibliography is prepared for subject areas for which requests are anticipated; this
type is given a control number and announced in the appropriate
publication in the same manner as individual reports. Another
type of bibliography is prepared in response to a specific request
for references related to a scientific or technical problem or project; in this instance, the user organization describes the problem
or project for which it seeks information. A computer search
strategy is then prepared by the Center. As a result of the search,
a computer printout describing pertinent documents is sent to the
user organization.

In addition to service with respect to reports of completed research and development, the Center, through its Research and
Technology Work Unit Information System, furnishes information
on research and development currently underway to federal
agencies. A data bank contains more than 24,000 résumés of
current efforts arranged in budget categories of research, ex-
ploratory development, advanced development, and management
support. As many questions can be answered as there are com-
binations of elements included on a research and technology
résumé form, prepared in terms of work unit descriptions. Information provided includes the title of the individual effort, ori-

ginating and performing activities, contract or grant numbers, key dates, and task approach. The data bank also includes résumés submitted by NASA which established the system jointly with the Department of Defense. Response is provided to requests in the form of statistical summaries, tabulations, or complete or partial printouts of selected résumés, generally in the format the user federal organization desires. The Center provides material which describes options available for requestors and furnishes guidance in making full use of the system. Information from the data bank not only keeps scientists and engineers current but also alerts them to organizations and personnel who are performing similar or related tasks. Limited access to this data bank to non-government organizations within the federal research and development community began in 1968.

The Clearinghouse for Federal Scientific and Technical Information, U. S. Department of Commerce, collects scientific and technical reports which result from scientific and technical work performed by government agencies and by industry and private institutions under contract to sponsoring federal agencies. The Clearinghouse announces, reproduces, and sells these reports at nominal cost. Scientists and engineers, employed both by government and by non-government organizations, obtain and use reports acquired from the Clearinghouse. The Clearinghouse also handles the processing, announcing, and distribution of unclassified Department of Defense reports to qualified DOD contractors.

The Clearinghouse collection contains over 540,000 titles and is increasing at the rate of approximately 40,000 titles per year. Reports are announced under twenty-two subject fields. Each subject field is further divided into several groups of topics.

To inform prospective users about new documents available each year, the Clearinghouse prepares and sells on subscription a series of publications:

1. U. S. Government Research and Development Reports: an abstract journal, this publication, issued semimonthly, describes in each issue over 1,000 government-generated research and de-

velopment reports and translations of foreign technical material recently released through the Clearinghouse.

2. U. S. Government Research and Development Reports Index: a companion publication to Reports, the Index provides data on documents announced in Reports by subject, author, source, report number, and contract number.

3. Clearinghouse Announcements in Science and Technology: designed for quick review of current scientific and technical reports, Clearinghouse Announcements provides a method for scientists and engineers to scan the flow of new scientific and technical information in such fields as defense, space, nuclear energy, transportation, housing and urban development, and air and water pollution. Clearinghouse Announcements is available in forty-six separate subject matter areas.

4. Fast Announcement Service: a method to bring selected research and development reports to immediate attention, Fast Announcement Service reviews new reports believed to have wide application and is available to subscribers in fifty-seven subject matter categories.

All documents announced in U. S. Government Research and Development Reports, Clearinghouse Announcements in Science and Technology, and Fast Announcement Service may be purchased from the Clearinghouse in paper copy or in microfiche. Microfiche is considerably less expensive than paper copy and easier to handle, store, and reproduce. Under a service called Selective Dissemination of Microfiche, the Clearinghouse makes automatic distribution of microfiche copies of scientific and technical documents. This service is available in several hundred categories. The user's selection options include ordering by subject, by originating agency, or by a combination of both. Distribution is made at the same time the documents are announced for public sale and at a price per title considerably lower than the cost of individual microfiche. The Clearinghouse single price/ prepaid document coupon system for paper copies and microfiche provides an effective device to facilitate the servicing of document requests.

On behalf of the Office of Water Resources Research of the U. S. Department of the Interior, the Clearinghouse also publishes and distributes, semimonthly, selected Water Resources Abstracts. This publication is designed to provide scientists and engineers with scientific and technical information on water-related aspects of physical sciences as well as related engineering considerations. The Clearinghouse also publishes the U. S. Government Research and Development Reports Annual Index which consists of subject, author, contract, and report number sections.

NASA maintains a document repository service which is linked with the Clearinghouse for certain distribution purposes. NASA collects documents related to all phases of science and technology involved in space exploration and aeronautics. Much of the information is generated by NASA in-house and contractor research and development work. The several hundred thousand documents in the collection are augmented by more than 75,000 titles each year. Scientific and Technical Aerospace Reports (STAR), a semimonthly NASA publication, contains abstracts and indexes of NASA collected information. Abstracts are arranged in thirty-four subject categories as follows:

> aerodynamics
> aircraft
> auxiliary systems
> biosciences
> biotechnology
> chemistry
> communications
> computers
> electronic equipment
> electronics
> facilities, research and support
> fluid mechanics
> geophysics
> instrumentation and photography
> machine elements and process
> masers
> materials, metallic
> materials, non-metalic

mathematics
meteorology
navigation
nuclear engineering
physics, general
physics, atomic, molecular and nuclear
physics, plasma
physics, solid state
propellants
propulsion systems
space radiation
space sciences
space vehicles
structural mechanics
thermodynamics and combustion
general

STAR has several indexes: subject, corporate source, personal author, report number, and accession number. Each document abstracted is indexed by several appropriate terms. To save time for scientists and engineers, reports in the subject index are described by notations of their content instead of a listing of titles. Cumulative indexes are published quarterly; the fourth quarter cumulative index covers the issues of the entire year. Subscriptions to STAR are obtainable from the Government Printing Office. STAR and the NASA documents abstracted in it are available, without charge, to NASA scientists and engineers, contractors, subcontractors, and grantees; other federal agencies and their contractors; libraries maintaining collections of NASA documents for public reference; and other organizations having a need for NASA documents in work related to the aerospace program. NASA documents listed in STAR are available either from the Clearinghouse for Federal Scientific and Technical Information or the Government Printing Office. Microfiche copies of NASA documents may be purchased from the Clearinghouse.

Organizations not engaged in aerospace activities may obtain NASA scientific and technical information by subscribing to the services of a NASA regional dissemination center. Such a center typically provides three services: selective preparation and dissemination of citations of documents on the basis of an individual organization's interest profile (copies of the full report and micro-fiche copies are available upon request), retrospective searches in response to scientific and technical questions by subscribing organizations, and distribution of NASA technology-utilization publications. NASA regional distribution centers at Blooming-ton, Detroit, Pittsburgh, and Durham are computer-equipped.

With support from NASA, the Technical Information Service of the American Institute of Aeronautics and Astronautics helps scientists and engineers to obtain information in aerospace science and technology which has appeared in worldwide published aero-space literature. A staff of specialists employed by the Service scans new documents to provide approximately 1,200 abstracts in each semimonthly issue entitled International Aerospace Ab-stracts. Approximately forty-eight percent of the abstracts pub-lished each year report on scientific and technical work done in foreign nations. Document characteristics are coded for com-puter input for use in machine retrieval of information. A cumu-lative index of abstracts appearing in the semi-monthly publica-tion is made quarterly and annually. A microfiche containing citation data, the abstract itself, and the complete text of the origi-nal document may be obtained for all non-copyrighted items re-ported in the semi-monthly publication. Over 50,000 documents are currently available on microfiche. The Technical Informa-tion Service library fills requests for reference services and photo-duplication, as well as microfiche. Scientists and engineers desir-ing to use the service of the Service may subscribe either to the semimonthly issues of the abstracts or to the cumulative index volumes.

With respect to the information analysis type of service, availa-ble data in a given field are obtained and evaluated by scientists and engineers who are professional analysts at the center. Eval-uated data are stored in machine-readable form. In response to individual requests, specific answers to technical questions are provided. Additional service provided may be the preparation of

[211]

state of the art reports, critical reviews, and bibliographies of evaluated literature.

Information analysis service is provided, for example, by the Atomic Energy Commission. AEC provides full or partial support for scientific and technical information centers in fields directly related to its mission. These centers collect, critically evaluate, and compile scientific and technical information in particular fields and make the evaluated information available as data tables, handbooks, critical state of the art reviews, and summaries of research and development programs in progress. Other services at these centers include answering technical inquiries and publishing specialized bibliographies and newsletters.

Most of the twenty-seven AEC supported centers are located at AEC laboratories where there are substantial literature collections and specialized personnel with subject matter competence. Qualifications for users of these centers vary, but generally scientists and engineers employed by government agencies, research organizations, educational institutions, and industry are eligible for service. Scientists and engineers seek assistance directly from the particular center involved. A directory of these centers is published by AEC.

NSF SCIENCE INFORMATION PROGRAM

Through legislation passed in 1958, the National Science Foundation is directed to arrange for indexing, abstracting, translating, and other services leading to a more effective dissemination of science information and to undertake programs to develop new and improved methods for making science information available. The Foundation does not operate a scientific and technical information center but it assists organizations which have storage and retrieval systems or wish to develop such systems.

The science information program of the National Science Foundation, which deals on a broad national basis with information requirements of scientists and engineers, provides financial support for information system development, for operations, for research and development, and for international information and translation.

Information system development involves an integration of information functions and services in major scientific disciplines matched with information requirements; exploiting technology to increase speed, selectivity and efficiency of existing services; and the creation of new communication channels. Greatest progress has been made in the development of an information system for chemistry. Because most chemical literature is compound-related, identification of compounds is a natural indexing link; hence, the literature of chemistry can be related to a central registry of compounds. With the development of suitable techniques, a compound registry system has been established. This system is maintained by the Chemical Abstracts Service of the American Chemical Society with NSF support. NSF is also helping the Service to create a total computer-based information system. Goals of the service are computer-controlled production of abstracts and indexes by 1971 and completed conversion of American Chemical Society journals to computerized production by 1974.

For a few other scientific disciplines, comprehensive programs of information system development under the leadership of scientific groups and with NSF support are being planned. In the case of a proposed National Physics Information System, for example, input materials will be subjected, as appropriate, to translation, editorial evaluation, bibliographic organization, storage, research, and retrieval. Users of the system, scientists and engineers in industry, government, and universities, will be provided with hard copy, microfilm, and machine-readable files. NSF strategy for the engineering sciences is to support a preliminary study of system requirements upon which engineering societies can base an implementation program supported by industry.

With respect to university-centered systems, support is provided for a systems approach to library modernization and improvement for the benefit of scientists and engineers using the traditional

[213]

library and for the benefit of librarians seeking to improve their services to scientists and engineers.

Support is also provided for studies directed at specific problems in order to develop and evaluate the feasibility of specific solutions to long range information problems.

Operational support is provided for publications and services which would otherwise be marginal or nonexistent. Such support is designed to assist scientists, through their societies and organizations, to keep pace with the rapid growth of information. Thus, journals are helped to reach new operating levels and scientific monographs are published with NSF financial assistance. Abstracting and indexing services and continuing bibliographic services for science and engineering, involving efforts to develop automated systems, are also funded. Another aspect of NSF operational support relates to the Science Information Exchange of the Smithsonian Institution.

Support for research and development involves studies of changing information requirements of scientists and engineers, as well as research on problems that emerge in the course of developing systems and services designed to satisfy changing requirements. This support consists of two categories of projects: individual research or study projects concerned with a single problem (such as studies aimed at determining the nature of information needs of scientists and engineers and the manner in which these needs are being met) and support of scientific information research centers (for example, the center at the Georgia Institute of Technology which has a program of theoretical research linked to a graduate degree program in information sciences).

Support for international information and translation provides published results of foreign research through acquisition of publications and through translations. Two types of translation activities make scientific and technical literature published in foreign languages available to, and usable by, U. S. scientists and engineers. Domestic translation projects are proposed to NSF by scientific societies on the basis of needs of their membership. Foreign translation projects, undertaken in foreign countries

[214]

through contractors using foreign currencies, are proposed to NSF by other federal agencies.

FEDERAL COORDINATION

Scientific and technical information activities of federal agencies are coordinated by the Committee on Scientific and Technical Information of the Federal Council on Science and Technology. The Committee reviews the scope and adequacy of present information programs and makes recommendations for improving systems for handling scientific and technical information. The Committee also stimulates organizations to seek new methods to improve their capabilities to communicate information. Under the guidance of this group, new systematic approaches have been developed and standards for information work have been established.

The work of the Committee is executed through panels and task forces whose members are drawn primarily from federal agencies. Members represent both operating programs and technical specialization. Panels of the Committee deal with such topics as operational techniques and systems, information sciences technology, management of information activities, education and training, and information analysis and data centers. Illustration of publications prepared or funded by the Committee are Guidelines for the Development of Information Retrieval Thesauri, Format Guidelines for Scientific and Technical Reports Prepared by Contractors and Grantees, Federal Microfiche Standards, Inventory of Information Sciences Technology Work in Progress, and Course in Information Tools, Techniques, and Resources for Scientists and Engineers.

GENERAL PROGRAMS RELATED TO SCIENTIFIC AND TECHNICAL INFORMATION RETRIEVAL

In addition to the availability of scientific and technical information through programs linked exclusively or primarily to science and technology, scientific and technical information is also available through general programs concerned with data

[215]

retrieval. Here, too, advances have been made in facilitating the storage and retrieval of scientific and technical information. The MARC (Machine Readable Cataloguing) Distribution Service of the Library of Congress illustrates a breakthrough in general library operations which aids scientists and engineers, as well as other specialists, by maximizing subject matter coverage while reducing the time factor.

The concept of the MARC Distribution Service is the conversion of cataloguing data to machine readable form. Under a pilot project started in 1966, the Library supported the design and development of computer programs for processing cataloguing data and for printing bibliographic records. A revised format based on pilot experience became the MARC program, available to all libraries for a fee beginning in 1969. The System provides, on a weekly basis, magnetic tapes containing bibliographic records representing monographic imprints. Each tape is 300 feet long, contains approximately 900 records, and is accompanied by a list of Library of Congress card numbers in numerical order identifying the records on the tape. It is expected that the program will be expanded to cover all current English language monographs catalogued at the Library of Congress.

The U. S. Office of Education administers a research support program concerned with the use of library resources, the development of library and information services, and the training of librarians and other information personnel. Under the program, the Office funds projects which hold promise of improved services and practices for all types of libraries. Grants are awarded to educational institutions, state governments, and other public or private nonprofit agencies, organizations or groups. Contracts are also authorized with public or private, profit or nonprofit agencies, organizations, and institutions.

Under the research support program of the U. S. Office of Education, a range of project types can be supported. These types include state of the art studies, feasibility studies, prototype development and hypothesis generation, testing and evaluation, and demonstration and implementation. Criteria used in

[216]

evaluating proposals include the significance of the proposal to the responsibility of the Office of Education in the total library and information science research effort, the promise of the proposed study to make a contribution to the improvement of library or information science, sound design or operation plan, and general applicability of local projects.

Individual projects having application to the storage and retrieval of scientific and technical information and funded by the U. S. Office of Education during fiscal year 1970 are summarized in Table V-2.

Table V–2

PROJECTS FUNDED BY U. S. OFFICE OF EDUCATION

Title of Project	Brief Description
Microfilm Reader Experiments	An investigation of the receptivity of observers to both wall-type screen displays and desk console models; an investigation of the effect of background luminance; an exploration of methods to allow the viewer to research rapidly several pages of microfilm material
Design and Preparation of Presentation to Increase Skill in Locating Information through Effective Use Of Federal Information Systems and Related Services	Development of a plan of audiovisual material by which a branching film format will allow the film to be used as a self-contained presentation for self-study or small groups while permitting its use as an integral part of large presentations
Determination of User Needs and Future Requirements for a Systems Approach to Microform Technology	Determination of appropriate environmental conditions for all aspects of microform use, including design and protoptype manufacture of an individual reader station for use of microforms; determination of elements of an effective system of bibliographic control of microforms
Development of a Low-Cost Microform Reader	Development of a good quality microfiche reader, meeting human engineering criteria and to be commercially available for under $50.
Preparation and Dissemination of a Bibliography on Information Science and Technology	Partial support of a bibliographic work which includes bibliography of 1968 literature

Source: OE data

Another program of the U. S. Office of Education supports research, planning projects, and operational programs which concern the application of computer technology and use in education. Project research support falls into several categories, one of which relates to data banks and information retrieval systems. These projects explore the potential of the computer for storage and retrieval of large bodies of information relevant to education and educational research. Typical projects in this category include studies to develop computer based systems for library use, the search of bibliographic holdings in on-line computer systems, and storage and retrieval studies. Examples of projects funded under the category of data banks and retrieval systems are the development and pilot operation of a system to reclassify old books and process new books under the Library of Congress classification system, a study of user requirements in identifying desired works in a large library, a study of the state of the art of dial-access-information retrieval, and a study of the acquisition of knowledge in relation to information storage and retrieval.

PROPOSALS FOR NATIONAL SCIENTIFIC AND TECHNICAL INFORMATION SYSTEM(S)

Active consideration is being given to the development of a national scientific and technical information system or series of integrated systems. Although coordination is provided for federal information systems, government and non-government storage and retrieval systems, as an aggregate group, are characterized by overlapping coverage, failure to cover in concert the full spectrum of basic subject matter, availability of service in some instances only to certain types of user groups, and widely differing procedures for users to follow to obtain information. Obstacles to integrated interconnections of information services between the federal and private sectors include the need for greater standardization and more compatibility of systems.

The question of a national information system or systems is further complicated by a series of factors which need to be carefully considered in connection with the establishment of a national system(s):

1. Computerization to retrieve original information, together with abstracts and indexes, is only a partial solution to the problem of retrieval. Other information sources, such as journals containing articles which summarize and evaluate ongoing work, are still necessary.

2. A variety of special user groups must be considered. Through specialized centers, information on subfields can be correlated for use of scientists and engineers engaged in highly specialized subject matter.

3. Personal contacts will continue to be important in information gathering. Informal conversations, conference attendance, and personal correspondence remain essential mechanisms.

4. A national system must not prohibit individual agencies from performing research on data processing and retrieval for their own benefit.

The Committee on Scientific and Technical Information of the Federal Council on Science and Technology, with input from its task groups, is engaged in broad planning and study efforts to tie individual federal programs of scientific and technical information with private sector programs to form a network of information systems. A task group of the Committee has investigated extensively the problem of planning for a national information system or systems. To obtain background information and to assess its relevance to the requirements and feasibility factors pertaining to national scientific and technical information systems concepts, the task group sponsored a series of research projects. One project examined the status of document handling and made recommendations concerning a national document handling system.[2] A second project was concerned with abstracting and in-

---

2. Systems Development Corporation, *Recommendations for National Document Handling Systems in Science and Technology,* 1965.

dexing services.[3] A third reviewed structures and functions of informal information communication systems.[4]

Separate from—yet related to—scientific and technical information storage and retrieval is the factual information content of a document. Concern for improving scientific and technical information storage and retrieval is often centered on documents, without reference to the nature of the data collected and selected for inclusion in the documents. Yet, ultimate use of the retrieved document is influenced by the features of the data it contains. One study funded by a task group of the Committee on Scientific and Technical Information had as its objective the surveying of scientific and technical data activities, data-related problems, and data system needs within government, the professions, and industry. Part of the input for this study was information obtained from approximately 300 experts who were asked to comment on ninety issues and recommendations relevant to national and technical data systems concepts.[5]

The report concluded, in part, that no effective means existed for coordinating and integrating data management and data handling activities of governmental, professional, and industrial sectors of science and technology; that the full utility of scientific and technical data was not being realized under existing data management and handling policies; that scientific and technical data handling practices did not fully employ available technologies; and that, to be effective, data service operations must be complementary to the normal work routines of scientists and engineers. Among recommendations, the report urged the creation of a National Advisory Council for Scientific and Technical Data to function as a review and consultative body and to evolve recommendations to guide the development of a national scientific and technical data program. The task group

3. Systems Development Corporation, *A System Study of Abstracting and Indexing in the United States,* 1966.

4. American Institutes for Research, *Exploration of Oral/Informal Technical Communications Behavior,* 1967.

5. Science Communication, Inc., *Study of Scientific and Technical Data Activities in the United States,* 1968.

is considering the results of this study within the framework of its broader mission to prepare recommendations and plans for the development of a national information system(s).

Plans for a national system or network of major information systems are still in the formulative stages. The development of networks and interconnections awaits solving a series of technical, managerial, and economic problems. Illustrations of such problems are determination of most efficient ways to organize large computer files for rapid, reliable, and economically feasible searches; programing of computerized systems with multiple access on a real-time basis; and the creation of a plan for assigning functional responsibilities in a way which meets the needs of scientists and engineers.

The creation of an effective information storage and retrieval program has been the subject of concern of engineering groups for the past few years. In 1965 a Tripartite Committee was established by the United Engineering Trustees (managers of the Engineering Societies Library), the Engineers Joint Council, and Engineering Index to develop a united engineering information system and center, provided these are needed and could be viable. Following several studies, the Committee made recommendations in 1966 to its constituent bodies in which steps to establish such a system were set forth. Subsequently, the Committee was authorized to continue in existence for the purpose of establishing a united engineering information corporation. The Committee determined that industry would support improved information services in a developmental phase if industry were presented with a concise engineered plan for solution of the recognized technical, socio-political, and economic problems involved and if the plan showed reasonable probability of success. The Committee, with a grant from the National Science Foundation, contracted for a study to develop such a plan. The study, completed in 1969, included system design specifications; a plan for system design, implementation and operation; plans for initial funding and achieving self-support; design of experiments for subsequent

[221]

evaluation and improvement of the system; and plans for continuing research and development of the system.[6]

After considering recommendations of a task force and reviewing the completed contract study, the Committee approved an action plan calling for the establishment of a United Engineering Information Service and recommended the plan to its constituent bodies. The proposed Service, to be established as a non-profit independent membership corporation, would provide a unifying force for the engineering community with respect to engineering information and data resources, help to train engineers and managers in better use of information resources, study needs of users of such information, develop improved methods of information transfer and demonstrate them, encourage others to improve their information services, and furnish certain information services for which there is a demonstrated need and means of support. The plan does not provide for referral services. The three boards of the constituent bodies which created the Committee have given careful consideration to the plan.

In 1969 the Committee on Scientific and Technical Communication of the National Academy of Science and National Academy of Engineering completed and reported on a three year study of the status and future requirements of the scientific and technical community concerning the organization, flow, and transfer of scientific and technical information. The Committee gave special attention to the private sector and to interrelations between the Federal Government and the private sector in connection with scientific and technical information. The Committee reviewed several government and non-government information systems and observed that diversity in information handling activities is essential because diversity promotes flexibility and responsiveness to user needs. The Committee stated that an aim of proposed changes is not to eliminate diversity but to spotlight areas

6. Battelle Memorial Institute, *The Final Report for Development of an Engineered Plan for a United Engineering Information Service for the Tripartite Committee,* 1969.

where greater effort is needed, to define roles and responsibilities, and to propose methods of more effective coordination.[7]

The Committee on Scientific and Technical Communication cited three problem areas: defining the relative roles of the Federal Government and private organizations in scientific and technical information; the economics of information services, particularly since different mechanisms provide for revenues and determine market prices for publications and services; and the impact of new techniques on scientific and technical information programs and practices. The Committee pointed out that scientific and technical societies must appreciate their critical role in information handling and take immediate steps to fulfill it; that increasingly numerous special user groups must be served more effectively; and that new mechanisms and policies are necessary to coordinate scientific and technical communication efforts of the for-profit and not-for-profit organizations and the government.

The Committee urged the creation of a Joint Commission on Scientific and Technical Communication, responsible to the Councils of the National Academy of Science and National Academy of Engineering. The proposed commission would coordinate information handling interests and programs of the private for-profit and not-for-profit organizations and facilitate their interactions with appropriate government policy-making organizations. The proposed commission would be knowledgeable about scientific and technical information activities and would provide guidance for public and private organizations in the development of scientific and technical communication programs.

Among its other recommendations, the Committee urged federal agencies to recognize their responsibility to fund literature-access services which are needed for the effective utilization of knowledge resulting from the research and technical activities which they sponsor. In so doing federal agencies should insure management of basic discipline-wide abstracting and indexing by

7. National Academy of Science—National Academy of Engineering Committee on Scientific and Technical Communication, *Scientific and Technical Communication*, 1969.

appropriate scientific and technical societies or federations of societies. The Committee also advocated a study of the costs of different methods of storage and retrieval of information. Estimates should be developed for the most desirable number of depositories as related to their users in order to clarify questions of centralization and decentralization.

Reports of the groups cited above are being considered in both the Legislative and Executive Branches of the Federal Government as well as by non-government organizations, prior to anticipated implementing action in the early 1970s.

ROLES IN FACILITATING STORAGE AND RETRIEVAL SERVICE

Five groups have distinct roles in facilitating the development and use of scientific and information storage and retrieval services: professional and technical societies, the Federal Government, industry, educational institutions, and scientists and engineers.

Because membership in professional and technical societies includes the main producers and users of scientific and technical information, these societies appear to be a natural group to collect, organize, and evaluate information which they disseminate through meetings, publications, and related services. The role of these societies includes increasing the quality and methods of generating and distributing primary data, providing abstracting and indexing of primary data, reprocessing and repackaging primary and secondary information for special user groups, and evaluating information services which they sponsor.

The Federal Government has a responsibility to support scientific and technical information activity required in the performance of its missions. Some federal agencies, such as NASA, have particular information functions assigned by law. Other agencies, such as the Department of Defense, administer information programs as basic to their primary line programs. In addition, the Federal Government provides support through federal agencies for non-government scientific and technical information efforts

[224]

deemed to be in the public interest. As employers, federal agencies should support scientific and technical information activities which are responsive to the needs of their own scientists and engineers.

Industry and educational institutions, as producers of scientific and technical information through their research and development activities, have a responsibility to assure that the results of research and development in which they engage are made available at the earliest appropriate time for subsequent use by others. These groups should participate in efforts to coordinate scientific and technical information handling. As employers, these two groups also need to support scientific and technical information activities which are responsive to the needs of the scientists and engineers on their payrolls.

Scientists and engineers have a major responsibility to seek to obtain all pertinent available scientific and technical data in the shortest possible time through whatever means are available. This responsibility includes using innovative methods of data acquisition as circumstances permit. Scientists and engineers are sometimes slow to change their habits of information storage and retrieval and in fact may show tendencies against using new and more effective information services. Continued reliance on most accessible and familiar sources of data frequently means greater expenditure of professional time than is necessary under available services.

To maximize the use of time while they are enhancing their insight and knowledge through data search and retrieval, scientists and engineers make extensive use of information facilities. Scientists and engineers can take better advantage of these facilities by developing an individual information-seeking capability, by regarding the use of information sources as an integral part of planning their work, and by orienting their management on the need for administrative support to insure continuing opportunities to use such service.

With respect to the development of individual information-seeking capability, scientists and engineers approach the task of obtaining scientific and technical information in different ways. Their ways are conditioned by such factors as personal knowledge of specific subject matter, ability to communicate, personal characteristics, habits of associates, time available for seeking information, time involved in obtaining information, and familiarity with sources. Scientists and engineers seek to use information sources most related to the problem or task at hand by reviewing and evaluating the potential of pertinent available sources of information related to anticipated or actual assignments, by determining information inputs desired, and by organizing information obtained for internal use.

With respect to the use of information resources as an integral part of work planning and performance, information acquisition and analysis requires man-hours which are estimated as a regular factor in work performance. The task of obtaining information is scheduled for specific periods of time and the relationship of such data to the assignment to be performed is shown. Work reports show the degree to which information sources are being utilized.

With respect to management orientation, it is useful for scientists and engineers to advise their superiors on suitable occasions about the vital role of information retrieval. Management support in the form of costs of in-house library and information centers, subscription fees, and literature search fees is required. Since large information centers are already million dollar operations, employers are expected to pay a share as they obtain benefits. Managers need to know and appreciate actual benefits if management support is to be forthcoming or to be continued.

In their role as users of facilities and centers, scientists and engineers improve the retrieval service they seek by following a few tested practices. Thus, scientists and engineers anticipate information needs as far ahead of time as possible, perhaps before the start of a new project; consult with local librarians and, when possible, information facility and center specialists to discuss the specific nature of information needs; specify their questions of need for data as precisely as possible; set forth the nature of re-

[226]

lated but unwanted information; place a maximum limit on the amount of material desired if, in fact, there is such a maximum; indicate any time period limitations relevant to the material desired; carefully follow instructions for payment of required fees; and provide feedback, after receipt of information, to indicate how adequately the request was answered.

More progress in the development of scientific and technical information storage and retrieval programs is necessary before the large majority of scientists and engineers can make adequate, regular use of this approach as a way to conserve time and effort while they are broadening their own scientific and technical knowledge. However, significant growth has been made during the past few years in this field.

Currently, professional and technical societies, government, industry, educational institutions, and other organizations are actively exploring ways of making greater use of technology to assemble and disseminate scientific and technical information. Examples of areas in which greater application of technology is being made are the more extensive use of computers to maintain data bases and dissemination of data retrieved in more useful formats. Demonstration projects related to such aspects as innovative data handling tools are also being undertaken. The pursuit of theoretical documentation research, experimentation with new variations of information systems, and intensified planning for national information networks are underway. Such activities, however, cannot overshadow the fact that the present status of storage and retrieval programs represents current opportunities for optimizing scientific and technical manpower utilization.

VI

DEFERRING GRADUATE STUDENTS

•

NATURE OF GRADUATE EDUCATION IN SCIENCE AND ENGINEERING

The complexity of science and technology today challenges the highest developed knowledge and skill of scientists and engineers. Curricula which are now articulated to stress basic science and engineering fundamentals at the undergraduate level and intense specialization at the graduate level substantiate the fact that, for many individuals, scientific and engineering talent nurtured to the baccalaureate level is only partially developed at that point. Termination of the educational process at the end of the undergraduate program for these individuals halts further formal talent development and induces underutilization of their scientific and engineering abilities.

Indicative of the integral relationship between undergraduate and graduate education in science and engineering is a major point made by the Goals Committee on Engineering Education in January 1968.[1] Through an investigation carried out over a five year period, the Committee accumulated extensive data on engineering education from educators, employers, and practicing engineers throughout the nation. In its final report the Committee stressed that graduate studies in engineering are a normal part of engineering education and that "the unreasonably restrictive conception that a bachelor's degree is sufficient preparation for more engineering work should not be perpetuated." Public and private employment policies and practices which identify many types of positions in science and engineering for which a master's or doctor's degree is an entrance requirement reaffirm the Committee's view.

---

1. American Society for Engineering Education, *Final Report of the Goals Committee,* 1968.

IMPORTANCE OF CONTINUOUS, ADEQUATE
FLOW OF GRADUATE STUDENTS

National policy should guarantee a continuous, adequate flow of qualified baccalaurate graduates into a variety of graduate education fields, including science and engineering. In this way scientific and engineering talent, initially developed through undergraduate curricula, is more fully developed through graduate study and thus is the basis for the performance of duties of a more complex character. Individuals already in possession of a baccalaureate degree in science and engineering and who continue without interruption through full-time graduate work develop their capabilities to a greater extent within a relatively short period of time and make more effective use of their scientific and engineering talent. Some federal programs, such as those providing fellowships and loans, are designed to increase the number of full-time graduate students in science and engineering while concurrently keeping to a minimum the time spent by such students in obtaining graduate degrees.

A national policy of graduate education interruption or threatened interruption by required military service raises sharp implications for scientific and engineering manpower utilization. The concern becomes heightened when the period of military duty does not entail for the individual his use of professional knowledge and skill acquired through completion of graduate work in science or engineering, or when the professional knowledge and skill attained by graduate training is in short supply for the civilian national or defense effort. The question to which this chapter is directed is not whether a group of graduate students in science and engineering should be exempt from military service. The question is whether a policy of exposing actual or potential full-time graduate students of high aptitude for advanced science and engineering work to the uncertainties of draft operations at a particular time in their careers—when they complete their baccalaureate degree and are scholastically prepared to proceed to higher education accomplishment—is in the national interest

[229]

from the viewpoint of scientific and engineering manpower utilization.

The strength of the nation is not in the total numbers, but in the quality, of its people. It is more than a coincidence that while the issue of an appropriate graduate education deferment policy is being deliberated, the Bureau of the Census has proclaimed that the population of the United States exceeds 204,000,000. This figure of one-fifth of a billion, however, is only approximately seven percent of the world's population. The supremacy of the nation depends upon the competency of this relatively small percentage of people. Within this small seven percent, there is a smaller percentage of scientists and engineers. Within this smaller percentage, there is a much smaller percentage of individuals academically capable of satisfactorily continuing, without interruption, graduate education in science and engineering.

A two or three year interruption in the educational process reduces the number of individuals who finally complete their graduate education and are prepared to use their highest talents. Veteran education benefits lose their incentiveness for some returning veterans who decide to start making a living and raising a family without recourse to further formal education. Even where the urge to continue formal education is strong in a returning veteran, time spent in the armed forces may necessitate a vigorous refresher program before one starts or restarts a graduate program. This necessity prevails especially in academic areas such as science and engineering where an individual's currency of undergraduate background is a practical requisite for graduate courses. The fields of science and engineering change so rapidly that a returning veteran, without scientific or engineering experience in military service, may be obsolete and his return to graduate work in science and engineering may be practically unrealistic. Furthermore, there is no evidence that returning veterans are pursuing graduate programs in science and engineering in numbers sufficient to approximate the probable number of graduate students in science and engineering who would have continued

[230]

their graduate education under a positive graduate deferment policy.

This is an age of specialization, achieved in science and engineeering through individual competencies acquired through sustained graduate work. Optimum utilization of scientific and engineering manpower of this nation depends, in part, on the numbers of scientists and engineers who complete their graduate programs without interruption and become available for both civilian and military assignments.

ESTABLISHMENT OF CONCEPT OF GRADUATE DEFERMENT

The Selective Service and Training Act of 1940 provided for the deferment of persons whose employment or activity was deemed necessary to the maintenance of the national health, safety or interest. Students were considered to be engaged in activities of this type, and students in science and engineering fields were generally deferred during World War II. Inductions stopped in October 1946 when it appeared that military manpower demands would be met by voluntary recruitment. The Selective Service and Training Act expired in 1947.

When the authorized level of military personnel for the Armed Forces was not being reached by voluntary recruitment methods in early 1948, President Harry S. Truman recommended legislation to re-establish a selective service system. The Universal Military Training and Service Act of 1948 became the first law authorizing induction of individuals for military service in peacetime. The act stated that "in a free society the obligations and privileges of serving in the armed forces and reserve components should be shared generally in accordance with a system of selection which is fair and just and which is consistent with the maintenance of an effective national economy." The act also stated that "adequate provision for the national security requires maximum effort in the fields of scientific research and development and the fullest possible utilization of the nation's technological, scientific and other critical manpower resources."

With respect to student deferment, the concept of an individual's essentiality as a civilian in a "hot war" period, applied by local boards during World War II, could not be similarly followed in a peacetime situation. The need of local boards for guidance became apparent. To emplement the administration of the act, the Director of the Selective Service System established six advisory committees whose membership represented experience in science and engineering as well as in other fields and whose objectives were to analyze the problem of student deferment and to recommend policy proposals. The recommendations of the committees favored student deferment and were transmitted to the Director of the Selective Service System in December 1948. He agreed in principle with them and sought further executive approval. Such approval was not immediately forthcoming because of lessened urgency of the student deferment problem: draft calls were made in December 1948 and January 1949 but an increase in enlistments resulted in no further calls until the beginning of the Korean War in June 1950.

After the outbreak of the Korean War, the six committees were reconvened to review their earlier student deferment recommendations in the light of the Korean conflict. Revised recommendations transmitted to the Director of the Selective Service System in December 1950 proposed, in part:

1. There should be established within selective service regulations a special class of registrants whose demonstrated educational aptitude was such that it was necessary that their preprofessional or professional training program be continued in order to increase their potential value to the national health, safety, and interest.

2. If a registrant were enrolled as a full-time student in the first year of a graduate program (other than for a degree in medicine or veterinary in which case different standards applied), he must have maintained a scholastic record in his last undergraduate year which placed him above the fiftieth percentile of his class in an accredited college or university.

3. If the registrant were enrolled as a full-time student beyond the first year in a graduate or professional program leading to a

graduate or professional degree (other than medicine or veterinary), he must be certified by the college or univeristy as making satisfactory progress and as likely to complete all degree requirements for the degree program in which he was currently enrolled.

4. After a registrant completed his training, he should be considered eligible for an occupational deferment if he engaged in a professional pursuit in an activity for which the nature and degree of his training were generally requisite and if the activity itself was essential to the national health, safety or interest.[2]

The recommendations of the six committees made no attempt to designate any specific college curriculum or graduate program as essential or as warranting consideration above that given to any other curriculum or program.

Subsequently, action on committee recommendations was taken by the President who issued basic regulations in March 1951. These regulations authorized the Director of the Selective Service System to prescribe categories of persons whose activity in study might be considered necessary to the maintenance of the national health, safety or interest and to require as a condition for the inclusion in such category either the maintenance of a required scholastic standing or the attainment on a qualification test of a score, or both.

Regulations promulgated by the Director of the Selective Service System advised local boards, with respect to graduate students, that activity in study might be considered necessary to the maintenance of the national health, safety or interest if a registrant were accepted for admission by a graduate school, if in his last full-time undergraduate academic year he had achieved a scholastic standing which ranked him for that year within the upper one-half of the full-time male students in his class or attained a score of 75 or more on the qualification test prescribed by the Director, and if the graduate school at which he was in attendance certified that he was meeting degree requirements and was expected to obtain his degree. Local draft boards made the

2. M. L. Trytten, *Student Deferment in Selective Service,* 1952.

classification determination according to the merits of the individual case.

The principle was established that the outcome of modern warfare and national defense in a highly complex society depends upon a range of specialties, education for which at the graduate level is a continuing national need even if a period of emergency or partial mobilization prevails. Concomitant with deferment for full-time graduate education has been the necessary acceptance of the responsibility by those registrants so deferred that, upon completion of their graduate programs, they respond to their duty to render military service on the same basis of liability for military service as is provided those not granted graduate deferment. Amendments to both selective service legislation and to regulations over the period 1951-1967 did not change this principle.

Under implementing selective service regulations established pursuant to executive order, occupational deferments were given by local boards to registrants including scientists and engineers. Such a deferment was based on findings by a local board that a registrant's employment and occupation were necessary to the maintenance of the national health, safety or interest and that he could not be easily replaced. Guidance was provided to local boards in the form of lists of critical occupations and essential activities prepared, respectively, by the U. S. Department of Labor and by the U. S. Department of Commerce and approved by the Interagency Advisory Committee on Essential Activities and Critical Occupations. Local boards made their classification decisions on the basis of the facts in each individual case. Occupational deferments for scientists and engineers were generally granted liberally.

LEGISLATION IN 1967

During the spring of 1967, in anticipation of expiration of the Selective Service Act on June 30, 1967, the findings and recommendations of two studies dealing with extension of the act were given careful consideration. One study had been prepared by the National Advisory Commission on Selective Service appointed by the President.[3] The other study had been prepared by the Civilian Advisory Panel appointed by the Committee on Armed Services of the U. S. House of Representatives.[4] In addition to several recommendations dealing with policy and operations of the selective service system, both studies recommended modifications in the deferment of graduate students, an area in which a liberal policy had prevailed under the law scheduled to expire on June 30, 1967.

These studies raised two issues concerning graduate education: whether graduate students (other than medical and dental students) should be deferred and, if so, which government unit would identify and make recommendations of specific graduate programs for deferment consideration. The majority of members of the National Advisory Commission on Selective Service recommended against graduate student deferments. The Civilian Advisory Panel recommended graduate deferments only for medical, dental, veterinary, or related allied specialty programs as designated by the National Security Council. The President's message to Congress proposing selective service extension urged no graduate deferments (except for students in medical and dental schools).

The Chairman of the National Advisory Commission on Selective Service testified before a Senate subcommittee in March 1967 that educational deferment should not be given. He stated that under the existing educational deferment program, the student had a choice of time for possible military service and hence he received an unfair advantage over the non-college person in these circumstances. Furthermore, the Chairman testified that the majority of the Commission members felt that there was no reason for educational deferments because no national needs for such deferments could be identified. He added that a minority of members of the Commission felt that educational deferments should be continued, partially because of anticipated difficulty in

3. *Report of the National Advisory Commission on Selective Service, 1967.*

4. *Report of Civilian Advisory Panel to the House Committee on Armed Services, 1967.*

[235]

recruiting officer candidates if educational deferments were to be eliminated.

Appearing before the same Senate group, the U. S. Commissioner of Education agreed with the recommendation of the National Advisory Commission that no further graduate deferments should be granted. He said that graduate deferments had too often become exemptions from military service and that college graduation is a convenient "cutting off point" for educational deferments. The Commissioner stated that an individual's graduate study would not be unduly hampered by an interruption for military service before graduate study began. He explained that in the establishment of a uniform policy of no deferment for graduate students, many of the administrative problems surrounding current deferment policies and many disparities in deferment procedures which existed among draft boards throughout the country could be eliminated. He called for an examination of federal fellowship and graduate school programs to assure that a veteran would be in no way subject to unfavorable discrimination in his subsequent pursuit of formal education because of his military service.

At a subsequent Senate Armed Services Committee hearing, the Chairman of the National Advisory Commission stated that the Commission did not have any evidence that abolishing deferments for graduate students, with a resulting interruption between college and graduate school for those called in the draft, would seriously disrupt the flow of trained professional manpower into society. Accordingly, the Commission concluded that deferments at this level of education—with the exception of deferments for medical and dental students—resulted in an unfair and an unnecessary avoidance of military service by those entering graduate school, without any corresponding national need which would justify such discrimination in treatment. The Chairman of the Commission pointed out that most members of the Commision believed that similar considerations should also result in the elimination of undergraduate deferments. The question could be raised whether abolishing student deferments would impair the flow of young men through the educational institutions, he said, but there was no evidence available to the Commission that an interruption at the sophomore year in college would be more harmful to the education of a young man than an interruption later, or indeed, that it would be harmful at all.

After each house of Congress had passed separate bills for extending the Selective Service Act, a Senate-House conference committee was set up in June 1967 to draw up a compromise approach agreeable to both houses. With respect to graduate education deferments, the joint agreement provided that:

1. The National Security Council would periodically advise the Director of the Selective Service System and coordinate with him the work of such state and local volunteer advisory committees which the Director might establish, with respect to the identification, selection, and deferment of needed professional and scientific personnel and those engaged in, and preparing for, critical skills and other essential occupations. In this connection, the Council would consider the needs of both the Armed Forces and the civilian segment. Thus, there would be established in the Council a responsibility to indicate under what circumstances deferments for graduate students should be given. All such deferments would be granted in the national health, safety or interest.

2. The President would be given wide latitude in providing future deferments for graduate students in medicine, dentistry or other subjects deemed essential to the national health, safety or interest. The intent was that the National Security Council initially would make the recommendations on which such graduate student deferments would be based.

3. The authority of the President to prescribe criteria for the future granting of graduate student deferments would remain unchanged. However, the legislation required the Council to assume the responsibility of recommending to the Director of the Selective Service System areas in which such deferments should be granted in the national health, safety or interest.

[237]

During discussion on the conference report in the U. S. House of Representatives, the proposed manpower role for the National Security Council was further discussed. Comments made by two Congressmen are particularly appropriate to an understanding of the intent of this manpower role.

The Chairman of the House Armed Services Committee pointed out that the original House language would have required the President to establish a National Manpower Resources Board to make recommendations on graduate student deferments. He added that the Senate conferees were strongly of the opinion that the functions of this Board were of such importance that they should be vested in the National Security Council itself. Therefore, in lieu of the establishment of a National Manpower Resources Board, the legislation provided that the functions proposed for the Board be performed by the National Security Council.

Representative Durward Hall of Missouri stated that he would like to make an explanation to be included in the legislative record insofar as the elimination of the National Manpower Resources Board was concerned. He explained that the conference committee did not want to establish another commission with another staff and felt that "it was the function of, and that there were adequate resources in, the National Security Council to handle this job of furnishing advice to the Director." Representative L. Mendell Rivers of South Carolina responded that Representative Hall had "a complete understanding of the view of the conferees on this matter . . . We agreed we should rely on the National Security Council, because it is in being, and this imposes the responsibility on them, and we are sure it will work. The gentlemen will remember the National Resources Manpower Board would also have worked in conjunction with the National Security Council. We will now leave it to them alone and see how it works. I am sure it will work."

During Senate debate on the conference report, Senator Edward Kennedy of Massachusetts raised objection to the proposed responsibility assigned to the National Security Council for advising selective service on student, apprentice, and occupational deferments, including identification of fields in which graduate deferments were authorized. The Senator stated that: "It is the judgment of the executive branch, communicated to the Armed Service Committee of both Houses of the Congress, that neither this Council nor its small secretariat has the time or resources to evaluate or make decisions on critical skills and essential occupations. On the other hand, the Interagency Committee has the full fact-finding resources of the six departments involved to evaluate the many hundreds of petitions from industry groups, employers, and individuals for inclusion on either of the two lists of essential occupations and critical skills. I think it is particularly inappropriate to vest this vastly detailed responsibility in the National Security Council, concerned as the National Security Council is with matters of broad policy for national security."

Senator Richard Russell of Georgia, Senate leader of the conference committee, upheld the proposed responsibility for the National Security Council by explaining that "this provision grew out of a provision in the House bill which provided for the creation of an entirely new executive agency, the National Manpower Resources Board . . . I did not want to create a new agency. I thought, inasmuch as the President was in direct control of the National Security Council, which was mentioned in the House provision, but which was given no direct duties, it would be better to give that agency this advisory function instead of creating an entirely new agency. For that reason I agreed to this provision. The Council would advise the President. The President is going to make regulations with reference to Selective Service. It is true that he is Chairman of the National Security Council. He will undoubtedly consult with the executive agencies and get their views before making any drastic changes in the system."

Both the Senate and the House of Representatives passed the conference committee report without change and the new law became the Military Selective Service Act of 1967.

[239]

ACTION BY THE NATIONAL SECURITY COUNCIL

Under the act of 1967, the National Security Council thus became responsible for advising the Director of the Selective Service System on the identification of fields of graduate study vital to the national health, safety, or interest. Students in fields so designated by the Council and subsequently approved by the Director would be eligible for graduate education deferment by local draft boards.

While the National Security Council was considering the exercise of its responsibility, an issue raised in educational circles was whether all or particular graduate fields (other than medicine, dentistry, and allied medical specialties) should be designated as deferrable. Organizations of science and engineering educators, such as the American Society for Engineering Education, and education officials, such as heads of departments in the physical sciences and deans of engineering, favored a graduate deferment policy for their fields. On the other hand, the Association of Graduate Schools in the Association of American Universities and the Council of Graduate Schools in a joint statement asserted that all fields of higher education were of equally critical importance to the continued welfare and balanced development of the nation and that no single discipline should be designated as more important or more critical than any others. The American Council on Education urged against graduate deferment by broad field but stated that there might be need for graduate deferments in narrow and critically needed specialties such as metallurgy.

To exercise its responsibility related to fields of graduate study, the National Security Council requested the Interagency Advisory Committee on Essential Activities and Critical Occupations to advise the Council on the identification of such fields. The Committee, composed of representatives of the Department of Agriculture; Commerce; Defense; Health, Education and Welfare; Interior; Labor; and the Selective Service System, had previously identified critical skills and essentials occupations vital to the national defense but had not been involved with college educational deferments. To carry out this assignment of the Council, the Committee appointed a Task Force on Graduate Student and Trainee Deferment to develop recommendations for the deferment or non-deferment of graduate students. Members of the Task Force were from the Department of Health, Education and Welfare; the Selective Service System; the Department of Labor; the National Science Foundation; the National Academy of Sciences; the Department of Defense; and the Executive Office of the President. The Task Force developed national supply-demand data and studied other information related to the education and employment of scientists, engineers, and other professional personnel. After evaluation of the data, the Task Force recommended to the Interagency Advisory Committee that full-time graduate study in science and engineering, as well as in certain other fields, was vital to the national health, safety or interest and that students in these fields should be considered for deferment. The Interagency Advisory Committee subsequently ratified the recommendations of the Task Force in November 1967.

In a joint memorandum dated February 14, 1968, the Secretaries of Labor; Commerce; and Health, Education and Welfare —contrary to the recommendation of the Interagency Advisory Committee—informed the National Security Council that "We have been considering the question whether student deferments . . . should be extended to graduate study in fields other than medicine and dentistry. We conclude that any such extension of the privilege of deferment from the obligations of military service is not essential for the maintenance of the national health, safety and interest." The joint memorandum added that "Graduate school deferments may be pyramided into exemption from military service. This is unfair to the thousands of other young men who lack the social and economic advantages to pursue graduate study. In a time of armed conflict it is patently unjust. The injustice would be compounded by allowing some areas of graduate study and not others to qualify for a preferred status of deferments."

[241]

On February 15, 1968 the National Security Council advised the Director of the Selective Service System that it was not essential for the maintenance of the national health, safety or interest to extend student deferments for graduate study to fields other than medicine, dentistry, and the allied medical specialties. This recommendation did not affect existing regulations governing deferments for graduate students who had entered their second or subsequent year of graduate study in the fall of 1967. The recommendation did affect those graduating from college in June 1968 and those who had entered the first year of graduate school in the fall of 1967 since the regulations provided that the latter group were to be deferred for one academic year only. The Council stated that it based its recommendation on several considerations: such graduate deferments were not required in the national interest, unfairness would result from exempting men in some graduate fields and not in others, inequities resulting from pyramiding of deferments should be eliminated, and there was absence of a significant military manpower need served by graduate deferments. The Director of the Selective Service System concurred in the recommendation of the Council and notified local boards accordingly on February 16, 1968. Thus, the "no graduate deferment" policy was established.

In summary, the following ideas undergirded the recommendation of the National Security Council:

1. The National Advisory Commission had recommended to the President a policy of no student deferments.

2. At Congressional hearings in 1967, the U. S. Commissioner of Education had advocated a "no graduate deferment" policy for students.

3. Detailed evidence on negative effects of a "no graduate deferment" policy had not been fully presented by educational organizations either to the Legislative or to the Executive Branches, prior to the Council recommendation.

4. A philosophy of equity for all Americans in matters of draft liability was prevalent.

The policy guidance issued by the National Security Council provided an opportunity for further consideration as subsequent circumstances warranted. A provision of the National Security Council advice to the Director of the Selective Service System stated, in part, that (1) a continuing surveillance over the nation's manpower and education needs would be maintained by four federal agencies in order to identify any area of graduate study that might warrant qualifying for deferment in the national interest and (2) whenever any such field would be so identified, the Council would be notified so that it might consider the need and advise the Director of the Selective Service System accordingly.

Dissatisfaction with the "no graduate deferment" policy was immediately registered. Greatest opposition to the policy was expressed by college and university presidents to officials of the Legislative and Executive Branches as well as to the press. For example, fifty-one college administrators predicted serious consequences for the nation's graduate education program and so informed a subcommittee of the Committee on Education and Labor of the U. S. House of Representatives which was undertaking an investigation of anticipated impact of the new policy on graduate education.

IMPACT OF "NO GRADUATE DEFERMENT" POLICY ON GRADUATE ENROLLMENT

With sharp differences of opinion prevailing between groups of educators and federal officials as well as among educators and among federal officials, interest centered upon the impact of the "no graduate deferment" policy upon graduate enrollment for academic year 1968-69. In actuality, the total number of graduate students (all fields combined) increased during academic year 1968-69, as compared with academic year 1967-68. However, the quality of graduate students as a whole seemed to have declined. Furthermore, women and foreign students made up a large part of the numerical increase. Formal and informal surveys were conducted to obtain a measure of the impact, as

[243]

related to graduate male enrollment and to graduate enrollment in the fields of science and engineering.

According to data compiled by the U. S. Office of Education, the number of full-time men in their first year of graduate and professional study (other than medicine) actually declined 5% between fall 1967 and fall 1968. The 5% decline compared with a 11% increase which had been projected before the "no graduate deferment" policy was promulgated. Hence, these figures meant a 16% drop in first year male enrollment over the figure earlier anticipated for fall 1968.[5]

Graduate enrollment of male, U. S. citizens in science and engineering dropped during academic year 1968-69 from the previous academic year. Estimates by the U. S. Office of Education indicated that the enrollment for first year male graduate students for fall 1968, as compared with fall 1967, dropped in chemistry (6.4%), mathematics (5.6%), engineering (1.8%), and physics (0.8%). A survey by the Engineering Manpower Commission showed that the full-time enrollment of 49,610 (fall 1967) in all advanced degree curricula in engineering decreased to 41,530 (fall 1968), or a drop of 16%; master's degree candidates in their second or later year of study in engineering declined 56%—a drop of approximately 8,000 men in this category.[6] EMC analysis of the data concluded that the elimination of graduate deferments cut deeply into graduate student enrollment. The U. S. Office of Education figures cited differ somewhat from the Engineering Manpower Commission figures primarily because of differences in the scope of the two surveys.

According to the American Institute of Chemical Engineers, a drop of 23% in the first year enrollment of male, U. S. citizens in graduate chemical engineering occurred between fall 1967 and fall 1968. The drop was lower than the average in larger graduate schools (16%) and higher than the average in

5. U. S. Office of Education, *Students Enrolled for Advanced Degrees in Selected Fields of Study, Fall 1968*, 1969.

6. Engineering Manpower Commission, *Engineering and Technician Enrollments, Fall 1968*, 1969.

smaller graduate schools (31%). Although it was impossible to identify the specific influence of the "no graduate deferment" policy with precision, the Institute attributed the decline, in part, to the elimination of graduate deferments.[7]

Three formal nation-wide studies were conducted during academic year 1968-69 to ascertain the military status of graduate students in science and engineering and related effects upon graduate enrollment. The first study by the Scientific Manpower Commission concerned students in science; the second, by the Engineering Manpower Commission involved students in engineering; and the third, by the Scientific Manpower Commission and member organizations concerned students in physics and chemistry.

The Scientific Manpower Commission through a survey of graduate science departments sought to determine the draft classification of graduate students as of mid-fall 1968.[8] The Commission received data from 1,237 science departments in Ph.D. granting institutions on the draft status of 20,047 male, full-time first and second year graduate students, 7,365 part-time graduate students who taught classes and 6,373 part-time graduate students who assisted in research. According to findings of the SMC study:

1. 38% of first and second year male, full-time science graduate students (including foreign students), or up to 46% of such U. S. students, would be potentially liable to induction in the months ahead.

2. Among male science graduate students (either full or part time) employed to teach, 43% of all first and second year students (including foreign students), or 50% of such U. S. students, would be potentially liable to induction in the months ahead.

3. Among male science graduate students (either full or part time) employed to conduct research, 40% of all first and second

7. American Institute of Chemical Engineers, *Study of Enrollments in Chemical Engineering Graduate Schools,* 1968.

8. Scientific Manpower Commission, *A Survey of the Draft Status of First and Second Year Science Graduate Students,* 1969.

year students (including foreign students), or 47% of such U. S. students, would be potentially liable to induction in the months ahead.

4. The number of U. S. males engaged in advanced scientific training in the nation's graduate schools would be substantially reduced during the ensuing months.

5. The nation's supply of newly trained Ph.D.'s in the sciences would be seriously curtailed in the early 1970's.

According to the SMC report, there appeared to be no substantial enrollment drop in fall 1968 as compared with fall of 1967. Higher than anticipated graduate enrollment for fall 1968 was attributed to low draft calls during the summer of 1968, a cutback in the number of military physical examinations given during the summer of 1968, slow reclassification of graduate students by some local boards, and a substantial enrollment of men who were draft liable. Information was sought from science department chairmen on whether their fall 1968 enrollment was above or below that which they might have expected, had there been no change in draft rules. Sixty percent of the responding chairmen felt that their enrollment was lower than expected; 80% of the chairmen so responding believed that changed draft rules and loss of research support caused the enrollment drop in equal measure; most of the remaining chairmen felt that changed draft rules constituted the major reason for the drop.

The Scientific Manpower Commission report stated that there was no way to predict accurately how many graduate students who were liable to induction would be called to military duty. Since regulations required that each local board fill its draft call with the oldest available men in the age group 19-25 years, it was thought by the Commission that inductions would likely be high among draft liable students.

A study of the draft status of graduate students in engineering curricula during academic year 1968-69 was made by the Engineering Manpower Commission.[9] Of a total of 122 schools of engineering to which questionnaires were sent, 55 replies containing information in usable form comprised the data for analysis. Figures submitted in this survey for students enrolled in the first and second year of graduate study represented approximately one-half of the nation's enrollment in these categories.

According to the EMC study, at least 31% of the 4,595 male U. S. citizens who were enrolled full time in the first or second year of graduate studies at the time of the collection of data were classified as available for military service (1-A) or in a class no longer applicable to them (II-S). Another 8% had occupational deferments although these registrants were full-time students. The complete classification of these individuals, by draft category, is shown in Table VI-1.

Table VI–1

DRAFT CLASSIFICATION OF GRADUATE STUDENTS IN
55 SCHOOLS OF ENGINEERING

Category	Percentage of Graduate Students
I-A—(available for military service)	19.7
II-S—(deferred because of activity in study)	11.5
I-D—(member of reserve component or student taking military training)	11.7
II-A—(deferred because of civilian occupation)	8.0
III-A—(registrant with child and registrant deferred because of extreme hardship to dependents)	13.5
I-Y & IV-F—(registrant not currently qualified under physical, mental or moral standards)	13.0
IV-A—(registrant who has completed service or is sole surviving son)	11.0
Other	11.6

Source: EMC study

The Scientific Manpower Commission, together with two of its member organizations, the American Chemical Society and the American Institute of Physics, conducted a study with depart-

9. Engineering Manpower Commission, *Draft Status of Graduate Students in Engineering Curricula, 1968-69,* 1969.

ments granting doctorates in chemistry and physics.[10] The purpose of the study was to determine the number of full-time, first and second year graduate students who had entered military service during academic year 1968-69 or who had been ordered for induction, time of which had been postponed until the end of the academic year. Analysis of the results based on questionnaire replies submitted in June 1969 by 114 (of 173) chemistry departments and by 96 (of 194) physics departments showed that 17% of first year male students in chemistry and physics (combined totals) and 13% of second year male students (combined totals) had entered military service or had been ordered for induction prior to June 1969. The survey did not deal with individuals whose local boards had given induction notices after June 1969. It should be noted that some prospective graduate students for academic year 1968-69 entered military service prior to the beginning of the fall 1968 term through operation of the "no graduate deferment" policy. The incidence of the latter two groups of students was not reflected in the SMC-ACS-AIP study.

Another dimension of the impact of the "no graduate deferment" policy on graduate enrollment is a sharp increase in the number of full-time, foreign graduate students in science and engineering in U. S. educational institutions. According to a study by the Institute of International Education, the total number of full-time, foreign graduate students in all fields in U. S. educational institutions increased from 48,209 during academic year 1967-68 to 54,034 during academic year 1968-69. Of the total of 54,034 students, 45.5% studied science (physical and life) and engineering, as contrasted with 38.4% during academic year 1967-68. The number of such students in science increased from 11,480 during academic year 1967-68 to 12,594 during academic year 1968-69. The number of such students in engineering increased from 10,394 to 11,915 during the same period.[11]

---

10. Scientific Manpower Commission, *The Effect of Draft Regulations on Graduate Education in the Sciences*, 1969.

11. Institute of International Education, *Open Doors 1969*, 1969.

During academic year 1968-69, foreign students constituted approximately 31% of the full-time enrollment for graduate engineering degrees. The comparable percentage for academic year 1967-68 was approximately 21%. A study by the Engineering Manpower Commission revealed that during academic year 1968-69 foreign students constituted 36% of the first year full-time enrollment for advanced engineering degrees and 30% of the second year students. To the Commission, it appeared that additional foreign students were accepted by U. S. educational institutions to replace the bachelor degree graduates of the previous year who had cancelled their plans to continue their education because of the elimination of graduate student deferments.[12]

A decline of United States citizens in full-time graduate education in the age group 21-25, without previous military experience, accompanied by an increase in the number of foreign students in the same field is also illustrated by results of a study by the American Institute of Chemical Engineers. The total first year, new graduate enrollment for fall 1968 in chemical engineering graduate programs decreased by 13% from fall 1967. The number of new foreign students as first year candidates in such programs increased 12% from fall 1967 to fall 1968. This 12% increase in foreign students partially offset the decrease of 23% in students who are U. S. citizens. For chemical engineering graduate programs in 24 major universities, the number of foreign graduate students as first year candidates increased by 26% for fall 1968 over fall 1967.[13]

The Federal Government has a special interest in the expanding enrollment of foreign graduate students in both science and engineering. Federal funds support a large portion of graduate education; hence, the Federal Government has a financial interest in this question. Particularly in periods of limited federal funding, students who are United States citizens are brought into

12. Engineering Manpower Commission, *Survey of Foreign Graduate Students Enrolled in Engineering Curricula in the United States,* 1969

13. American Institute of Chemical Engineers, *Study of Enrollments in Chemical Engineering Graduate Schools,* 1968.

[249]

increased competition with foreign students for science and engineering graduate education benefits provided by federal funds. Such competition tends to impede the development of scientific and engineering talent of individual United States citizens. Furthermore, the native countries of many of these foreign students are experiencing a rise in the role of science and technology and will presumably attract more foreigners with advanced degrees away from the United States to meet the needs of these nations. It does not seem plausible to consider foreign nationals as a reliable continuing source of scientific and engineering manpower for the United States. A national objective should be to stimulate, not hinder through the "no graduate deferment" policy, the development of adequate numbers of qualified U. S. citizens as graduate scientists and engineers.

IMPACT OF "NO GRADUATE DEFERMENT" POLICY ON OCCUPATIONAL DEFERMENT

Another type of impact of the "no graduate deferment" policy has been a greater use of occupational deferment for individuals who previously would have been deferred for graduate education purposes.

As part of its responsibility under the Military Selective Service Act of 1967, the National Security Council became responsible for advising the Director of the Selective Service System on the subject of occupational deferment. The identification of critical occupations and essential activities vital to the national interest had been carried out by the Interagency Advisory Committee on Essential Activities and Critical Occupations which promulgated advisory lists. Such lists were then made available to local draft boards for use in their determination of occupational deferments. However, at their discretion local draft boards gave occupational deferments to individuals in occupations whether or not they were included on the lists.

On February 15, 1968 the National Security Council, reflecting advice contained in a joint memorandum signed by the Secretaries of Labor, Commerce, and Health, Education and Welfare, advised the Director of the Selective Service System to suspend the use of the advisory lists. The Council asserted that the needs of the armed forces and of the civilian economy did not require such occupational deferments. The Council also cited, as reasons for suspending the use of the lists, "the inherent inequity, at a time when men are called upon to risk their lives for the nation, in any such occupational deferments from military service which may in practice turn into permanent exemptions" and lack of justification for such deferment list. The Director agreed to the suspension of the use of the lists and so advised local boards on February 16, 1968.

Local boards, however, have continued under the act to grant occupational deferments to registrants in occupations deemed essential to the national health, safety or interest. Local boards also grant occupational deferments on the basis of essential community needs. Other requirements for occupational deferments are that an employer must show that a replacement of similar competence is not available and that the loss of the individual registrant to the draft would have an adverse effect on the employer's ability to carry out essential work. Occupational deferment decisions are made by local boards on the basis of the facts in the individual registrant's case.

Individuals employed as full-time faculty members or researchers continue to be eligible for consideration for occupational deferment. However, local boards were advised by the Director of the Selective Service System on April 25, 1968, that a full-time graduate student cannot be considered for occupational deferment on the basis that he is engaged in part-time teaching. Several institutions established full-time junior teaching staff positions below the rank of instructor in order to permit the institution to request deferment for employment of graduate students teaching at the undergraduate level. Some local boards have granted occupational deferments to such individuals while other boards have not. One result of differing board practice, according to educators, has been uncertainty on the part of educational institutions and anxiety on the part of such registrants.

The existence of occupational deferments has acted as encouragement to some students completing their baccalaureate degrees in science and engineering to accept full-time employment in industry with the possibility of receiving an occupational deferment. The choice of entering graduate work, without a basis for an educational deferment, or accepting employment with a good chance for an occupational deferment, has meant that countless numbers of bachelor degree graduates in science and engineering have accepted industrial employment. In reality, some of these baccalaureate graduates who entered industry have been subsequently deferred; others have not.

Thus, the "no graduate deferment" policy has encouraged students with a baccalaureate degree in science or engineering to seek the early substitution of an occupational deferment for an educational deferment. This action results in an underdevelopment and underutilization of individual scientific and engineering potential.

MILITARY USE OF COLLEGE GRADUATES AS ENLISTED MEN

Since an effect of the "no graduate deferment" policy is to increase the number of men having baccalaureate degrees in science and engineering who are available for military service, the question of the use of this type of manpower in the military has been raised.

Department of Defense policy on the utilization of college graduates in enlisted positions is reflected in a memorandum sent by the Assistant Secretary of Defense (Manpower) to the Assistant Secretaries of the Army, Navy, and Air Force in August 1968. The Assistant Secretary of Defense (Manpower) pointed out that a far larger number of enlisted men with college degrees than the armed services had experienced in the past would be taken in the services during the ensuing period and that it was of utmost importance that these young men be used in assignments which take maximum advantage of their education and which contribute to a feeling that their abilities are recognized. The Assistant

[252]

Secretary of Defense (Manpower) then set forth a series of general principles to govern the distribution, assignment, and utilization of college graduates, as follows:

1. Each service should develop and maintain an accurate inventory of the intake of enlisted college graduates and their assignments.

2. Each service should develop systems to classify and assign such individuals; in this process each service should give careful attention to the type of education possessed by each, consider individual differences, and take best advantage of their civilian-acquired education, training, and capabilities in meeting service requirements.

3. Special attention should be given to individuals with unusual or particularly high educational qualifications to try to insure their assignment to the most appropriate duties.

4. Each man should be provided the training he needs but he should not be required to undergo any unnecessary training.

5. Many of these individuals should attend only portions of formal training courses and it might be possible to modify certain courses for them.

6. All enlisted college graduates should be given the standard basic military training provided by the particular service.

7. The performance of these men should be continuously evaluated.

8. Each service should be able to evaluate the overall impact on the service from the influx of large numbers of enlisted college graduates.

9. An adequate periodic reporting system in each service should be provided in order to inform the Secretary of Defense and others with current information on the distribution, assignment, and utilization of these men.

Pursuant to Department of Defense policy, each of the assistant secretaries of the three services transmits to the Assistant Secretary of Defense (Manpower) a monthly narrative report of the experience of the service with college graduates, including statistical summaries and an explanation of any training modifications and of special assignment programs. The reports are monitored to ascertain ideas for subsequent broader application in the services and to identify possible problems requiring adjustment.

Army experience with enlisted college graduate accessions dominates the military personnel utilization picture. Except for relatively few Marine Corps accessions, Army accessions have been the only ones involving induction. Most information available, therefore, centers on the Department of the Army.

In anticipation of increased numbers of college graduates on active duty, the Department of the Army in 1968 established a classification of priorities of assignment, based on abilities, technical knowledge, and leadership potential of such men. The priorities are as follows:

Priority I: skills which can be directly correlated to college academic fields or personal preferences such as skills included in the scientific and engineering assistance program;

Priority II: skills which will challenge the leadership or technical capability of a college graduate such as leadership potential in the combat arms or as a capability in automatic data processing;

Priority III: skills which are essential but do not fully challenge the average college graduate.

Because of the termination of deferments for college graduates, the number of such persons entering the Army as enlisted men sharply increased, beginning the first half of fiscal year 1969. Approximately 15% of the total enlisted accessions by the Army during fiscal year 1969 were college graduates. This figure compared with previous figures of from 5% to 8%. Specifically, during fiscal year 1969, the total number of college graduates entering the Army as enlisted men was 44,795. During the same year, 41,924 were given specialized occupational training assignments. Assignments to priority I totaled 26,000 or 62% of the 41,924; to priority II, 15,828 or 37.8%; and to priority III, 96 or 0.2%.

Proper interpretation of the preceding priority figures requires an understanding that priority I is composed of three categories: men with preferred assignments, men with enlisted commitments for military occupational specialty training, and men with preferred training having an academic correlation. Therefore, those men receiving the training for which they volunteered—whether or not the training is directly related to their formal education—are counted in priority I. Furthermore, the inclusion of certain specialties in priorities I and II is somewhat debatable. Nevertheless, although questions about the classification system may be raised and although sizeable numbers of college graduates have been assigned to duties which previously had only a token representation of college graduates, the fact is that the Army has been attempting to make proper use of increasing numbers of college graduates as enlisted men in the light of its manpower needs. Data which relate numbers of enlisted men having degrees in science and engineering to the specific priorities cited and to the type of assignment within each priority are not available.

However, preliminary information on the utilization of college graduates in science and engineering as inductees during the latter part of 1969 was developed by the Scientific Manpower Commission. In June 1969 the Commission and the Office of Manpower and Reserve Affairs of the Department of Defense began a pilot program designed to insure that the Army was made aware of the qualifications of outstanding young graduates and graduate students who were being inducted. Potential draftees were informed through a notice in Science magazine that the Commission might be able to assist them in obtaining Army assignments that would utilize their civilian training if they would contact the Commission as soon as their date and place of induction were known. During the first five months of the program, approximately 700 college graduates so contacted the Commission. Approximately 85% of these persons had had graduate training and approximately 97% had degrees in science or engineering. After the Commission obtained personnel details from each individual, pertinent information was provided to the Department of Defense for input into the assignment system.

Assignments to advanced individual training for a military occupation specialty or to a direct duty post are generally made at the end of the eighth week of basic training. The training assignments of 176 men who were inducted by the end of September were subsequently known and were tabulated by the Commission in December 1969 in an analysis covering the first five months period of the program. Of these 176 individuals, 45 were subsequently given an advanced training assignment related to their civilian professional competence, including direct assignments to the science and engineering aide program of the Army: 64 were given unrelated, noncombat assignments such as training for military police work; and 58 were given combat arms assignments. One hundred sixty-seven cases are insufficient data on which to base firm conclusions. However, if subsequent analysis covering larger numbers of such inductees continues to show similar proportions for the three types of assignments cited, the scientific and engineering talent of college graduate inductees is being very seriously underutilized.

Although most enlisted skills do not require men with a college education, many of the enlisted assignments challenge the abilities of the college graduates. Under the circumstances, the objective of the Army in utilizing college graduates has been to gain the maximum benefit from their education, experience, and training while maintaining equitable treatment for all other personnel.

The Marine Corps has a small number of college graduates as enlisted men—slightly more than 1,000 in January 1970. Most of these men are inductees. The Corps seeks to place enlisted college graduates, upon completion of basic training, in available assignments which correlate with certain specific college backgrounds. As in the case of the Army, the Marine Corps has been hard pressed to find an adequate number of assignments which require a college education for enlisted personnel.

Despite efforts to achieve a match between manpower requirements and manpower assets, it appears that during 1969 approximately 40% of enlisted men who are graduates in science and engineering were not utilized in the professional field in which they were educated. This condition is not necessarily the fault of an internal military assignment system. The condition is the inevitable result of the difference between the nature of gross manpower needs in the military service and the knowledge and skills of those men entering the military through the recruitment policies employed.

CHANGES IN 1969

On May 13, 1969, in a message to Congress in which he recommended amendments to the Military Selective Service Act of 1967, President Richard M. Nixon stated that the policy against graduate deferment should be continued (except for medical and allied fields) in order to prevent pyramiding of student deferments into a total exemption from military service. However, during the fall of 1969, the President announced three actions which had a direct impact upon graduate students.

On September 19, he stated that the programed draft calls for November (32,000) and for December (18,000) would be cancelled and that the draft call previously announced for October (29,000) would be phased out over the final quarter of calendar year 1969. An effect of this curtailment was to reduce the number of college graduates inducted in the Army and Marines during the last quarter of 1969.

On October 1, the President announced a modification in the application of the "no graduate deferment" policy: he stated that graduate students about to be inducted would be permitted to finish the academic year before being inducted. Previous policy, set forth by the Director of the Selective Service System in November 1968, had permitted a delay only until the end of a term. Technically, the policy change announced by the President on October 1, 1969 resulted in a recommendation to this effect from the National Security Council (of which the President is chairman) to the Director of Selective Service. In its communication to the Director, the Council related that "In courses of graduate study, an interruption at the end of a term, other than the final term of the academic year, is costly to the student in terms of expenses and academic progress and therefore, contrary to the national interest."

On November 26, following Congressional action which he had recommended, the President approved an amendment to the Military Selective Service Act of 1967. The amendment eliminated a prohibition which had prevented him from reversing the practice of taking the oldest first of those in the prime age category eligible for induction. Coincident with his approval of the legislation, the President through an executive order and a proclamation announced that he had determined that a method of random selection would provide the most equitable basis for selection of registrants for military service. He stated that a random selection sequence of birth dates would be established by a drawing, to be conducted on December 1, 1969.

Under the draft procedure in effect through calendar year 1969, a registrant began his time of maximum vulnerability to the draft at age nineteen; if he did not volunteer for service, he remained in that status until he was drafted or until he reached his twenty-sixth birthday. Selection among registrants in this age group was on an oldest first basis. Under the revised system, a first priority selection group has been established which normally constitutes the only group from which men are called involuntarily. Registrants not selected for induction during their twelve month period of maximum vulnerability are placed in a lower priority selection category and are not normally inducted unless the first priority selection group is exhausted.

Under the revised system, during 1970, the transitional year, the first priority selection group included all draft eligibles, aged twenty through twenty-five years at the beginning of 1970. This broad inclusion of registrants was provided so that no individual eligible for induction under previous rules could escape vulnerability because of the change to the revised system. However, after 1970, the first priority selection group for induction is limited to draft eligibles in their nineteenth year of age at the beginning of the year and to those registrants between the ages of nineteen and twenty-six whose deferments expired during the year. The draft age period for each registrant is predictable—either the year following his attainment of age nineteen or in the year after he ceases to be deferred.

At the time of the establishment of the random selection method, a White House announcement noted that the actual chance of an individual registrant's being reached for induction depends upon many factors including future military strength requirements. The announcement stated that best judgment at that time was that registrants whose birth dates appeared in the top one-third of the random selection sequence had a "high probability" of being drafted; those in the middle one-third, an "average probability"; and those in the bottom one-third, a "relatively low probability."

Pursuant to the President's decision, the Director of the Selective Service System placed into effect the random selection procedure by conducting, as scheduled, the initial drawing of birthdates for individuals who were between the ages of nineteen and twenty-five as of December 31, 1969. The resultant sequence of birth dates was followed by local draft boards beginning January 1970 in making selections to fill draft calls. It should be pointed out, however, that the revised system did not apply to those graduate students who had received postponed orders of induction granted to them during September-December 1969 in order to permit them to complete academic year 1969-70.

Reducing the period of time of individual vulnerability to the draft increases the necessity for better utilization of college graduates in science and engineering as enlisted men. Maximum draft liability extending during the period of 19-26 years of age acted to stimulate within this age group countless volunteers to the armed forces. With a period of maximum vulnerability reduced to one year, a lessening in the number of draft-motivated volunteers may be expected. If increases in inductions take place for this reason, while the number of billets requiring science and engineering

[259]

capabilities remains relatively constant or decreases, the induction of college graduates in science and engineering (as "constructive" 19 year olds) may result in serious underutilization of their scientific and engineering capabilities. The nature of such a problem tends to be aggravated where the individuals so underutilized are inductees instead of volunteers.

OVERVIEW

With respect to academic year 1968-69, the first academic year after the promulgation of the "no graduate deferment" policy, an objective attempt to generalize from information obtained suggests that an unknown, but apparently a significant, number of students in science and engineering discontinued their graduate education or immediate plans for same because of the policy. Discontinuance took the forms, primarily, of immediate employment, with subsequent occupational deferment, and of entrance into the armed forces by either voluntary or involuntary methods. The impact of the policy takes on added significance in the face of increased numbers of college graduate enlistees and inductees beyond apparent Army needs for such manpower under prevailing conditions.

Although conclusive data on the adverse impact of the "no graduate deferment" policy are limited, it is clear that the actual impact during the first academic year took place during a period when numerous local boards were slow to reclassify college graduates out of the student deferment category, when local boards permitted graduate students in many cases to complete their graduate term before induction, and when monthly draft calls were often relatively light. The changed academic status of individual registrants merely through the passage of time, prompt local board reclassification out of Class II-S of individuals who complete their baccalaureate degree in science and engineering, and a continuation of the needs for a similar number of new recruits as sought in 1969 will undoubtedly produce a profound effect upon scientific and engineering manpower utilization if the "no graduate deferment" policy continues.

The full impact of the revised system upon graduate students in science and engineering during academic year 1969-70 is not observable. However, under the circumstances prevailing at the time of the adoption of the random selection method, it appeared that at least one-third of the full-time, male, United States citizen, graduate students pursuing science and engineering during academic year 1969-70 would be subject to call-up before they completed their graduate study objective.

The continuous formal education development of students in science and engineering, without interruption through master's and doctorate programs, produces a group of individuals qualified to perform at the highest levels of science and engineering Interruption of this development is a deterrent to optimum utilization. The adverse effect of the "no graduate deferment" policy on scientific and engineering manpower utilization should be given the most careful, immediate consideration, particularly because of the scheduled expiration of the Military Selective Service Act in 1971.

VII

MINIMIZING THE IMPACT OF
DEFENSE CUTBACKS

•

REDUCTIONS IN LARGE SCALE FUNDING

The Federal Government funds a series of national programs having a strong science and technology content and hence requiring the services of large numbers of scientists and engineers. These services are provided by scientists and engineers primarily as employees of industry, government, and colleges and universities.

Ultimately, when decisions are made to reduce these programs in any significant way, the need for scientific and engineering personnel is drastically curtailed. The larger the reduction in funding and the shorter the time period during which the program reaches the decreased funding stage, the more adverse is likely to be the impact of the curtailment upon the optimum utilization of scientific and engineering manpower.

A fluctuation in employment of scientists and engineers, caused by relatively slight changes in funding over a period of time, is a normal event with respect to any program. Changes of this type are usually taken in stride, particularly when manpower adjustments can be effected by local action of employers and other groups with a minimum of disruption to the effective utilization of scientific and engineering talent.

However, in the case of broad programs based on large scale funding, the total number of scientists and engineers participating at the peak of these programs is large, and the impact of decreased funding is potentially much more severe. The complex nature of large national programs is such that, in connection with a reduction of scientific and engineering personnel, employers—either individually or as a group—are unable to meet the full challenge of minimizing the impact of decreased funding upon a large number of scientists and engineers involved. In such cases, realistic solutions to the problem of scientific and engineering manpower utilization are affected by actions taken by several sectors in the nation.

A potential threat to the maximum utilization of a large group of scientists and engineers is the impact of defense cutbacks, incident to the complete cessation of hostilities in Vietnam, upon scientific and engineering manpower employed in the defense program. Major changes in other large scale programs, such as the national space program, also endanger the effective utilization of sizeable number of scientists and engineers and also merit special consideration. However, the concern of this chapter is the defense cutbacks related to the end of the Vietnam conflict.

There are many facets to the Vietnam defense cutback problem which are of great importance to the nation. Such facets include the redirection of federal funding to civil technology to assist with social problems, the need to spend some sizeable amount for the defense effort for such items as modernization of defense equipment and new weaponry, and the effect of changed spending patterns upon monetary and fiscal policies. Another facet is minimizing the impact of Vietnam defense cutbacks upon optimum utilization of scientific and engineering personnel.

EMPLOYMENT OF SCIENTISTS AND ENGINEERS IN THE DEFENSE EFFORT

Under the Department of Defense-NASA Economic Information System (EIS), defense contractors report at six month intervals on their employment of personnel on defense prime contracts and subcontracts. For smaller contractors not reporting their employment, defense-generated employment is estimated by applying census factors to prime contract awards data. Statistics on civilian and military personnel at defense installations are obtained from DOD reports.

Through use of data derived from EIS, the Department of Defense reported in 1968 that during the period June 1965 to

[263]

June 1967 total defense-generated employment increased by 1,600,000 persons. Of this figure, 700,000 employees worked in prime contractor plants, 200,000 were civilian employees in defense installations in the United States and 700,000 were military personnel.

This increase in defense-generated employment was approximately 70% of the increase in all U. S. employment (civilian and military) over the two year period. Total defense-generated employment of scientists and engineers increased approximately 87,-000 during the same period. Of this total, 74,000 were employed in private industry and 13,000 were in the Department of Defense. The estimate of 87,000 represented 90% of the increase in the employment of scientists and engineers over the two year period.

In one study the Department of Labor made estimates of employment generated by military expenditures in fiscal years 1965 and 1967. These estimates were derived by using an inter-industry economic model. Detailed estimates of military purchases of final goods and services were processed through the model to obtain the total of direct and indirect output necessary to produce these purchases. Estimates of defense-generated employment were obtained by converting industry outputs to employment figures by using productivity factors for 1965 and 1967. Through this method the Department estimated that defense-related civilian employment increased from about 3.0 million (fiscal year 1965) to 4.1 million (fiscal year 1967). This increase represented about 23% of the total increase in civilian employment during the period.[1]

The Department of Labor also made a study of worker skills required in civilian defense-related employment in fiscal years 1965 and 1967. Occupational estimates were derived from a set of estimates of defense employees in industry for fiscal years 1965 and 1967. A pattern of occupations was developed for

1. R. P. Oliver, "The Employment Effect of Defense Expenditures," *Monthly Labor Review,* September 1967, pp. 9-16.

each of eighty industries defined in the basic economic structure model. Through computer operation, employment in a given industry was multiplied by the percentages of the occupations in the industry pattern to find the number of workers in each occupation in the industry. These industry numbers were added to obtain national totals for various occupational groups. Among occupations for which information was developed were chemistry, physics, and engineering.[2]

Table VII-I shows estimated chemist, physicist, and engineering (civilian) employment attributable to defense expenditures during fiscal years 1965 and 1967.

Table VII-1

SCIENTISTS AND ENGINEERS IN DEFENSE
GENERATED EMPLOYMENT, FY 1965 AND FY 1967

Types	FY 1967 (thousands)	FY 1965 (thousands)	Increase from FY 65 to FY 67 (thousands)	1967 Defense Employment as Percentage of Total 1967 Employment
Chemists	11	8	3	10
Physicists	9	8	1	38
All engineers	216	173	43	18
Aeronautical	41	33	8	61
Chemical	5	5	0	10
Civil	18	15	3	10
Electrical	58	46	12	20
Industrial	20	16	4	14
Mechanical	43	34	9	19
Metallurgical	4	3	1	10

Source: Dept. of Labor study

According to Table VII-1, 38% of all physicists employed in 1967—or 9,000—were engaged in defense work. Eighteen percent of all engineers employed in 1967—or 216,000—were so engaged. With reference to specific types of engineers, 61% of all aeronautical engineers employed in fiscal year 1967 were in defense employment, followed by electrical (20%), mechanical

2. M. Rutzick, "Worker Skills in Current Defense Employment," *Monthly Labor Review,* September 1967, pp. 17-20.

(19%), and industrial (14%), engineers. Ten percent of all chemical engineers in 1967 were in defense employment. The same proportion characterized civil engineers and metallurgical engineers.

Table VII-1 also reveals that electrical engineers comprised the largest number in defense employment (58,000), followed by mechanical (43,000) and aeronautical (41,000). Each of these three types of engineers increased significantly since 1965.

Table VII-2 gives the distribution of defense employment of engineers, classified by selected industries.

Table VII–2

DISTRIBUTION OF EMPLOYMENT OF ENGINEERS
IN SELECTED DEFENSE INDUSTRIES

Industry	Number of Engineers (thousands)	Percentage of Engineers
Total Engineers in Defense Employment	216.	100.
Aircraft and Parts	70.0	32.4
Electrical Machinery Equipment and Supplies	40.5	18.7
Ordnance and Accessories	14.0	6.5
Machinery	8.5	3.9
Government (DOD)	7.5	3.5
Construction	3.5	1.6

Source: Dept. of Labor study

According to Table VII-2, slightly more than one-half of these engineers (51.1%) were engaged in aircraft and parts and electrical machinery equipment and supplies. The survey also indicated that considerable numbers of engineers in defense employment were spread throughout the economy.

In a study prepared in 1969, the Department of Labor used fiscal year 1968 budget data and, with the aid of the inter-industry economic model, estimated the number of scientists and engineers whose employment was generated by defense expenditures during fiscal year 1968.[3] The study also included revised

3. M. Rutzick, "Worker Skills in Current Defense Employment," *Monthly Labor Review,* January 1970.

data for fiscal year 1967 (which were contained in the earlier study): the revised fiscal year 1967 data incorporated subsequent DOD information and reflected improved techniques of analysis. Table VII-3 shows the (revised) occupational distribution of scientists and engineers for fiscal year 1967 and for fiscal year 1968.

Table VII-3

NUMBER OF SCIENTISTS AND ENGINEERS IN DEFENSE-
GENERATED EMPLOYMENT, FY '67 AND FY '68

Types	Number FY '67	Number FY '68
Scientists (total)	37,169	40,553
Chemists	10,239	11,364
Geologists and Geophysicists	1,835	1,995
Mathematicians and Statisticians	10,524	11,692
Physicists	8,027	8,711
Other Physical Scientists	6,544	6,791
Engineers (totals)	203,156	228,777
Aeronautical	37,734	44,503
Chemical	5,453	6,150
Civil	16,490	17,363
Electrical	53,319	59,474
Industrial	20,592	23,607
Mechanical	39,651	44,492
Metallurgical	4,502	5,100
Mining	803	902
Sales	6,956	8,038
Other	17,656	19,148

Source: Dept. of Labor study

The proportion of total employed scientists who were engaged in defense-generated employment in fiscal year 1968 cannot be determined because of lack of basic data. However, it is estimated that approximately 19% of total employed engineers in the United States were engaged in defense-generated employment during fiscal year 1968. The addition of the indirect effect upon this employment, not measured by the Department of Labor approach, increases the percentage to approximately 30%.

Comparison of defense-generated employment of scientists for fiscal year 1968 with that for fiscal year 1967 shows an increase of 9% in the one year period. Increases were registered in every

[267]

science occupation. Largest increases took place among chemists (11%) and among mathematicians and statisticians (11%). Comparison of defense-generated employment of engineers for fiscal year 1968 with that of fiscal year 1967 shows an increase of 13% in the one year period. Increases were registered in every engineering branch. Largest increases took place among aeronautical engineers (18%). Changes in defense-generated employment of scientists and engineers between fiscal year 1967 and fiscal year 1968 are shown in Table VII-4.

Table VII-4

CHANGE IN DEFENSE GENERATED EMPLOYMENT
OF SCIENTISTS AND ENGINEERS, FY '67 AND FY '68

Types	Number of Scientists and Engineers FY '67	Change FY '67-FY '68	Percentage of Change
Scientists (total)	37,169	3,384	9%
Chemists	10,239	1,125	11%
Geologists and Geophysicists	1,835	160	9%
Mathematicians & Statisticians	10,524	1,168	11%
Physicists	8,027	684	8%
Other Physical Scientists	6,544	247	4%
Engineers (total)	203,156	25,621	13%
Aeronautical	37,734	6,769	18%
Chemical	5,453	697	13%
Civil	16,490	873	5%
Electrical	53,319	6,155	12%
Industrial	20,592	3,015	15%
Mechanical	39,651	4,841	12%
Metallurgical	4,502	598	11%
Mining	803	99	12%
Sales	6,956	1,082	16%
Other	17,656	1,492	8%

Source: Dept. of Labor study

Analysis of the data contained in the preceding tables, modified by informal estimates of changes during calendar year 1969, suggests that in early 1970 approximately 250,000 scientists and engineers in a variety of branches in these two fields were engaged in defense-generated employment.

[268]

EMPLOYMENT OF SCIENTISTS AND ENGINEERS IN THE AEROSPACE INDUSTRY

The largest identifiable group of scientists and engineers in defense-related employment concerning whom recent comparable data are available is the aerospace industry. A survey of aerospace industry employment covering fifty companies representing approximately 80% of total employment in the industry was made by the Aerospace Industries Association of America in 1969. The survey indicated that employment of scientists and engineers in this industry totaled 214,000 in December 1969.[4] Data contained in the survey do not differentiate between scientists and engineers, but it is estimated that engineers constitute approximately 90% of the combined scientists and engineers figure.

Table VII-5 presents estimated distribution of employment of scientists and engineers in the aerospace industry, by product group, for March 1969 and December 1969.

Table VII–5

ESTIMATED DISTRIBUTION OF EMPLOYMENT OF SCIENTISTS AND ENGINEERS IN AEROSPACE INDUSTRY, BY PRODUCT GROUP

| | March 1969 | | December 1969 | |
Product Group	Employment (thousands)	Percentage of Total Employment	Employment (thousands)	Percentage of Total Employment
Aircraft	117	53	113	53
Missiles and Space	94	42	91	42
Non-Aerospace	11	5	10	5
Total	222	100	214	100

Sources, AIAA study

Table VII-6 shows an estimated distribution of employment of scientists and engineers in the aerospace industry, by geographical area, for the same time periods.

---

4. Aerospace Industries Association of America, *Aerospace News,* October 31, 1969.

Table VII–6

ESTIMATED DISTRIBUTION OF EMPLOYMENT OF
SCIENTISTS AND ENGINEERS IN AEROSPACE
INDUSTRY, BY GEOGRAPHICAL AREA

Geographical Area	Percentage of Employment March 1969	Percentage of Employment December 1969
New England and Middle Atlantic	23.8	24.8
East North Central	4.1	4.1
West North Central	5.5	5.3
South Atlantic	7.5	7.6
South Central	5.5	5.3
Mountain	2.2	2.6
Pacific	43.8	43.2
Undistributed	7.6	7.1
Total	100.	100.

Source: AIAA study

Table VII-7 presents estimated distribution of employment of scientists and engineers engaged in aircraft research and development and production, by geographical area. To prevent disclosure of individual company data, the AIAA study does not show separately any geographical area having four or less establishments.

Table VII–7

ESTIMATED DISTRIBUTION OF EMPLOYMENT OF SCIENTISTS
AND ENGINEERS IN AIRCRAFT RESEARCH AND DEVELOPMENT
AND PRODUCTION, BY GEOGRAPHICAL AREA

Geographical Area	Percentage of Employment March 1969	Percentage of Employment December 1969
New England and Middle Atlantic	37.1	38.6
East-West North Central	13.6	13.3
South Atlantic	5.3	5.4
South Central and Mountain	9.8	9.5
Pacific	25.9	25.3
Undistributed	8.3	7.9
Total	100.	100.

Source: AIAA study

Table VII-8 shows estimated distribution of employment of scientists and engineers working on missiles and space, by geographical area.

Table VII–8

ESTIMATED DISTRIBUTION OF EMPLOYMENT OF SCIENTISTS
AND ENGINEERS IN MISSILES AND SPACE,
BY GEOGRAPHICAL AREA

Geographical Area	Percentage of Employment March 1969	Percentage of Employment December 1969
New England and Middle Atlantic	3.4	3.5
East-West North Central	3.7	3.5
South Atlantic	9.9	10.1
South Central and Mountain	4.8	5.6
Pacific	71.6	71.4
Undistributed	6.6	5.9
Total	100.	100.

Source: AIAA study

Several observations may be noted from a review of data presented in the preceding tables: the decline during the period March-December 1969 in the level of employment of scientists and engineers in the aerospace industry (3.7%), a relatively small number of scientists and engineers employed by aerospace companies who work in non-aerospace work (10,000), a spread of employment generally throughout the nation but with a very high concentration in the Pacific area (43.2%), the New England and the Middle Atlantic area as the leading section in employment in aircraft research and development and production (38.6%), and the predominance of the Pacific area in employment in missiles and space (71.4%). It is clear that defense cutbacks in the aerospace industry have disproportionate effects in diverse sections of the nation.

SELECTED STUDIES RELATED TO
DEFENSE CUTBACKS

Fortunately, results of research offer insights on the effect of defense changes upon scientific and engineering manpower. A series

[271]

of defense cutbacks in 1963-1964 resulted in the loss of employment and in other job changes for many types of personnel, including scientists and engineers. These cutbacks occurred in several geographical areas in the nation during a two year period and caused job adjustments among a relatively sizeable number of scientists and engineers. It has been estimated that 31,000 scientists and engineers were so involved. The 1963-1964 experience caused the initiation of a series of studies designed to develop manpower data related to the impact of defense cutbacks.

Since 1964 eleven federal agencies have sponsored research projects to seek answers to certain aspects of the impact of defense cutbacks upon segments of the nation's manpower, including scientists and engineers. Most of these studies, however, have been funded by four agencies: the Arms Control and Disarmament Agency, the Department of Defense, the Department of Labor, and the National Aeronautics and Space Agency. The research projects have been actually carried out by either the federal agency funding the research (such as the Department of Labor) or by a contractor (such as another government agency or non-government body like an educational institution) on behalf of a federal agency.

Among the research studies carried out, one of particular relevance is a study dealing with the transferability and retraining of defense engineers.[5] The specific aims of this study, funded by the Arms Control and Disarmament Agency in 1967, were to determine critical barriers to the transfer of defense engineers to commercial positions and to analyze the role of retraining in overcoming such barriers. Information was obtained from 2,100 engineers and 100 managers in 14 industrial companies. Twenty-four percent of the total respondents had made defense-to-commercial transfers while thirty-three percent had made commercial-to-defense transfers.

5. U. S. Arms Control and Disarmament Agency, *The Transferrability and Retraining of Defense Engineers,* 1967.

Through the ACDA study, a series of barriers to such transfers were identified: a presumed lack of cost consciousness among defense engineers, an attitude of commercial managers that defense engineers are not well suited to commercial work, different specialty requirements, and a demand for more generalists instead of specialists in commercial industry. On the other hand, among those engineers who had experienced transfers, more than three out of five felt that defense-to-commercial transfers were about equal in difficulty to other kinds of transfers they had made. Furthermore, there was a willingness on the part of those persons employed in defense who were satisfied with their present work to undertake commercial work. No important barriers to transfer with respect to age, martial status, or number of dependents were detected in the study.

Managers responding in the ACDA study were generally optimistic about the transferability of engineers from the point of view of skills and attitudes, but these managers were less optimistic about the ability of commercial industry to absorb large numbers of defense engineers. Managers set forth a series of views: that commercial engineers are product-oriented while defense engineers tend to specialize in more technical fields; since there are substantially larger proportions of defense engineers than commercial engineers engaged in documentation activities, defense engineers may meet serious transfer problems; aeronautical engineers may have transfer problems since the demand for engineers in both commercial and military aircraft production may level off or decline; commercial industry focuses on manufacturing feasibility and the balancing of cost and performance while defense engineers give greater emphasis to striving for technical limits to achieve maximum performance; commercial engineers are more concerned with marketing considerations than are defense engineers; and while individual engineers are transferable, groups of engineers are not.

According to the ACDA study, engineers and managers agreed that where retraining is required, it should be generally done through in-house programs. Managers thought that attitudes,

[273]

such as those related to cost-consciousness and reliability, cannot be successfully altered through formal training; these attitudes can be changed while defense engineers are being absorbed in commercial industry. Product orientation was likewise considered appropriate for in-house retraining.

However, managers asserted that if large scale changes in skill specialties are required, formal training might be preferable. If the "mix" of specialties of transferees differs from defense industry to commercial industry, more extensive training might be required and educational institution participation might be desirable. Managers said that where transfer problems are serious, retraining requirements should be identified. Some managers claimed that educational institutions show little regard or awareness for the practical problem which engineers face in their reorientation to commercial industry.

Another observation of the ACDA study concerned a comparison of types of engineers in defense industry and in commercial industry. There is a larger proportion of mechanical engineers in commercial industry than in defense industry. By contrast, there is a larger proportion of electronics engineers in defense industry than in commercial industry. Thus, it was pointed out it may be easier for mechanical engineers to transfer from defense to commercial industry and more difficult for electronics engineers to transfer from defense industry to commercial industry.

Two states completed formal studies by state groups to analyze the impact of defense cutbacks upon the economy of the state. Both reports were based on general assumptions, were careful to avoid absolute judgments, and were optimistic in outlook. A few additional states have indicated similar interest in the defense cutback problem.

In 1967 in Pennsylvania, the Governor requested his Economic Advisory Council to determine whether defense industries located in the state could make the transition from a war to a peacetime economy without creating serious unemployment problems. The Council's report was submitted to the Governor in 1967 and revised in 1969. The Council concluded that it appeared that

[274]

the diversity of the industrial complex in the state, the concentration of defense work in cities where disruption could most readily be absorbed, and other factors were sufficient to sustain the state in the event of a reduction in the flow of defense funds.[6]

The Council revealed that approximately 130,000 employees were employed in 1969 in defense-related industries in the state and pointed out that scientists and engineers comprised an ever-growing portion of the total employment. The Council did not separate scientists and engineers from defense employees as a group in its analysis. The Council said that because defense workers' skills are highly marketable, the possibility is small that a large pool of unemployables would be created by defense cutbacks.

The Council commented that a sudden and substantial cut in federal spending in any labor market area "is most unlikely." Regardless of type of economic realignment that eventually occurs, the Council held, "it is unlikely" that change will take place overnight. According to the Council, the majority of firms were preparing for reduction of defense contracts by making plans for commercial products. In its revised report, the Council noted that defense spending is "a constantly changing picture" and that information becoming available since the study was completed "sheds new light on the subject."

In 1968 in New York State, a Post Vietnam Planning Committee was appointed by the Governor to plan and recommend public and private action to ease the economic and social transition in the state when peace comes in Vietnam. The report of the Committee, based on a series of assumptions related to the status of the national economy and to Federal Government action, was forwarded to the Governor. Committee concern was much broader than scientific and engineering manpower, yet this type of manpower was included in Committee considerations. The Committee concluded that "with sound planning, limited demobilization and cutback in defense spending will have only a

6. *Defense Spending in Pennsylvania: A Report to the Pennsylvania Governor's Economic Advisory Council,* 1969.

[275]

minor and short lived impact on the economy of New York State unless the national economy is undergoing a recession."[7]

The Committee determined that New York State had $3.3 billion of prime defense contracts in 1967. The Committee found that private, defense-generated employment in the state in June 1968 totaled approximately 144,000 employees of all types and that between 20,000 and 50,000 of these employees would be eventually laid off over a two year period due to contract cancellation. The Committee did not specify the portion of scientists and engineers which would be included in the total layoff figure.

The Committee stated that contracts for research, development, testing, and evaluation (RDT&E)—amounting to fifteen percent of the state's total prime contract dollar volume—"seem less likely" to be cut than production contracts and, if terminated, "may be replaced" by other defense projects. Holding this belief, the Committee stated that "the effect on employment should be slight." The Committee also said that its survey showed it unlikely that many of the scientists and engineers doing RDT&E work would be laid off during de-escalation. According to the Committee, many large defense contractors believed that such employment "may actually increase" after the end of hostilities in Vietnam, due to dormant RDT&E projects being brought forward and due to new and expanded activities in the space program. Highly skilled persons, the Committee added, are in short supply, have greater mobility than the average defense worker, and "should have little difficulty" in finding other jobs if laid off."

The Committee made no recommendations concerning manpower. Instead, it recommended that area post-Vietnam planning committees be set up in eleven areas of the state to plan for peace. These area committees would consider suggestions to meet unemployment problems. The Committee also recommended that the Governor appoint a state post-Vietnam coordination committee from his cabinet and a staff to serve as liaison agency with

---

7. *Plans for New York State to Meet the Economic Consequences of Peace: Post Vietnam Planning Committee's Report to the Governor,* 1968.

the eleven area committees, to plan priorities of capital construction, and to coordinate state assistance to displaced defense employees.

Although the findings of any one study of this type cannot be applied to a whole industry, the attitudes and opinions of individuals participating in the cited surveys provide an understanding of difficulties which may be anticipated at the time of defense layoffs.

ANALYSIS OF IMPACT STUDIES

Thirty-one studies which have assessed, directly or indirectly, impacts of defense cutbacks upon scientific and engineering personnel have been funded by federal agencies, since the defense cutbacks 1963-64. Review of these studies suggests a series of general observations, formulated on the basis of the aggregate content of the studies.

Some individuals believe that abrupt personnel layoffs in science and engineering are an essential part of the free enterprise system and cannot be avoided. According to this belief, business organizations cannot be run efficiently if management cannot make layoffs at will. There are times when unfavorable business conditions demand layoffs. However, in the case of defense employers, layoffs have occurred during years of record profits for employers involved. Another aspect of layoffs by defense employers is that such layoffs often are periodic. Within a year of one layoff, the same defense employer may start an extensive recruitment program for the same types of professional personnel previously laid off.

Scientists and engineers constitute a most complex group within the labor force. Their heterogeneity is reflected in the multiplicity of specialties within these fields, diverse levels of education, and a wide array of work experiences. Individuals classified as engineers, for example, range from those with no degree to those with Ph.D. degrees. Sometimes, degree-holders working in the field have degrees in fields outside traditional science and engineering branches. Many scientists and engineers

[277]

work in areas which cut across traditional, academically-oriented disciplines. With reference to the array of work experiences, some scientists and engineers are engaged in basic research work, some in design and development work, some in production work, and others in a combination of these areas.

Due to the highly diversified and individualized character of science and engineering employment, an analysis of an employer layoff experience is very difficult. Two professionals having the same academic degree in a particular field and same experience may encounter sharp differences in their efforts to secure new employment. Certain highly individualized variables, such as inherent abilities, differences in work histories, and performance ratings, almost defy quantification.

A distinctive feature of position adjustment for scientists and engineers is the highly diversified nature of available employment information. Newspapers carry advertisements of vacancies for scientists and engineers. Some private employment agencies specialize in scientific and engineering personnel. Professional and technical societies, scientific and technical journals, and alumni offices of educational institutions serve as job information sources. The U. S. Department of Labor, through the Training and Employment Service, also has a system for providing information on available professional positions.

Another determinant in the reemployment process is the degree of substitutability of knowledge and skills possessed by different scientists and engineers. This aspect may be illustrated by the fact that in one study, during the time of a layoff in a geographical area, newspapers continued to carry multi-page advertisements for engineering vacancies which remained unfilled in the same engineering branches as those in which individuals were being laid off. In this case, the specific knowledge and skills offered by the laid-off engineers were not those required at that time by employers in the area. Data on the degree of transferability of skills to new positions are needed. Without such data, effort may be wasted in attempts to teach certain new tech-

[278]

niques to scientists and engineers whose backgrounds are insufficient to permit them to benefit from the new techniques.

The mission of the Department of Defense is to maximize the effectiveness of the armed services. Some individuals believe that this Department should not be expected to include among its goals the maximum utilization of scientific and engineering personnel not directly employed by the department. If an attempt to stabilize fluctuations in the use of scientists and engineers generally should interfere with its primary goal, the Department is faced with a dilemma. Nevertheless, it is in the national interest to seek full utilization of the nation's scientific and engineering manpower. The precise degree to which the Department of Defense has responsibility for helping to stabilize the utilization of scientists and engineers generally is not fully established.

An objective, quantifiable measure to determine the degree of obsolescence of individual scientists and engineers is needed. Perhaps after a scientist or engineer seeking new employment incident to a defense layoff indicates his area of professional interest, an examination could be prepared and administered by a committee of educators and professional and technical society representatives. The examination could be designed to test whether the scientist or engineer is currently knowledgeable in a particular subject matter field. The examination might consist of a series of questions based, in part, on subject matter in current publications in a specialized field. The difference between the perfect score and the actual score of the scientist or engineer would be considered an indicator of his obsolescence. Results of such examination would presumably give insight into the need for updating at that point in time as preparation for his reemployment.

A wide range of recommendations is contained in the thirty-one research reports funded by federal agencies since the defense cutbacks of 1963-64. Classified on the basis of the initiator of followup action, a résumé of selected recommendations has been compiled to reflect views of those who conducted the individual studies and developed suggestions for action. From the array of material produced through the studies, a series of action recommendations are herein presented. Based on research reports and studies, these recommendations are intended for immediate consideration by employers of scientists and engineers, professional and technical societies, scientists and engineers themselves, educators, the Federal Government, and state governments. It is suggested that members of each of these groups select recommendations which are appropriate to their own situation and initiate follow-through steps consistent with the recommendations.

RECOMMENDATIONS FOR EMPLOYERS

Employers should give scientists and engineers who have worked a minimum period of time for their employer, such as a year, a reasonably advance notice of an involuntary termination. A substantial number of experienced scientists and engineers involved in the 1963-64 defense cutbacks were given very short or no advance notice of their pending layoffs. One study indicated that one-half of the employees laid off received less than two weeks advance notice. A reasonably long advance notice reduces hardships caused by massive layoffs and facilitates the reemployment process.

Employers should apprise scientists and engineers at the time of their appointment that continuation of their employment depends upon the award of a particular contract or upon continuance of a certain contract, if such is the case. Defense companies sometimes hire scientists and engineers on a temporary basis during the process of bidding for contracts without the newly employed scientist or engineer having this knowledge. If the company is not awarded a contract or if the contract is not extended, jobs may be abruptly terminated. If a scientist or engineer knows that his employment depends upon the acceptance of a particular company proposal or extension of a contract, the individual is not faced with an emotional shock and resultant loss of productive effort which an unexpected termination often brings.

[280]

Employers should institute liberal severance pay policies. Severance pay has been an important source of financial assistance for the unemployed scientist and engineer. Severance pay, coupled with unemployment insurance, has not been an adequate source of financial support during the transitional period. Individuals who remained unemployed for three or four weeks often have had to depend upon liquidation of their savings for economic survival. In some cases, no severance pay has been provided.

Employers should actively assist a "laid-off" or "about-to-be-laid-off" scientist or engineer in obtaining employment elsewhere. Evidence indicates a wide type of employer response in this situation, ranging from no assistance to significant assistance. For example, an employer may provide assistance to the scientist or engineer in the preparation and distribution of employment resumes. During the advance notice period, firms may permit the scientist or engineer who is to be released to search for new employment on official time. Employers may also permit and encourage officials of other firms, private employment agencies, and the public employment service to interview on employer premises scientists and engineers who are to be laid off. Employers may circulate to other firms and to employment agencies individual employment résumés of scientists and engineers to be displaced.

Employers should provide ample continuing education opportunities for scientists and engineers to enable them to keep up-to-date in their own and related scientific and technical fields. In the past, employer activity in this respect has been irregular. Employers may establish in-plant training for long-term employed scientists and engineers to inform them of new developments. Employers may provide symposia and seminars to help familiarize scentists and engineers with latest information. Continuing education facilitates job transfers within the organization and, when terminations are required, helps job adjustment through the process of external transfers.

[281]

Professional and technical societies should hold meetings to find solutions to common problems associated with job displacements of their members. Relatively little action of this type has been taken by such groups in the past. The suggested meetings may attack specific or general phases of the displacement issue. For example, the National Society of Professional Engineers showed concern for this problem by holding a symposium in California, following the 1963-64 defense cutbacks in that state; the symposium was entitled "Engineering Employment—Can We Meet the Challenge?"

Professional and technical societies which have job placement facilities should evaluate their effectiveness and, as may be necessary, strengthen the operation of these facilities. In former periods of defense cutbacks, society efforts in this regard have not been particularly effective. In some cases, efforts to acquaint members as well as employers with the availability of society employment service may be increased. In other cases, the institution of a follow-up process with applicant members and prospective employers may be undertaken. Periodic evaluation of the placement efforts of such facilities often shows weaknesses in the system not otherwise apparent.

Professional and technical societies should sponsor, on a more active basis, specific continuing education opportunities for their members. A useful, but relatively restricted, contribution to continuing education related to potential job change has been made by these societies. Continuing education opportunities may be accelerated through greater chapter activity and may be attuned to members living in a geographical area. Such opportunities may be related also to a broader membership base and be offered in conjunction with state or national meetings. Flexibility for differing types of assignments is usually characteristic of a scientist or engineer who is reasonably up-to-date in his professional field.

Professional and technical societies should represent the professional interests of their members before legislative and executive branches of government on issues involved in defense cutbacks. Societies generally have not been contributors to government policy-making efforts in previous defense cutbacks. Federal Government policy decisions directly affect the whole defense cutback effort, including contract renegotiation and contract termination. For many policy issues raised, the voices of the scientists and engineers—as articulated by professional and technical societies—should be an important influence in the policy-making process.

Professional and technical societies should sponsor research to seek facts related to key, yet neglected, aspects of the scientific and engineering employment situation as modified by actual or anticipated defense cutbacks. In spite of the relatively large number of manpower research projects which have been undertaken, there are still critical areas for which conclusive information is not yet available. The subject of mobility of scientists and engineers is one of these areas. Decisions are made on the basis of the best data available; however, knowledge gaps persist in the over-all fund of defense cutback information.

RECOMMENDATIONS FOR SCIENTISTS AND ENGINEERS

Scientists and engineers should use discretion in selecting future employers. Scientists and engineers may wish to avoid firms which have a history of periodic mass layoffs. As a result of the previous layoffs, some scientists and engineers reported that they subsequently accepted job offers with lower salaries than some available offers after they had taken into account the growth pattern and the past record of employment stability of their prospective employers. It is realized that alternative employment opportunities may not often exist in a cutback period, but evidence suggests the desirability of the applicant's making discriminating employment decisions insofar as this step is possible and practicable.

Scientists and engineers should plan to be geographically mobile, especially if they are in a geographical area where defense contracts predominate the local economy. Failure of scientists and engineers to obtain new jobs has often been linked to an individual's decision not to move to another location under any circumstances. Being geographically mobile means that scientists and engineers consider themselves available for employment opportunities outside of the geographical area in which they are working. The factors which initially determined the location of a defense plant may be subsequently modified to such an extent that the outlook for employment in a particular geographical area may be highly uncertain. Without the ability to be geographically mobile, scientists and engineers may find their science and engineering future very seriously impaired.

Scientists and engineers should prepare financially for experiencing a period of unemployment or for a reduced salary income after an inevitable defense cutback occurs. Research findings show that scientists and engineers who shift from defense-oriented employment to other types of employment often are required to accept salary reductions. Salaries for scientists and engineers in defense work often are higher than salaries in positions requiring comparable basic skills in commercial, government or academic settings. Although scientists and engineers often place non-monetary job satisfactions higher than monetary income, the salary factor may be vital in view of personal responsibilities. Arranging one's finances during a period of defense employment, with the possibility in mind of a subsequent temporary cessation of employment or reduction in salary, permits the scientist and engineer to undergo subsequent transitional periods without undue personal hardship.

Scientists and engineers should make every effort to keep up-to-date professionally in their own and related fields. According to surveys of previous defense layoffs, significant numbers of scientists and engineers admitted to non-participation in meaningful updating activities. In the present environment, continuing education opportunities prevail in a variety of forms. Employers, educators, professional and technical societies, and government have distinct roles to play in providing such opportunities. Yet, the basic responsibility for taking advantage of these opportunities belongs to the individual scientist or engineer.

Scientists and engineers should maintain familiarity with basic scientific and technological developments in the civilian part of the economy, regardless of their own specialized field. Numerous scientists and engineers fail to become familiar with science and engineering challenges beyond their own narrow defense-oriented spheres. The existence of a series of emerging areas of technology—typified by programs in air and water pollution, mass transportation, and housing—contribute greatly to increasing the scientific and engineering opportunities not only for the present but also for the long-range future. The anticipated availability of funds for work in these and other civilian areas strengthens the belief that much greater participation in non-defense-oriented activity will become one of the basic characteristics of scientific and engineering employment in the decade ahead. One source of employees for such activity is a portion of the group of scientists and engineers presently employed in defense work.

RECOMMENDATIONS FOR EDUCATORS

Educators should offer the use of collegiate placement services for scientists and engineers who are employed or who seek employment in that geographical area. College placement offices already provide assistance to their alumni and are usually active centers for industrial and government recruiters. The collegiate placement services should be broadened to include assistance, on a fee basis, to those who seek professional referral aid, regardless of whether the individual scientist or engineer is a graduate of the institution.

Educators should undertake manpower research to ascertain the precise nature of actual and potential employment of scientists and engineers in their geographical area. Such research should determine the changing nature of employment, should project trends, and should develop data useful for reaching local policy and program decisions which would minimize negative effects of future scientific and engineering personnel adjustments.

Educators should establish detailed programs to facilitate the transfer of new science and technology concepts from the R&D stage, for consideration for application and implementation by local employers. Through assistance in the transfer process as may be provided by an educational institution, employers in the area would be helped in their determination of directions toward which their future science-oriented and technology-oriented efforts could be pointed. Probable changes in the employment of scientists and engineers could then be more realistically anticipated.

Educators should assess their curricula in science and engineering to assure adequate inclusion of broad scientific and engineering principles, in contrast to highly specialized subject matter content. In some instances, educators may find it practical to broaden the subject matter base. Curriculum stress on general principles tends to promote subsequent transferability of scientists and engineers from one type of position to another, with a minimum of professional adjustment.

Educators should evaluate the desirability of establishing or increasing the availability of off-campus continuing education opportunities for scientists and engineers at or near defense employer locations. Formal graduate courses, refresher programs, and seminars are among methods designed to bring new scientific and technical data to the attention of the working professional. Acquisition of newer knowledge not only increases the capability of a scientist or engineer to change his program emphasis and maintain or increase his level of employment but also facilitates subsequent individual mobility incident to future layoffs or promotions as they occur.

RECOMMENDATIONS FOR FEDERAL GOVERNMENT

Recommendations for the Federal Government fall into two categories. One series of recommendations contained in the research reports pertains to the Federal Government without reference to a particular agency; other recommendations pertain to

[286]

identified federal agencies. With respect to the Federal Government in general, several recommendations are offered.

The Federal Government should provide funds "earmarked" for continuing education opportunities for scientific and engineering personnel involved in the defense program. Furthermore, these funds should be allocated on a standby basis to avoid the lag time between the request for funds and the actual setting up of such opportunities. One objective of such funds would be to utilize a prime contractor's facility and supervisory personnel for retraining formerly employed scientific and engineering personnel for positions elsewhere.

The Federal Government should sponsor legislation to encourage greater commercial R & D spending and hence to raise the level of scientific and engineering opportunities offered by commercial companies. The transfer of scientific and engineering personnel between defense and non-defense work will become more widespread if commercial firms offer positions as attractive as defense industries. Such opportunities are possible when extensive R & D programs are established in commercial industries.

The Federal Government should undertake a series of research studies designed to develop more meaningful manpower data on which policies and programs may be formulated. An example of such proposed studies is a detailed analysis of job relationships between defense-related scientific and engineering positions and non-defense-related scientific and engineering positions. A reorientation of some defense-experienced scientists and engineers is inevitable. Precise information is needed on questions such as how an aeronautical engineer with ten years of experience can convert to a non-aviation engineering assignment and how non-degree engineers can compete in a declining market with degree engineers, especially with the latter individuals who have graduated in the past few years. Another example is pre-layoff research that would assess the potential effect of a layoff and point out specific counteracting remedies. Funds should be provided for such research in addition to the funds provided for other re-

[287]

search if the proposed research task is to receive the attention it actually deserves.

The Federal Government should share directly in the cost of relocation allowances for scientists and engineers who have been engaged in the defense effort and who are unable to obtain local jobs. Loss of earnings while one is in the process of moving to another location for reemployment purposes and loss of money through the forced sale of a home may represent serious barriers to mobility. Partial subsidization of these costs might represent a profitable contribution to the improved functioning of the employment market. Resultant economic benefits from the work efforts of such employers might actually exceed the costs contributed by the government.

The Federal Government should prepare and maintain a reserve list of national programs of public significance and involving science and technology. The list would represent long range thinking. Programs on the list would be activated on a selective basis as part of projected national economic growth as individual defense projects are phased out. Through a range of federal incentives, contracts for the development of non-defense science and engineering oriented industry would replace, in a sense, defense contracts and could be accelerated or slowed down at a pace determined by officials of the Federal Government.

Some recommendations for federal action which are contained in the research reports are linked to specific federal agencies as initiators of action. Thus, the following recommendations are presented.

The Department of Defense should review cases of short-notice contract cancellation, examine factors which necessitated this type of termination, and avoid repetition of such action in the future. Greatest manpower dislocation occurs when contract cancellations are abrupt. The Department should balance immediate monetary savings which may accrue to it through sudden termination with other federal costs, direct or indirect, resulting from short notice cancellation.

The Department of Defense should require prime contractors to furnish directly to the public employment service periodic information on occupations and on numbers of scientists and engineers working on defense contracts. In the absence of relatively current data, it is difficult, if not impossible, to conduct meaningful analysis as preliminary to assessing prospective impact as well as specific followup activity.

The Department of Defense should encourage prime contractors to adopt the Dictionary of Occupational Titles, in addition to any employer position classification system, for use in identifying defense-related scientific and engineering positions. Presently there is lack of uniformity in the use of position titles. Adoption by all employers of common position definitions and titles would permit a clearer analysis of types of positions involved and would aid in the conversion of scientists and engineers from defense-related to non-defense related positions.

The Department of Defense should urge defense contractors to establish reasonable standards of advance notice to be used in connection with defense layoffs. The proposed standards would be based on the individual's length of service in the company or on a defense contract, quality of performance, and other relevant factors.

The Department of Defense should give earlier notice of impending layoffs, through an early warning system, to the Training and Employment Service of the Department of Labor. The latter would then be able to start administrative action basic to the creation of special programs or services to assist in a layoff program.

The Department of Labor should obtain and set aside "standby" funds for immediate administrative use in connection with large scale layoffs of scientists and engineers. Regular placement staff cannot be expected to cope successfully with the volume of placement work associated with a sizable layoff. One aspect of strengthening placement service would be the acquiring of placement officers who are themselves specialists in science and engineering manpower. Working closely with professional and technical societies, the education community, and other employers and groups, these specially qualified placement assistants could presumably perform placement work more effectively than the generalist placement assistant.

The Department of Labor should prepare for regional distribution lists of names, addresses, and particular occupational skills of scientists and engineers who are available for employment because of defense layoffs, provided such personnel request this service. These lists could be issued at regular intervals and sent to employers in various geographical areas in which scientists and engineers prefer work. A brief resume of available scientists and engineers would also be prepared and made available to prospective employers. Since relatively few scientists and engineers submit applications to public employment offices, this type of assistance would enhance the job referral process of the department.

The Department of Labor should set up a compatible, detailed system of classifying positions of scientists and engineers engaged in defense-related industrial and governmental work and non-defense-related industrial and governmental work. The purpose of such a system would be to expedite the matching of vacancies for scientists and engineers with available individuals. The development of a meaningful code tying together these four types of positions should reflect, realistically, current assignments of scientists and engineers.

RECOMMENDATIONS FOR STATE GOVERNMENTS

State governments should make an assessment of the impact of defense cutbacks upon scientists and engineers employed within the confines of the state. This assessment should be made either through an ad hoc committee appointed by the governor or by a regular state agency such as a state department of commerce. The assessment should be made in detail and should reflect the situation in various geographical sections of the state in which defense employers are located.

State governments should draw up a master plan for the establishment of new and expanded science-oriented and engineering-oriented industry in the state. The master plan would become a pattern for coordinated state action related to policies and programs dealing with education and taxation. Implementation of the plan should be undertaken on a scheduled basis to generate new employment opportunities for scientists and engineers now residing and working in the state.

State governments should sponsor a series of meetings within the state to alert interested groups, such as employer associations, chambers of commerce, and professional and technical societies, about the nature of problems which defense cutbacks would raise in the state and seek advice and cooperation of representatives of these groups with respect to appropriate action to be taken by state government officials.

EXAMPLE OF DIRECT ACTION

Defense cutbacks in 1963-64 motivated the State of California to initiate an experimental effort to apply advanced engineering techniques, pioneered in defense activities, to social, political, and economic problems. The actual and threatened impact of the cutbacks in the state at that time prompted the state to feel that federal funds might be available to industries in the state which could successfully demonstrate a systems analysis approach to the solution of problems of a non-defense, non-space nature.

In the first stage of the effort, the State of California made contracts, each for $100,000 and for six months duration, with four aerospace companies located in the state. Aerojet-Corporation contracted with the state to study problems in waste management and pollution abatement; Lockheed Missiles and Space Company, to analyze the establishment of a statewide information network to satisfy data needs of state agencies; North American Aviation, to study problems in integrating air, land, and water transportation; and Space-General, to study detection, processing, rehabilitation, and control of the state's criminal population. Each of the problems was thought to be subject to improvement through research and development and to systems analysis. Each state request for bids required that the con-

[291]

tractor identify R&D needs in problem areas and utilize a systems approach. A fifth California company, Systems Development Corporation, was engaged by the state to act as its advisor for the four studies.

Completion of the four contracts and review of the results prompted the state to enter into a subsequent series of contracts, larger in scope and funding than the initial four. Thus, TRW Systems contracted to develop and demonstrate a land use information system; Space-General, to provide systems analysis and development in the field of social welfare by defining and analyzing the target population, by developing mathematical models of the welfare system, and by developing an improved information system to facilitate welfare transactions; Aerojet-General, to make a systems study of solid waste management for a combined urban-rural region and to develop an optimum solid waste management system for that region; Lockheed Missiles and Space Company, to develop a criminal justice information system and to assist the State Department of General Services in the development of details of requirements for a state-wide federated information system.

The amounts of individual contracts ranged as high as $350,-000. In some cases, federal financial support was obtained from such agencies as the Department of Housing and Urban Development; Department of Health, Education and Welfare; and the Department of Justice. Illustrations of completed projects are system design and specifications in the area of criminal justice and system design and specifications for a solid waste disposal program for the Fresno area. A California law enforcement telecommunications system based on one of the studies is operational. The state is funding additional systems studies in more advanced stages.

The experience of the State of California in funding the experimental effort in advanced engineering techniques motivated much interest in their wider application to social, economic, and political problems. For example, a Special Subcommittee of the United States Senate Committee on Labor and Public Welfare held hearings in California in 1965 to learn details of the California effort. Subsequent Subcommittee hearings were held in Washington in 1966 and in 1967 to obtain further indication of concern for, and the feasibility of, the systems approach in solving broad, non-defense type problems.[8]

In order to determine the extent to which systems technology was being used or considered for use by state and local levels of government, the Subcommittee in 1968 sent questionnaires to 80 government jurisdictions. All 50 states and 22 cities were contacted. Analysis of 58 responses indicated that over 75% of the jurisdictions were engaged in some level of systems analysis activity—from preliminary consideration of the approach to the establishment of multiple systems designed to assist high-level decision-making. Many letters to the Subcommittee, which accompanied the executed questionnaires, placed special stress on the scarcity of available specialized manpower for this type of activity. Some respondents referred to the need for recruitment of such personnel; other respondents pointed out the need to train or retrain government personnel; others indicated an eagerness to make more extensive use of consultants and consulting firms for systems advice. Respondents identified eleven federal agencies providing funds to state and local governments, within program limitations, to support systems analysis work.

Systems analysis concepts are currently being developed and applied to social, economic, and political problems by several defense-oriented companies. For examples, in the field of transportation, projects involving systems analysis are being carried out in connection with high speed ground transportation to meet intercity transportation requirements and with the use of communications satellites for relaying voice communication between aircraft and ground; in the field of water resources, in connection with exploration and evaluation of plans for the coordinated use of ground and surface water to meet the needs of an area and with membrane processes such as reverse osmosis to desalinate

8. U. S. Senate Committee on Labor and Public Welfare, *Systems Technology Applied to Social and Community Problems*, 1969.

water economically; in the field of urban affairs, in connection with improvement in the efficiency of mobile systems for deployment of police patrol cars through the use of advanced communication systems and with the development of criteria for use in the design of land use information systems; in health, in connection with automated medical examination systems and with integrated communication-logistics-data handling systems in medical centers.

The State of California experiment in pursuing systems analysis projects through contracts with defense companies was an innovative step which has aroused wide concern. The application and use of advanced engineering techniques, initially evolved in the defense effort, represents one possible major phase of the national transition from defense to non-defense activity. Essential to the use of such techniques is systems expertise, possessed by a significant segment of scientists and engineers engaged in the defense effort. A post-Vietnam period involving an emphasis on advanced engineering techniques for social, economic, and political problem-solving illustrates the need for the adoption, on a coordinated basis, of several of the recommendations set forth in the preceding section of this chapter.

REORDERING OF NATIONAL GOALS

The issue of defense cutbacks is inextricably linked to the larger problem of goals, policies, and programs which the Federal Government adopts as the Vietnam conflict comes to a conclusion. The types of services which government can properly provide for the people of the nation at any one time outstrip the financial ability of government to furnish these services. Thus, government must identify and determine priorities of national goals, along with policies and programs to reach these goals. Reduction in defense expenditures caused by the cessation of the Vietnam war requires a reordering of national priorities, either by affirmative national decision after analysis and debate or by default. The choice of goals made now and in the period ahead, together with the selection and timing of policies and programs to implement these goals, sets boundaries for subsequent participation by scientists and engineers in post-Vietnam programs and has a direct effect upon the utilization of such personnel.

Since 1963 the Presidents of the United States have appointed ad hoc groups of key government officials to assess effects of the cessation of the Vietnam war upon the national economy. In connection with their assignments, these groups have also identified national goals, policies, and programs for possible adoption for post-Vietnam America. The reports of these groups do not constitute a precise blueprint for action. As a matter of fact, their views are somewhat diverse, often speculative, and sometimes based on very broad assumptions. Yet, the views collectively represent some of the difficult choices which must be faced. A review of highlights of the reports of these groups provides a base for further analysis of the basic problem of determining national goals, policies, and programs in the early 1970s.

In July 1963, President Kennedy authorized the establishment of an informal committee under the leadership of the Chairman of the Council of Economic Advisers to review and coordinate the work of federal agencies related to the economic impact of defense and disarmament. In December 1963, President Johnson formalized the committee by designating it as the Committee on the Economic Impact of Defense and Disarmament. He made the group responsible for reviewing and coordinating activities of federal agencies designed to improve understanding both of the economic impact of defense expenditures and of changes in the composition and total level of such expenditures.

In its report to President Johnson in 1965, the Committee stated that programs to deal with defense adjustments should be designed to advance national economic goals. The Committee suggested that defense resources no longer needed for military purposes could be used to finance such objectives as better education at all levels, more vocational and technical training, better mental and physical health, and the prevention of delinquency and crime. The Committee observed that there would be a significant opportunity during the coming years to devote more technical manpower to the strengthening of civilian technology and to give increased emphasis to space exploration and the peaceful uses of atomic energy. The Committee recommended that it, or some similarly constituted body, should carry on similar activities of analysis, coordination, evaluation, and stimulation, without operational responsibility. Shortly after the report was transmitted to the President, United States participation in the Vietnam conflict was increased considerably and the question of defense cutbacks became much less urgent.[9]

In January 1967, the need to establish priorities before the end of the Vietnam war was pointed out in President Johnson's Economic Report to the Congress.[10] The President stated that the resources being claimed by the war could be diverted to peaceful uses and could hasten the attainment of desired national goals. He added that when peace comes, rapid adjustments in economic policies would be needed and the nation must be prepared for these adjustments. The President reported that he was instructing heads of relevant federal agencies, under the leadership of the Chairman of the Council of Economic Advisers, to begin a major and coordinated effort to review the nation's readiness. The President asked these officials to take six specific actions:

1. Consider possibilities and priorities for tax reduction.

2. Prepare, with the Federal Reserve Board, plans for quick adjustments of monetary and financial policies.

3. Determine which high priority programs can be quickly expanded.

4. Determine priorities for the longer range expansion of programs to meet the needs of the American people, both through new and existing programs.

5. Study and evaluate the future direction of federal financial support to state and local governments.

9. *Report of Committee on the Economic Impact of Defense and Disarmament*, 1965.

10. *Economic Report of the President*, 1967.

6. Examine ways in which the transition to peace can be facilitated for workers, companies, and communities engaged in supplying defense needs and for the men released from the armed forces.

The President directed that initial reports be prepared on all of these and related problems and that thereafter the reports be kept continuously up-to-date. A few weeks later, in March 1967, the President asked the Secretaries of Treasury, Defense, Commerce, and Labor; the Director of the Bureau of the Budget; and the Chairman of the Council of Economic Advisers to form a cabinet committee to coordinate economic planning for the end of the Vietnam hostilities. As the initial assignment, the committee was given the six tasks mentioned in the President's Economic Report of 1967.

In January 1968 the Chairman of the Council of Economic Advisers reported on activity of the Cabinet Coordinating Committee which had taken place since March 1967.[11] He stated that the Committee was continuing to study the transitional period under various assumptions related to the magnitude and timing of the phasing down of military activities. The Chairman explained that with an assumption that defense outlays would return essentially to the 1963-65 level of spending, the major part of the manpower and expenditures reductions associated with this pattern might be accomplished over a period of approximately one and one-half years after the cessation of hostilities. This projected result assumed as rapid a phasing down as could be reasonably expected on the basis of past experience. The Chairman pointed out that the analysis necessary to establish priorities among the various proposals was being pursued by interagency working groups.

The final report of the Cabinet Coordinating Committee was sent to the President in January 1969.[12] The Committee explained that the choices among alternative fiscal adjustments during demobilization should be guided by "longer run" priorities

11. *Economic Report of the President, 1968.*
12. *Economic Report of the President, 1969.*

[297]

which should be weighted in advance of action to launch new programs, to strengthen existing programs, or to reduce taxes. A highlight of the Committee's report was a statement that, assuming the transition to peace would be essentially completed by 1972 and that the 10% income tax surcharge and certain excise taxes would have expired by that time, a "peace and growth dividend" available for federal spending purposes or for tax reduction would amount to $22 billion by fiscal year 1972 and would increase $7 to $8 billion a year thereafter.

The Cabinet Coordinating Committee stated that possibilities for expansion in the defense area are vitally unlimited and that the need for defense expenditures will depend upon international developments. New programs proposals prepared for illustrative purposes by the Department of Defense and submitted for Committee consideration totalled $6.5 billion annually; this amount included programs for aircraft development, modernization of naval forces, and advanced strategic and general purpose weapons items.

New civilian programs and major expansions of existing civilian programs were set forth by the Committee as possible uses of the "dividend." These suggestions totaled $40 billion for fiscal year 1972. Proposals having science and technology aspects amounted to $10.6 billion (of the $40 billion). Examples from the Committee report of such new and expanded programs are shown in Table VII-9.

The Cabinet Coordinating Committee stressed that difficult choices must be made between increased expenditures and tax reductions, between defense and non-defense programs, and among competing civilian programs. The fact was stressed that demobilization will require some shifts in employment patterns, such as from defense industries to those producing civilian goods and services and such as from one geographical area to another. It was estimated that 1.3 million persons may seek civilian employment over a period of six quarters following the Vietnam truce. The Committee observed that some individuals who lose defense jobs will not possess required skills for other jobs while other individuals will be geographically isolated from job opportunities. The Committee stated that federal programs should be undertaken to ease the impact of demobilization upon seriously affected individuals. The establishment of a Readjustment Operations Committee was recommended to assume responsibility for detailed planning of federal readjustment assistance and to work closely with state and local authorities.

Table VII–9

ILLUSTRATIONS OF PROPOSED POST VIETNAM PROGRAMS

Proposed programs	Cost (billion of dollars)
Quality of environment (including air pollution, water pollution, and solid waste disposal)	$1.7
National resources (including water resources)	1.4
Urban development (including urban mass transportation, urban facilities, and renewal)	5.5
Transportation (including airport modernization, rapid urban ground transit, and modernization of merchant marine)	1.0
Science and space exploration (including scientific research in oceanography and communications)	1.0

Source: CCC study

In January 1969, President Nixon, by executive order, established the Cabinet Committee on Economic Policy, composed of the Vice-President, four department heads, the Director of the Bureau of the Budget, the Counselor to the President, and the Chairman of the Council of Economic Advisers (who was also named committee coordinator). The Committee was given the task of advising and assisting the President in the development and coordination of national economic programs and policies. Shortly after its creation, the President charged the Committee with responsibility for carrying out programs to ease post-Vietnam adjustment problems. In this connection, he also set up a special study committee to work under the direction of the coordinator of the cabinet committee and to make regular progress reports to the Cabinet Committee.

[299]

The special study committee working under the cabinet committee coordinator prepared a report for internal use late in the summer of 1969. Public discussions by high officials who had knowledge of the contents of the report indicated that relatively little money for new federal programs would apparently become available at the time of the end of the Vietnam war. Factors which entered into such belief included the cost of implementing housing goals contained in the Housing Act of 1968, proposals to reduce tax levies by approximately $8 billion, and the possible passage of three major proposals made by the President to Congress and dealing with welfare reform, mass transit, and federal sharing of tax revenues with the states. Such discussions underlined the need for an ordering of national priorities on the widest possible basis in order that adjustment would be effected at the end of the Vietnam conflict with a minimum of dislocation of scientific and engineering manpower.

Meanwhile, the National Planning Association established in 1966 quantitative standards for a series of sixteen proposed national goals and provided estimates of dollar costs to meet these goals. Under subsequent contract with the U. S. Department of Labor, the Association translated dollar costs of these goals into their manpower requirements classified by occupation and including scientific and engineering personnel requirements. This study, published in 1969, provides a base for assessing potential impact of shifts in national priorities following the end of the Vietnam conflict. The shifts anticipated in the study involved a lesser priority for the national defense goal and higher priorities for civilian-oriented goals such as those relating to natural resources, to non-defense research and development, and to transportation.[13]

In the Association study, a $20 billion cutback in defense orders was estimated. The study indicated that the total decline in defense spending would exceed $20 billion because of reductions in military and civilian payrolls within the Department of De-

13. National Planning Association, *Manpower Needs for National Goals in the 1970's*, 1969.

fense which would accompany reduced defense orders. Distribution of the estimated $20 billion cutback in defense orders is shown in Table VII-10.

Table VII–10

DISTRIBUTION OF ESTIMATED CUTBACK IN DEFENSE ORDERS

Industry	Percentage of Total Cutback
Aircraft	32
Missiles, Ordinance and Weapons	28
Communications and Electrical Equipment	10
Petroleum and Chemicals	5
Shipbuilding	5
Construction	4
Food	3
Instruments	3
Vehicles	2
All Others	8

Source: NPA study

By contrast, the study suggested that spending for defense-related research and development would scarcely decline because of a changed Vietnam situation.

According to the NPA analysis, a net increase in the total employment in the private sector would occur because of a shift in expenditures from defense-related industries to industries directly serving consumers and to the construction industry. Under assumptions set forth in the study, a total of 232,000 professional and technical employees would be released from employment in the private sector by the cutback in defense orders while 177,000 of the same types of employees would be needed in new jobs created by offset programs in the private sector.

The NPA analysis made estimates of new employment created by a projected $10 billion tax cut and by a projected $10 billion increase in public spending for urban development and social welfare. Employment changes projected for scientists and engineers under these assumptions are shown in Table VII-11.

Table VII-11

PROJECTED EMPLOYMENT CHANGES

Occupations	Persons released from employment by a $20 billion cutback in defense orders (thousands)	New employment created by $10 billion tax cut $10 billion greater public spending (thousands)	Net change (thousands)
Scientists	14	4	—10
Engineers	112	34	—78
TOTAL	126	38	—88

Source: NPA study

Goals related to urban development and social welfare represent objectives likely to receive greater emphasis as defense expenditures decline. If goals having a content of science and technology higher than the content in urban development and social welfare are given top priorities, estimates of new employment for scientific and engineering personnel would be greater than those shown in the preceding table.

It should be stressed that the estimates cited in the preceding table refer to potential employment changes. The extent to which potential employment becomes a reality depends upon several factors, including program priorities and manpower policies. It should also be pointed out that the broad estimates of employment changes tend to underplay the fact that the knowledge and skills of individuals who are released from defense employment and are available for employment in other programs are often widely different from the knowledge and skills required of individuals in the same occupational fields in the other programs. This situation often makes an orderly transition of scientists and engineers from defense to non-defense work very difficult.

Reports of all of these committees and groups have been reviewed by high-level federal officials and constitute part of the data base which underlies official action to be taken as deemed appropriate.

Thus, the selection of various goals and policies and programs to reach these goals will have diverse effects on the employment

[302]

and the utilization of scientific and engineering manpower. Some proposed goals involve policies and programs using significant amounts of scientific and engineering manpower; other proposed goals involve the use of very little scientific and engineering personnel. As contrasting possibilities, rapid expansion of high priority programs may center on further space exploration and oceanography or on welfare and broader health care; federal aid to state and local governments may accentuate expansion of existing grant programs dealing with air and water pollution or may create a system of shared tax revenues spent primarily on goals, policies, and programs determined at the full discretion of state and local governments. In any case, the alternatives are not mutually exclusive. In reality, a combination of diverse goals, together with accompanying policies and programs, will probably be the ultimate federal response. The extent of the "mix" of goals becomes very critical but it is not yet visible. In determining the "mix," one criterion should be consistency in the effective utilization of scientific and engineering personnel.

NEED FOR POSITIVE RESPONSE

The defense program has utilized the knowledge and skills of a large segment of the nation's scientists and engineers—engineers in much larger numbers than scientists. If defense spending and defense-generated employment returns to 1965 levels, as many as 100,000 scientists and engineers will be forced to change their assignments. If defense spending is reduced by a lesser amount to permit such activities as a reasonable amount of defense R&D and the procurement of sophisticated defense hardware, as few as 50,000 scientists and engineers will be involved in job curtailments. In any event, complete cessation of Vietnam hostilities will bring significant shifts in the utilization of scientific and engineering manpower engaged in the defense program.

The time to analyze scientific and engineering manpower implications of major change in the defense effort and to start mitigating steps is now. Coordinated patterns of positive action can

[303]

be created without delay. For example, integrated measures can be planned, on an orderly basis, to facilitate the mobility of certain types of electrical engineers in defense industries to selected non-defense industries and to state and local government employment if a high priority is placed on water pollution control measures backed by larger amounts of federal grants to state and local governments. Additionally, some actions involving multi-sector effort and requiring a long lead time can also be initiated before final decisions to reduce defense expenditures by sizeable amounts are made. While some steps are properly taken at the local and state levels, other steps are most effectively taken at the regional and national levels.

Reductions in the Vietnam effort of the nation were begun in 1969 as a matter of national policy. Decisions recalling U. S. military personnel from Vietnam and reducing the amount and number of defense contracts were forerunners of the eventual cessation of Vietnam hostilities. Increasing numbers of scientists and engineers are finding their defense assignments being changed or eliminated.

Action to reduce the impact of defense cutbacks upon scientific and engineering personnel is a responsibility of several sectors of the nation—scientists and engineers, employers, professional and technical societies, government, and educators. However, the lines of responsibility for specific actions in these sectors are often imprecise. What each sector thinks are its responsibilities and the responsibilities of other sectors is a vital element in the adjustment process. Hence, a clear understanding by each sector of the scientific and engineering manpower utilization issue and the need for coordinated action are paramount. The goal of optimum utilization of a large segment of the nation's scientists and engineers depends in large measure upon the nature of the total positive response to the defense cutback problem.

VIII

SETTING FORTH A CHALLENGE

•

CHARACTERISTICS OF THE SCIENTIFIC
AND ENGINEERING MANPOWER POOL

In a very real sense, scientists and engineers constitute a manpower pool. Tributaries connected to the pool are two types: inflow and outflow. Inflow tributaries carry entrants to the pool directly from colleges and universities and from other sources such as military separation centers. Outflow tributaries, such as those leading to non-scientific and non-engineering type duties and to retirement, carry pool members temporarily or permanently from the pool. Ever-flowing tributaries make the pool a dynamic body. This basic characteristic makes pool analysis difficult.

The composition of the pool and the collective action of pool members in using their scentific and engineering knowledge and skills to the fullest possible extent are affected by external and internal changes. Acting externally upon the pool, the tributaries bring in and take out scientists and engineers with a constantly changing variety of knowledge and skills. Acting internally, a series of factors, such as accumulation of experience, reassignments, training, transfers, and promotions, continuously modify the attributes of those who remain in the pool. Strategies for improvement of utilization depend upon the identification and assessment of actual or anticipated characteristics of the pool or a portion of the pool at a particular point in time.

Statistics showing the precise composition of this pool in 1970 do not exist. However, some understanding of this composition can be derived from studies which presented analyses of the pool as of 1966, 1967, and 1968.

The Department of Labor made total estimates of science and engineering employment by aggregating separate estimates for

[305]

each of six sectors of the economy for which data on science and engineering employment were available. Within private industry, estimates were derived separately for 31 industry groups. According to this analysis, there were 1,262,200 scientists and engineers employed in 1966. Of this number 266,200 were scientists and 996,000 were engineers.[1]

Based on type of employer, the Department of Labor analysis produced the distribution set forth in Table VIII-1.

Table VIII–1

ESTIMATED EMPLOYMENT OF SCIENTISTS AND ENGINEERS, 1966

Type of Employer	Number of Scientists (thousands)	Percentage Distribution of Scientists	Number of Engineers (thousands)	Percentage Distribution of Engineers	Total Number (thousands)
Private Industry	162.8	61	812.2	81.5	975.0
Manufacturing	114.7	43	538.1	54	652.8
Non-manufacturing	48.1	18	274.1	27.5	322.2
Government	34.4	13	144.1	14.5	178.5
Universities & Colleges	63.7	24	35.1	3.5	98.8
Nonprofit Institutions	5.3	2	4.6	.5	9.9
All groups	266.2	100	996.0	100	1262.2

Source: Dept. of Labor study

In 1969 the Department of Labor updated the largest segment of the preceding study by preparing estimates of the number of scientists and engineers employed in industry in 1967.[2] Table VIII-2 shows the distribution of such employment, based on size of industry.

1. National Science Foundation, *Employment of Scientists and Engineers in the United States, 1950-1966,* 1968.

2. U. S. Department of Labor, *Scientific and Technical Personnel in Industry, 1967,* 1970.

[306]

Table VIII–2

ESTIMATED EMPLOYMENT OF SCIENTISTS AND ENGINEERS IN INDUSTRY, 1967

Types	Small sized industry (under 100 employees)	Medium sized industry (between 100-999 employees)	Large sized industry (1,000 or more employees)	Total Employment
Chemists	13,379	34,718	37,150	85,247
Physicists	843	3,601	11,728	16,172
Metallurgists	906	2,597	8,475	11,978
Geologists & Geophysicists	5,769	7,463	3,166	16,398
Other Physical Scientists	528	2,119	2,884	5,531
Mathematicians	2,732	10,234	18,359	31,325
Engineers	138,464	234,765	450,799	824,028
Totals	162,621	295,497	532,561	990,679

Source: Dept. of Labor study

During 1967 industrial employment of scientists increased approximately 2.5% over that of 1966 while industrial employment of engineers increased approximately 1.5% for the same period.

Diversity of characteristics of scientists is shown in a profile of scientists prepared by the National Science Foundation and based on 187,219 scientists in six selected categories who reported in 1968 to the National Register of NSF.[3] Individuals are considered eligible for inclusion in the National Register if they have full professional standing based on academic background and work experience, as determined by an appropriate professional society. Data for the National Register are obtained directly from individual scientists and engineers through the mailing of questionnaires by professional societies. The distribution

3. National Science Foundation, *Reviews of Data on Science Resources*, No. 16, 1968.

of the number of scientists in the 1968 group is shown in Table VIII-3.

Table VIII–3

DISTRIBUTION OF SCIENTISTS IN SELECTED CATEGORIES

Field	Number of Scientists
Chemistry	93,788
Earth and Marine Sciences	23,746
Atmospheric & Space Sciences	5,745
Physics	32,491
Mathematics	24,477
Computer Sciences	6,972
Total	187,219

Source: NSF study

The NSF study developed data on three key aspects of scientists in the pool, as represented by the National Register. These aspects relate to the highest degree awarded, the type of employer, and the primary work activity.

With respect to the highest degree awarded, 40% of these scientists had bachelor's degrees, 30% had Ph.D. degrees, and 29% had master's degrees. The distribution of highest degree awarded for each of the six selected categories is shown in Table VIII-4.

With respect to the type of employer, 44% of these scientists were employed by industry, 30% were employed by educational institutions, and 10% were employed by government. The distribution of type of employer for each of the six selected categories is presented in Table VIII-5.

With respect to primary work activity, 33% of these scientists were engaged in research and development, 20% were engaged in management or administration, and 16% were engaged in teaching. The distribution of primary work activity for each of the six selected categories is reflected in Table VIII-6.

Table VIII–4

HIGHEST DEGREES AWARDED TO SCIENTISTS IN SELECTED CATEGORIES

Degrees	Chemistry	Earth & Marine Sciences	Atmospheric & Space Sciences	Physics	Mathematics	Computer Sciences	Total
Ph.D	28,973	4,956	514	14,311	6,929	469	56,152
Prof. Medical	211	1	0	7	3	1	223
Master's	20,121	7,651	1,555	10,776	12,094	2,736	54,933
Bachelor's	43,127	10,893	3,168	7,239	5,147	3,513	73,087
Less than bachelor's	160	59	39	5	29	3	295
No report	1,196	186	469	153	275	250	2,529
Total	93,788	23,746	5,745	32,491	24,477	6,972	187,219

Source: NSF study

Table VIII–5

EMPLOYMENT OF SCIENTISTS, BY TYPE OF EMPLOYER

Types	Chemistry	Earth & Marine Sciences	Atmospheric & Space Sciences	Physics	Mathematics	Computer Sciences
Educational Institutions	20,510	5,890	757	15,522	12,837	921
Federal Government	5,247	2,982	1,857	3,717	1,354	516
Other Government	1,221	1,064	72	86	308	102
Non-profit Organizations	2,121	249	114	882	681	475
Industry & Business	53,291	9,809	537	9,436	7,289	4,513
Self-employed	1,069	2,019	36	249	222	45
Military	1,442	373	2,184	603	481	141
Other employed	539	92	26	41	219	62
Not employed	6,180	882	107	1,132	786	147
No report	2,168	386	55	823	300	50
Totals	93,788	23,746	5,745	32,491	24,477	6,972

Source: NSF study

[309]

Table VIII–6

EMPLOYMENT OF SCIENTISTS, BY PRIMARY WORK ACTIVITY

Types	Chemistry	Earth & Marine Sciences	Atmospheric & Space Sciences	Physics	Mathematics	Computer Sciences
R&D	33,492	3,737	1,079	16,380	5,147	2,661
Management or Administration	20,908	3,935	1,510	5,123	5,122	1,555
Teaching	9,762	4,034	293	6,899	9,491	212
Production & Inspection	14,318	1,554	66	183	184	88
Consulting	1,315	734	89	363	1,065	440
Exploration, forecasting & reporting	823	7,134	1,970	577	926	1,231
Other work	2,726	618	406	336	745	427
Not employed	6,180	882	107	1,132	786	147
No report	4,264	1,118	225	1,498	1,011	211
Totals	93,788	23,746	5,745	32,491	24,477	6,972

Source: NSF study

Diversity of characteristics of engineers is shown in a profile of engineers prepared by the Engineers Joint Council and based on questionnaires returned by 53,000 engineers in 1967. This group represented an estimated 565,000 individual members of 45 professional and technical societies. From the data obtained, EJC extracted attributes for a group of 438,000 clearly identified, actively employed engineers. The population of 438,000 represented only those engineers who at the time of the survey were members of professional and technical societies.[4]

The EJC study developed data on four key aspects of engineers in the pool, as represented by the planned sampling procedure. These aspects relate to the highest degree awarded, the type of employer, the employment function, and the employed

4. Engineers Joint Council, *The Engineering Profession: A New Profile,* 1969.

area of technology and are expressed as percentages of the group of 438,000 engineers. For 70% of the engineers, the highest degree awarded was the bachelor's. Seventy percent were employed in industry and business. Twenty-three percent were managers of research and development or worked in R&D. Activities related to work management and control—such as process design, work simplification, and reliability—constituted 18% of the total specialties. The distribution for each of these four aspects is shown in Tables VIII-7—VIII-10.

Table VIII–7

ENGINEERS: HIGHEST DEGREES AWARDED

Types	Percentage of Total
Ph.D.	5
Master's	22
Bachelor's	70
Less than Bachelor's or No Degree	3

Source: EJC study

Table VIII–8

ENGINEERS: TYPES OF EMPLOYER

Types	Percentage of Total
Industry & Business	70
Federal Government & Military	10
Education & Non-Profit	6
State & Local Government	5
Self-employed	4
Others & No Report	3

Source: EJC study

Table VIII–9

ENGINEERS: EMPLOYMENT FUNCTION

Types	Percentage of Total
Management, Administration & Technical Supervision	21
Research & Development	15
Design	15
Consulting & Construction	12
Production, Maintenance, Quality Control, Testing	10
Management of R&D	8

[311]

Table VIII–9 (Continued)

Types	Percentage of Total
Sales	6
Planning & Analysis	5
Other	4
Teaching	3

Source: EJC study

Table VIII–10

ENGINEERS: AREAS OF TECHNOLOGY

Types	Percentage of Total
Work Management & Control	18
Electronics	12
Other	11
Mechanical	10
Environmental Control & Human Factors	10
Construction & Structures	9
Electrical machinery & power	8
Materials	6
Mining, Petroleum, Geological	5
Chemical	4
Science & Mathematics	4
Flight	2
Marine & Ocean	1

Source: EJC study

The Department of Labor analysis provides a bridge which links scientific and engineering employment in the same time frame. The studies of the National Science Foundation and the Engineers Joint Council underscore the very wide diversity of characteristics of scientists and engineers who constitute the pool.

In addition to the complex nature of the scientific and engineering manpower pool as described through the studies reported, the total size of this pool has expanded to the extent that it is currently estimated as approximately 1,500,000 scientists and engineers.

NATIONAL DEPENDENCY UPON POOL

The United States is becoming ever more dependent upon the capabilities of the scientific and engineering manpower pool for responding to difficult national problems. At the present time, four basic factors make this dependency very noteworthy:

1. The defense of the nation and the free world is built on science and technology. The maintenance of scientific and technological superiority of the United States over any potential enemy means that the intricate defense weapons of this nation must be effectively developed and counter-measures against an enemy's weapons must be created.

2. Serious economic issues require the best of science and technology in order to produce practical solutions. These issues range from the need to reduce economic costs of mass housing to additional applications of automation to reduce human effort.

3. Persistent social problems call for solutions, some of which are based on science and technology. Efforts of scientists and engineers are required in overcoming such social problems as increasing crime rates and adverse effects of air and water pollution.

4. On the international scene, developing nations want to experience some of the better life. They increasingly seek scientific and engineering know-how of this nation to help them raise themselves to a higher standard of living.

In a positive response to this dependency, maximum utilization of scientific and engineering manpower is essential. Such essentiality is based on two particular factors: the nature of scientific and engineering challenges which exact as a price for accomplishment a requirement of the maximum use of scientific and engineering brainpower and the high cost investments in science and technology. The need to achieve such utilization is also made evident by current and anticipated shortages of qualified scientists and engineers in specific fields at particular locations. Available evidence, although "spotty," suggests that shortages in particular branches of science and engineering exist and will continue to exist at least until 1975. Undergraduate and graduate enrollment figures, for example, indicate that the number of graduates in science and engineering who will become available during the next few years will not meet total identifiable needs, even from a quantitative view. Faced with growing shortages of qualified scientists and engineers at a time of changing and expanding demands for such manpower, the nation needs to take every appropriate step to make best use of the present supply. Although the concept of optimum utilization merits action independent of a supply-demand relationship, unmet demands add to the concern for maximum utilization of the existing supply.

NATURE OF UTILIZATION PROBLEM

With respect to the current status of scientific and engineering manpower utilization, a wide array of policies, programs, and actions have been undertaken by all sectors involved—employers, educators, government, scientists and engineers, professional and technical societies, and related groups—with the objective of improving the utilization of such manpower. It is evident that for particular phases of the utilization problem and in specific situations, efforts put forth to improve the use of scientists and engineers have been very effective. Nevertheless, the fact remains that the current total efforts of all sectors are grossly inadequate in relation to the nature of the problem of attaining optimum utilization of scientific and engineering manpower.

Six aspects of the utilization problem have been singled out and described in the preceding chapters as having special significance at this time. Specifically, it has been suggested that the use of scientific and engineering manpower will be greatly enhanced through steps to strengthen selected personnel functions, to increase the availability and use of engineering technicians, to broaden the role of continuing education, to facilitate the retrieval of scientific and technical information, to defer graduate students, and to minimize the impact of defense cutbacks. The utilization of such personnel will be considerably improved if steps are taken to nurture this human resource through the application and extension of tested and innovative policies, programs, and actions, many of which have been described heretofore.

One characteristic of the present effort is that positive steps pursued in one individual sector are often undertaken independently of, and without full knowledge or regard for, actions taken or about to be taken in another sector. In fact, actions at cross purposes are occasionally taken in the same sector. For example, in 1969, several federal agencies were granting graduate fellowships to young scientists and engineers to help them enter and remain in graduate school while at the same time the "no graduate deferment" policy called for the induction of many of these same individuals. In the light of multiple responsibilities for scientific and engineering manpower utilization, effective leadership is fundamental to interpret the issues and to induce voluntary, coordinated action in connection with areas where policies, programs, and actions merge or overlap and require program integration to be fully responsive to overall needs.

Effecting changes to optimize utilization involves an expenditure of funds which may not be readily available. The costs of instituting changes, however, usually are more than offset by monetary savings and by other benefits such as higher morale. For example, with respect to employer action, the operation of an exit interview program costs money; however, it is expensive to recruit new professional personnel. Expenses for operating an exit interview program should more than pay for the operation in money saved through the reduction of recruiting costs.

The utilization problem is a complex issue. There are no simple, cure-all approaches which can be taken today or tomorrow to solve, once and for all, the high incidence of malutilization. Producing solutions to this problem is often a time-consuming process as sufficient time is necessary to initiate effectively positive policies, programs, and actions which improve individual situations. The voluntary nature of most responses acts to increase the time span for effective action. In the final analysis, each approach needs to be analyzed and tailored to meet the specific situation.

CALL TO ACTION

It is essential for every sector involved in the utilization problem to play a more active role in order to reap greater benefits. To illustrate, for employers, optimum utilization means greater opportunity to provide a higher quality service or product as well as to obtain more effective work performance for the science and technology dollar. For the Federal Government, it means greater fulfillment of national goals which require an input from science and technology. For educators, it means greater attainment in the transmitting of pertinent knowledge and skills through the learning process. For professional and technical societies, it means greater enhancement of the scientific and technical competency of their membership. For individual scientists and engineers, it means greater job satisfaction arising from increased individual productivity and accomplishment. All sectors share in the credit for the accomplishments in scientific and engineering manpower utilization. All sectors should be responsive to an appeal to increase their efforts in this direction.

Early in this century, a successful nationwide crusade was undertaken by groups and individuals under national leadership to stress the importance of the conservation of natural resources of this nation. Today, there is need for another nationwide crusade, a crusade for the better utilization of human resources of the nation. Groups and individuals have a vital part to play in this new crusade. A call to action to embark upon this crusade is the thrust of OPTIMUM UTILIZATION OF SCIENTIFIC AND ENGINEERING MANPOWER.

INDEX

INDEX

[319]

Interagency Advisory Committee on Essential Activities and Critical Occupations, 234, 240-241, 250

J

Jet Propulsion Laboratory, 177
Johnson, President Lyndon B., 17-18
Joint Advisory Committee on Continuing Engineering Studies, 168-169

K

Kennedy, President John F., 15-16

L

Labor Department: see Department of Labor
Langley Research Center, 177
Lewis Research Center, 178
Library of Congress, 216

M

Manpower planning, 50-55
Manpower pool: characteristics, 305-312; national dependency, 313-314
Manpower Training and Development Act, 175
MARC Distribution Service, 216
Match between capabilities and actual duties, 42-43
Military Selective Service Act of 1967, 239; as amended, 258
Military use of college graduates as enlisted men, 252-257
Minority group members, 35-36
Mohawk Development Service, 34

N

National Academy of Sciences: Committee on Utilization of Scientific and Engineering Manpower, 16-17; member of President's Committee on Scientists and Engineers, 7
National Academy of Sciences-National Academy of Engineering Committee on Scientific and Technical Communication, 222-224
National Aeronautics and Space Agency: continuing education program, 173, 174, 177-178; defense cutback studies, 272; document repository service, 209-211; RECON system, 200-201
National Advisory Commission on Selective Service: recommendation against graduate deferment, 235-237; study, 234-235
National Advisory Council on Vocational Education, 79-80
National Commission on Technology, Automation and Economic Progress, 17-19
National Conference on Industrial Hydraulics, 13
National Council on Marine Resources and Engineering Development, 21-22
National Defense Education Act of 1958, 77
National goals, reordering, 294-303
National Institute of Public Affairs, 67
National Institutes of Health, 172-174
National Planning Association, 300-302
National Referral Center for Science and Technology, 202
National Register of Scientific and Technical Personnel, 58-59

National Science Foundation: continuing education program, 173, 174; contract with AID, 178; funded study of continuing education, 129-132, 139-140, 186-187; funded study of information systems, 196; salary survey, 58; science information program, 212-215; sea grant program, 21; sponsorship of studies, 4; study of characteristics of employment of scientists, 307-310

National Scientific and Technical Information System(s), 218-224

National Security Council: action concerning graduate deferment, 240-243; recommendation for induction delay, 257

National Society of Professional Engineers: concern for utilization, 5; continuing education study, 122-125, 164; continuing education program, 164-165; Institute for Certification of Engineering Technicians, 110-112; liason with utilization program, 13; salary survey, 58; symposium on engineering employment, 282

Naval Post Graduate School, 188

Newark College of Engineering, 35-36

New York State Post-Vietnam Planning Committee, 275-277

Nixon, President Richard M., 257-260

"No graduate deferment" policy: impact on graduate enrollment, 243-250; impact on occupational deferment, 250-252; recommendation by National Security Council, 241-243

O

Occupations, critical, 234, 250
Office of Civil and Defense Mobilization, 14, 15
Office of Emergency Planning, 14, 15

Old Dominion College, 177
Oregon Technical Institute, 84-85

P

Panel of Consultants on Vocational Education, 77-78
Parallel ladders for advancement, 60-62
Pennsylvania Economic Advisory Council, 274-275
Pennsylvania State University: Capitol campus, 82-83; continuing education study, 118-122; educational technology program, 157-158
Performance appraisal system, 55-56
Physical environment, 38-40
President's Committee on Scientists and Engineers: establishment, 5-7; utilization program, 7-14
President's Science Advisory Committee: concern of Manpower Panel, 22; study of manpower needs, 15-16
Presidential Task Force on Career Advancement, 68
Project CO-TIE, 158-159
Project SURGE, 158
Public Health Service, 172-173

R

Random selection method, 258-259
Recognition, 62-63
RECON system, 200-201
Rewards for achievement, 55-63

S

Science Information Exchange, 202-203
Scientific American, 69
Scientific and Technical Information Centers, 201-212

[324]